This
Cybernetic
Age

A Source Book
of vital readings,
selected, edited,
co-authored and synthesized
by DON TOPPIN
for the Department of Adult Education,
Ontario Institute for Studies in Education
and The Human Development Corporation.

This
Cybernetic
Age

Published by
HUMAN DEVELOPMENT CORPORATION
NEW YORK, N.Y.

Dedicated to
My Fellow Human Beings
whoever and wherever they may be,
especially to my teen-age sons, Bob and Warren,
and to leaders of the twenty-first century.

D. T.

© Copyright, Human Development Corporation,
New York, N.Y., 1969

This
Cybernetic
Age

MACHINES—ESPECIALLY COMPUTERS, ROCKETS
AND SATELLITES—ARE CHANGING YOUR
WORLD ! ! !

Every human on earth—INCLUDING YOU—
will be changed by

This
Cybernetic
Age

WAR, VIOLENCE AND POVERTY
CAN BE ELIMINATED!
SECURITY AND SELF–FULFILLMENT
CAN BE YOURS!

"The Development of Machines Could Make Work Obsolete"

Distinguished leaders bring you this guidebook to the future

Edited and co-authored by DON TOPPIN

"For to him that is joined to all the living, there is hope."
Ecclesiastes (9:4).

"THIS CYBERNETIC AGE" deals with this unique moment, called today, when, for the first time, man can be joined to all the living through the machine. Hopefully, war and poverty will end as man and machines learn to interact to the benefit and self-fulfillment of Man. "Man" is brief for "Homo Sapiens", which, assuredly, includes women and youth who seemingly have the much-needed capacities for love, humanization and hope.

This book is for general readership throughout the world. We try to use words from the Basic English Vocabulary for Global Communication (Appendix I, Page 413). Other words you will understand by context. Newer technical words and terms are defined in Global English in the special dictionary at the back of the book —Glossary of Timely Terms (Appendix II, Page 419). The "Statistics on the Good Earth" will be found in Appendix III, Page 433.

Although simple to read, it will make you think. As a matter of fact, it is our hope that some of the expressed thoughts may challenge our most profound thinkers to action.

This collection of essays and speeches, in adapted form, has been assembled for self-study and, hopefully, group discussion. At the end of each part, you will find (1) Books for Further Study, with (2) "Questions to Consider" as Appendix IV, Page 445.

Consequently, this can become the starting point for discussion by groups in schools, colleges, universities, churches, service clubs, industries, communities, governments, etc.

But even the casual reader should find this book to be timely, interesting and helpful.

"The Alternatives that face man in these apocalyptic times lead either to a mechanized society, in which man is caught like a helpless cog, and to eventual destruction by thermonuclear war, or to a renaissance of humanism and hope, a society that puts technique, not first but second, as a servant of human well-being."

ASHLEY MONTAGU, Author of *The Human Revolution*

"Cybernation is not a device with which to outlaw, displace or dispense with man. . . . It is a means for increasing man's stature and extending his ability to produce in greater volume with less physical effort or mental strain.

F. G. WOOLLARD, *Machines in the Service of Man*

Cybernetics is the science of automatic control; for example, a thermostat on your wall can be set to control your heat. Cybernetics deals with the communication and control of organisms. New machines, such as computers and satellites, are organisms. The most powerful organism of all is the human brain.

Cybernation, for the purpose of this book, means automation through the application of cybernetics. This usually, but not necessarily, refers to automated processes in which the computer is involved.

"This Cybernetic Age" is concerned with the relationship between men and machines, especially in the elimination of war, violence and poverty, and the guaranteeing to every human a life of self-fulfillment.

Preface

THIS COULD BE
THE MOST IMPORTANT BOOK YOU OWN!

This Cybernetic Age is a very important book—one of the most important books ever compiled.

For the first time, some of the world's greatest thinkers have focused their attention on the nature of this man-machine era and how, without question, it has changed, is changing, and will further change your life. These changes can be of enormous benefit to you, if you understand now.

This Cybernetic Age is also unique because, again for the first time, the book itself is cybernetic in nature: it is automatically self-adjusting to the reader, whoever and wherever he may be. Consequently, it can be of value to anyone and is a "must" for many.

It should be read by every teacher, every university professor and every leader in every walk of life for it tells them where their specialty fits into the changing patterns of the world. The excellent bibliographies branch the interested reader into depths of his choosing.

For those who are involved in government and public affairs, this reading is mandatory because, again for the first time, the destiny of the universe is within our grasp, provided we and they can learn to communicate and cooperate, swiftly and effectively.

"This Cybernetic Age" should be read by every mature individual. It doesn't tell what is going to happen in the next thirty years but what can be made to happen. In cybernation, through global communication and distribution systems, we have the makings of a new golden age. For the first time, man can be joined to *all* the living—by the machine.

That is why this book has been designed to be read by anyone who understands the "Basic English Vocabulary for Global Communication"—the "Glossary of Timely Terms" translates technical and sophisticated terminology into words which are understandable, even to the average grade-three student.*

The reason for this unusual approach is to cut across the usual communication barriers between levels and groups so that important subjects may be considered by everyone.

Machines, especially computers, rockets and satellites, are changing your world faster than you can read this sentence. As the book emphatically states, "the greatest challenge of our civilization is awaiting our response. Simply stated, this challenge is to utilize fully our scientific and technological potentials through cybernation and global communication systems to create a brotherhood of men who have both food and freedom."

The message is clear and universally shared. But the average human being today feels helpless and terrified, somewhat like a mosquito in a hurricane, as war, violence and poverty increase around the globe. We are captives of things we do not understand and, consequently, cannot control. *Through the power of the cybernetic approach, however, war, violence*

---

* The editor also has an answer for those who do not read or understand any English and has prepared a system of Instant English which will train anyone to read, write, understand and speak "Global English" in less than one hundred hours. This is not included, although details are mentioned in "Appendix I". "Instant Global English" is briefly noted here to emphasize the cybernetic approach of this book. In brief, it can bring the wisdom of the masters to every inhabitant of the world.

and poverty can be eliminated. The requisite and vital co-ordination and communication can be assured if every human would read, understand and apply even just *the principles* which are introduced in this unique and invaluable source-book.

It has been said that there are less than 500 people on earth who understand the tremendous changes which are being wrought daily by modern science and technology. Each of us, in the civilized world, has become a specialist. The specialist simply does not have the time to think, particularly if he is a busy president of a university or a corporation . . . or a prominent doctor, lawyer, teacher, theologian or politician. The heavy duties of each day consume all of the energies of most leaders, and they lose touch. Ask any of them how to end war, poverty and violence and you will discover what we mean!

If these leaders don't know, how can you and I be expected to know?

Yet, there are thinkers who have specialized in probing, thinking and planning. Over thirty of them meet for the first time within the covers of this book:

In Part One, Lord Ritchie Calder gives a background to cybernetics and, while John D. Rockefeller, Jr. praises the young revolutionaries, Norman Cousins, the distinguished editor of Saturday Review, relates why this is an exciting time to be alive. Then follows some of the fascinating predictions from the Hudson Institute and the brilliant analysis of social trends by Dr. Burnham Beckwith. These trends effect everyone, just as computers, rockets and satellites will change the role of everyone.

In Part Two, famous pioneers such as John Diebold, C. C. Killingsworth, A. J. Hayes, John Snyder, Norbert Weiner, John Rose and Arthur Porter zero in on the real problems of the man-machine society. They are hopeful that leaders and members of union, industrial and government groups can get together so that everyone can enjoy the benefits of abundance and leisure which are now possible.

In Part Three, the vital issues of communications are explored by world leaders Colin Cherry, Marshall McLuhan, Gordon Thompson, Henry Cassirer and Satoru Takatsuks. Included is a statement from UNESCO on the application of mass media.

In Part Four, in recognition that we do live in a global village, Barbara Ward (Lady Jackson), the Rt. Hon. Lester B. Pearson, World Federalist Reuben Schafer and World Bank Director Robert McNamara agree that there is specific action which can be taken today.

In Part Five, we go to Russia for the profound observations of "The Sakharov Manifesto". Kenneth Galbraith sees greater freedom emerging from the industrial state. Martin Stone, a keen member of "The Young Presidents' Club", emphatically states that elimination of want is now a matter of survival and calls for a guaranteed minimum income. This latter is also defined by pioneer Robert Theobald in his now classic essay on this subject.

Professor John Farina, cooriginator of the book, explores the question of leisure created by automation. His essay is followed by "Impact of Change on Work and Leisure" by Dr. H. L. Wilensky; "Art and Culture in the Cybernetic Age" by Professor Harley Parker; "The Community for Human Development" by Prof. D. M. Smyth, and "Matching the Old and Making the New" by industrial engineer Barrington Nevitt.

In Part Six, top social scientist Van Court Hare tells us why things don't happen. Historian Elting Morrison makes a profound proposal; famed Eric Fromm hits the keynote in his appeal for humanization and the beloved president of India writes on the never-ending pursuit of learning. Then comes another rocket from Russia—soft and verbal—which can, if observed, provoke more action than Sputnik. But this time the action will be global and for good. The book ends with a "checklist of enemies", which may incite you if you have been listed, and with "Afterwords"—a provoking synthesis and declaration for discussion and action.

Appendices include:

1. The Basic English Vocabulary for Global Communication;
2. A Glossary of Timely Terms—for those who want to understand this book as well as any university professor;
3. Statistics on "The Good Earth"—to show us how lucky we are and where to begin, and
4. Questions to consider and provoke thought and discussion.

In brief, the book recognizes that the day of the machine has arrived; that scarcity of goods and continuation of war are unpardonable. It also places emphasis on the need for better communications between all the people of the world, including the neighbour next door. But, equally as important as machine cybernetics is mental cybernetics which, in brief, can bring human development to you—whoever you may be —right now! No computer can compete with a human brain.

People with vested interests, although they have more to gain than to lose, will probably resent the collaborators. Those who do not understand it will dismiss the book as unexciting or academic, just as people have always opposed what they have not understood. But many more will pick up ideas which will lead to self-realization.

To say the least, this book is a brain-stretcher and highly valuable to anyone who can read at or above the level of the Basic English Vocabulary for Global Communication.

If 5,000,000 people use this book as a discussion item in schools, churches and community groups around the globe, war, poverty and violence will come, we predict, to an end.

The editor has made predictions before which, much to his amazement, came true. When Bonanza's Lorne Greene, then the National News Voice of Canadian Radio, wrote an introduction to his book "From Cradle to Grave", he said: "I've known Don Toppin for many years. You don't have to agree with him—he doesn't ask you to agree—but he certainly makes you think. He's sincere about everything he says and does and this book embodies ideas which could derive only from his unique background of philosophy, business and human relations."

I am happy to echo these words and to add that his vast experience qualifies him to do exactly what he has done.

If you read "This Cybernetic Age", it will make you think, if you think you will act, if you act you will benefit.

> J. Rae Perigoe,
> Editor, *Personnel*
> (Official Journal of the Federation of Canadian Personnel Associations.)

Foreword

1

This book is intended to help you think—along with me —about this age in which we live—This Cybernetic Age.

Are we on the threshold of a wondrous world civilization guaranteeing satisfying lives to all members of the global community? Or are we to be destroyed—physically and psychically—by the science and technology which modern man is creating more rapidly than ever before?

H. G. Wells once said: "Civilization is in a race between education and catastrophy". But education for what?

One thing which I have already learned from compiling this book is that there is very little communication between the educators and the leaders themselves: each is a busy specialist. The comprehension and credibility gaps are enormous, even among the experts. Consequently, the layman becomes hopelessly confused—and for good reason. The revolt of youth is one very obvious result.

The English philosopher Albert North Whitehead warned against this back in 1929 when he wrote [1] "This situation has its dangers. It produces minds in a groove. Each profession makes progress, but it is progress in its own groove. Now to be mentally in a groove is to live in contemplating a given set of abstractions. But there is no groove of abstractions which is adequate for the comprehension of human life. Thus

[1] From *The Aims of Education* The Macmillan Company, New York.

in the modern world, the celibacy of the medieval learned class has been replaced by a celibacy of the intellect which is divorced from the concrete contemplation of the complete facts. The dangers arising from this aspect of professionalism are great, particularly in our democratic societies. The specialized functions of the community are performed better and more progressively, but the generalized direction lacks vision."

One of the purposes of this "Source Book" is to bring together authorities with directive wisdom and to relate them, in a generalized way, to life in the future.

"Bring Us Together!"

If I recall correctly, these were the words on a placard which a teenager bequeathed to President Richard Nixon as his theme. We hope he succeeds in bringing Americans together. This would be a fine example.

What about the rest of the world?

2

Perhaps there are advantages in writing from Canadian soil:

(1) Apparently there is less thought-control in Canada. For example, a recent CBC program on gas warfare was telecast from coast to coast without the necessity of clearance from any agency, whereas a similar program in the United States, it was reported, had to be cleared by over fifty agencies.

(2) Certainly there is less communist witch-hunting in Canada. We live between the U.S.A. and Russia and Red China. We trade with the U.S.A. and Russia and Red China. We are close to socialized Britain as part of a Commonwealth of Nations which have almost nothing in common except tradition and participation itself. Conservative governments were already socializing our hydropower before Lenin had any hydropower to socialize. The welfare state has been promoted by our socialist party for over 35 years and implemented by

both Liberals and Conservatives. Our economy is mixed; the world economy can also be mixed with state, corporate and private ownership. Moreover, the new industrialist states, as Kenneth Galbraith emphasizes, are global; organized labor is global. Corporate shareholders and union members are also human beings with common interests; global bonds already exist. It is psychologically unfortunate that, in the minds of some, America still stands for capitalism and Russia for communism while, today, both terms are rapidly becoming outdated. In the long run, the interest of the majority of people of the world must be served. Compared with the space beyond, our globe is now very small.

(3) Geographically, Canada is the second largest nation in the world; next to the USSR. Surprisingly, a recent United Kingdom survey shows Canada to be the most affluent country in the world—based on percentage of householders owning central heating, refrigerators, cars, telephones, washings machines, and television sets. In all six categories, Canada easily leads the world, but, like United States and other countries, and in spite of our affluence, we have not solved the problems of poverty, education and equality, and our unit labor cost is one of the highest in the world. We desperately need more automation and more humanization.

(4) Canada is a peace-loving nation. We have never started a war and have always actively supported both the League of Nations and United Nations. As a matter of fact, our UN delegates have already successfully served as mediators and have averted at least one major war. Our former Prime Minister won a Nobel Prize for peace. He is now courageously talking about the United States of the World and working closely with Robert McNamara of the World Bank. An International Development Centre in Ottawa is proposed as a service to governments of developing nations and to the organizers of international aid programs. Expo '67 was the animator of the communications revolution.

Therefore, we have created this anthology for the people of

the world who want to be "brought together" in order to enjoy the better lives which can be made possible through the full utilization of the resources and techniques which are now available for the first time since the origin of man.

3

The idea for the book originated during a discussion with a publisher about man's automatic rejection of new ideas and machines since the beginning of time. A few days later, at a luncheon at the University of Toronto Faculty Club, I casually mentioned the conversation to Dr. Arthur Porter and Dr. John Farina.

It was one of those rare days when the past, present and future converged into one meaningful pattern. Professor Porter is an internationally-known authority on automation and the inventor of one of the first computers. Professor Farina is a social scientist who has lectured for many years on automation, especially as it pertains to the increase in productivity and the creation of leisure time. We recognized that the team would not be complete without the observations of Canada's famous communication prophet, Marshall McLuhan. We later called in Gordon B. Thompson, who has been referred to as "Canada's One-man Think-tank on communications systems."

My designated role was to select significant statements from assorted leaders and to interrelate them to the basic issues of the times. My work on the project on Communication and Cybernation for the Department of Adult Education of the Ontario Institute for Studies in Education facilitated the development of this book and I am deeply greatful to my associates, especially Dr. Roby Kidd, Dr. James Draper and Dr. Norman High. Special thanks for editorial assistance are due J. Rae Perigoe, editor of *Canadian Personnel and Industrial Relations Journal,* and to Carol Evans who has been most helpful in handling the typing and the multitudinous details which accompany such a venture.

We have been blessed by excellent cooperation from the various contributors and publishers as listed. This, of itself, is an exemplification of cooperative action.

4

As a reader, you may wish to read in depth many of the books on the Rcommended Reading Lists from which passages have been selected. Some of these books are already becoming "classics" among the specialists, though unknown to the multitudes of readers whose futures are very much involved.

Because this is intended as a book which can be read and understood by every man, woman and child, *This Cybernetic Age* is *not* about the complicated *science* of cybernetics as created by Dr. Norbert Weiner, and which has been defined as "The study of human control functions and of mechanical and electric systems designed to replace them involving an application of statistical mechanics to communication engineering". More simply, cybernetics (from Greek, meaning Helmsman) is the communication and control of organisms; men and machines.

Immediately, we are more interested, as you must be, in the full utilization of cybernation toward maximized productivity of goods and services at minimized per-unit costs. We are also interested in verbal and visual communication which can now, by satellite, be instant and global. The coordination of these two concepts will change the world environment. There are vast social, economic and political implications. *For instance, war and poverty can be eliminated. The Global Village can become humanized.*

However, if the warnings go unheeded, men will continue

to destroy themselves with the tools they have created until this so-called civilization ends as all other civilizations have ended—except that this end could be the end of species known as Homo Sapiens.

Or we might, for a while longer, keep "muddling along" with increasing conflicts between racial groups, religious groups, economic groups, geographic groups, social groups, political groups. In this situation, population, poverty and strife will continue to increase until life, for both rich and poor, will become a living hell. The assassination of a Kennedy or a Martin Luther King or a union leader could become commonplace. Germ destruction, or hermicide, could happen in any community. Affluence would make no difference. No one could escape.

This book recognizes that mankind now has a clear-cut choice between self-fulfillment or self-destruction. We take the optimistic view that there is enough intelligence to "bring together" men, machines, materials, money and management for the ultimate benefit of the entire human race. Without coordination, on a global basis, there is no reason for optimism. Humans have this capacity to coordinate. The new machines can change the world environment so that, for the first time, the destiny of the universe is within man's grasp.

DON TOPPIN.

Centennial Acres
Box 960, Bracebridge, Muskoka
Ontario, Canada
January, 1970

Contents

Productivity and costs

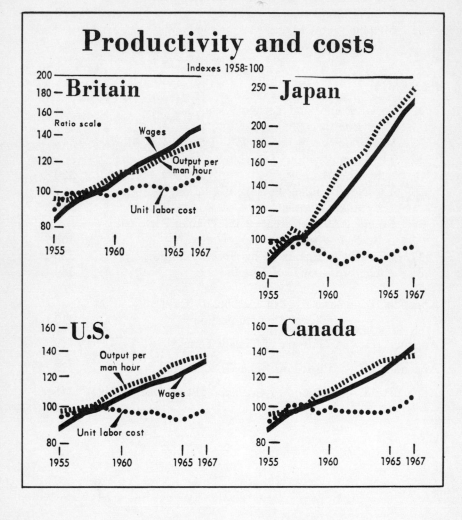

Indexes 1958=100

Britain

200
180
160
Ratio scale
140
Wages
120
Output per man hour
100
Unit labor cost
80

1955   1960   1965 1967

Japan

250
200
180
160
140
120
100
80

1955   1960   1965 1967

U.S.

160
140
Output per man hour
120
Wages
100
Unit labor cost
80

1955   1960   1965 1967

Canada

160
140
120
100
80

1955   1960   1965 1967

PART ONE

We now begin our exciting adventure in understanding, discovery, and choice.

Marshall McLuhan tells of an interviewer who accused him of being Utopian. McLuhan reminded him that Utopia in Greek is "NOWHERE".

Jean-Paul Sartre might say, "You may select for yourself: 'Utopia is No Where' or 'Utopia is Now Here.' " It's up to you to make a choice. When you choose, you are participating in a choice for all mankind. Think about it!

Chapter One emphasizes that tomorrow is here. The great decisions about war and poverty must be made now. This overview gives you a glimpse of the nature of both the book and the future.

In Chapter Two, top-ranking scientist-writer Lord Ritchie Calder brings you some background to the science of cybernetics which, because of its continuing capacity for feed-forward, feed-back, self-correction and development, can, mentally and mechanically, change the world.

In this connection, John D. Rockefeller III (Chapter 3) gives amazing praise to the young revolutionaries around the globe who are saying important things which some people do not wish to hear.

In Chapter 4, Norman Cousins, distinguished editor of Saturday Review and President of Federation of World Federalists, recognizes the urgency of the moment and, after comparing this period in history with other great periods, concludes that this is an exciting time to be alive.

Chapter Five forecasts the nature of the future, spells out some specific predictions, and clearly identifies trends which are already underway—if we survive.

Appendix IV is comprised of questions on the thought and material of each Part, which can be used to test your comprehension and to provoke conversation, discussion and action. There is also a list of suggested books for those who wish to pursue the study in greater breadth and depth.

CHAPTER 1

Tomorrow Is Today!

by Don Toppin

This chapter developed from the editor's project on
"Communication and Cybernation" for the Department
of Adult Education, Ontario Institute for Studies in
Education. Special thanks to Gerald Brander, publisher
of MacLean's, "Canada's National Magazine", for permission to adapt and reprint the opening paragraphs
from "The Next Revolution Will Happen in Your
Living Room".

Don Toppin is an internationally-known Training
Systems Consultant who has been a pioneer innovator
since, as a teenager, he initiated the Young Canada
Hour and the first public affairs program on the first
coast-to-coast radio network in Canada. His biography
has been published by the editors of "Who's Who in
America" in "Who's Who in the East", 66-69, 70, etc.
He is a Certified Adult Educator and Guidance Coun-
sellor who specializes in Manpower Training, Communications and Individually Prescribed Programmed
Instruction which he is now coordinating for the re-
cently-planned Global College for Private Study and
Career Development.

1

QUENTIN R. SMITH wrenches the top off another beer, hunches over the console of his home communicator and spins the dial through its circle of channels. The stolid images and flat voice of the news channel flash by, the public-affairs network has some professor talking about scrolls, the movie channel is playing a German thing, and the financial channel has stock reports and the sports network is featuring international hockey. Ah, that's more like it—a Bonanza rerun on the entertainment band. Quentin leans back, sucks his beer, sighs with contentment.

Upstairs, Quentin's daughter Nasturtium is finishing her last class of the day on the education channel; downstairs, in the recreation room, Mrs. Smith, a culture buff, has just slipped the video record of an old Jerry Lewis Special into the family's third television set, and it doesn't look as if the washing and ironing will get done this afternoon after all.

Across the street, the Wenceslas T. Jones family is busy at the communicator, too. Wenceslas has just dialed the Daily Star; he is watching the editorials read out onto the livingroom scanner and muttering imprecations at the dunderheads who run newspapers. (Why do they still call them newspapers, anyway, when you read them on a screen?) Wenceslas, Jr. has slipped off to his room to scan a book. Well, not just any book; actually, he has dialed the public library and is having the riper passages from Fanny Hill fed to his bedroom screen. Mrs. Jones is ordering groceries through the Dial-A-Mart ("One Call Buys it All"), but with a distracted air; she is thinking of other things, thinking especially, that she must really nag Wenceslas tonight about fixing the auto-toboggan in case anybody wants to go out tomorrow.

Oh, didn't I tell you? The Joneses and the Smiths live in Frobisher Bay, NWT.

Through a global network, this type of service is available around the world and throughout space. United Nations channels run continuing programs on education and world affairs. Programs can originate in any language; then, they are translated by computer into Global English for universal coverage. At the option of the UN member, the program can be retranslated into a native language. Or natives may prefer to tune to a third UN channel which teaches Global English and other languages around the clock. Those who do not have the full set, complete with UHF video can pick up the audio portion by transistorized radios which can be worn like watches.

Admittedly, this is a projection, but the technical skill to produce every element in this sketch is available today. These are not developments that could conceivably take place: they almost certainly will. We are already caught up in a communications explosion that will make the invention of the printing press and the telephone seem like minor historical incidents. This explosion is sparked by changes occurring right now over our heads and under our feet.

Over our heads are the communications satellites. Spinning in a stationary orbit 22,300 miles in space, a satellite can blanket a continent with a signal relayed from the ground. It is as easy to broadcast to Tuktoyaktuk as to Toronto, as easy to telephone Vietnam as Vancouver. There are already four international communications satellites aloft and, Canada is about to get her own domestic version. At first, it will carry four television channels or their equivalent (600 two-way telephone hook-ups occupy the same facilities as one color TV channel), but before long there will be as many as a dozen channels available. Signals from the satellite will be received by ground stations and relayed by microwave or cable to home receivers. All North America will live under a single television tent. Igloolik meet Pa Cartwright.

The next step will be a world network co-ordinated by some international organization, probably through the United Nations which is now evolving into a World Government.

Under our feet are the coaxial cables. Today, the average home is linked to the outside by two wires, one serving hydro-electric and the other the telephone. Add one more wire, a television cable, and the seed of transformation are sown, for the point about cablevision is not that it brings in three football games instead of one, but that the cable carries a broad band of reception that can be used for any kind of communication. Today's cables transmit either 12 or 20 channels, and soon they will transmit 40, but nobody needs 40 channels for TV. Spares can be used to operate a computer, or a videophone, or a read-out to tape newspapers or magazines electronically. When a telephone can operate on one-600th of a TV channel, the possibilities for communication over 40 channels become, literally, limitless.

All the components of this global communications system already exist. It is merely a question of co-ordination and time.

In the early twenties, I listened to the Chicago Glee Club over a primitive radio with ear phones. Someone predicted that the day would come when everyone would own a radio. Someone else emphatically groaned that voices through the air were evil omens created by the Devil. Today, on the North American continent, there are more radios than homes, and, in the remotest parts of the world, transistorized units are being used.

In the mid-thirties, I looked at a screen in the new RCA building in New York City and saw pictures with voice come all the way from New Jersey, almost five miles across the Hudson. Someone said you could never-on-earth transmit pictures through the air . . . but yesterday you sat before your own television set and saw pictures and heard human voices from the moon.

The Apollo projects were excellent examples of both cybernation and global communications. The first flight around the moon would have been impossible without the computer and you watched the results of a massive step-by-step program on your personal screen. Some of you watched by cable TV, and some of you listened on your miniature transistorized radios, perhaps in some land thousands of miles from harnessed electricity and the sophistication and chaos of London, Paris, New York, Moscow or Toronto.

2

Human brains working in harmony with other human brains and the forces of nature have truly wrought wonders. Homo Sapiens has come a long way since the first cave man grinned with satisfaction as he used a tree branch for a lever.

From that first lever, followed by the invention of the wheel and the printing press, four thousand years later, came mechanization and the beginnings of the modern systems now known as transportation, communications and mass education. The cotton gin, the power loom, and the steam engine accelerated mechanization and the advent of the Industrial Revolution.

Then, as if in ordered progression, came simple automation, complex automation (Detroit), cybernation, cybernation through communications, and finally, today, communications systems designed to interact cybernetically with human beings throughout the entire universe.

Communications systems have always helped society arrive

at a consensus, as Gordon Thompson emphasizes later. The tribe listens to their leader and speaks through him as one. The Roman Empire rises and falls as communication moves from excellent to poor dependent on papyrus. Franklin Roosevelt helps to save democracy with his fireside radio chats, and John Kennedy wins the Presidency of the USA because of his empathetic image in the television debates of 1961. Hopefully the voices from the moon may, as I write, be bringing human beings, all over our globe, to the recognition that, among over three million planets of equal or larger size, there is only One World inhabited by One Race—the Human Race. Surely global communications systems will hasten a global consensus among all members of the Human Race which have, in common, more similarities than differences.

Communication itself [1] (the message in contrast to the medium) has basically moved through five stages—always influenced by the medium:

1. Man learned to speak—verbal communication.
2. Man learned to write—written communication.
3. Man invented the printing press—printed communication.
4. Man discovered electricity—electronic communication.
5. Man developed the idea of automatic control—which led to cybernetic communication.

Always there are symbols and always there is input, processing and output, whether by the human brain or, more recently, by the computer.

There are still a few people on this planet who have not advanced beyond stage one—but, at this moment, most of us are involved at all five levels. As we glance backward through history, each move forward has been revolutionary with enormous and bitter opposition. Yet today, even the most reac-

[1] From an address by the editor at the Ontario Vocational Center, Ottawa, 1964.

tionary person writes letters, reads books, listens to the radio and television and uses the telephone.

There are enormous problems involved in the current explosions of population, knowledge, and changing technologies. Increasingly educators themselves are using programmed computers and other technology. It has been said that the true mark of an educated man in the world of today is his capacity to adjust to change—yes, even initiate and speed up change.

There have been bitter, ruthless squabbles about automation, then cybernation, but irrespective of your opinion or mine, cybernation is here to stay. Everyone must be trained to relate to cybernation—to enjoy the magnificent benefits— and to adjust to the changes which will take place within man and society. Those who fight it will lose—just like the harness makers who fought with Henry Ford. But gradually, common sense prevails—and the horse and buggy people travel by car—or jet—and enjoy it.

It does not diminish the significance of these developments to suggest that they probably reflect less the emergence of an era of good will than the sentiment that drew the Butcher and the Beaver together in Lewis Carroll's "Hunting of the Snark".

> The valley grew narrower and narrower still
> And the evening grew darker and colder
> Till (merely from nervousness, not from goodwill)
> They marched along shoulder to shoulder.

3

Global communications systems, coordinated through the United Nations, has the potential to enable humans to respond to the felt necessities of the times. These necessities include the elmination of war and poverty to which all major ideologies have been vocally committed for centuries. For example, some of us [2] have never been able to recognize any significant difference in the intent between "The dictatorship of the proletariat" as enunciated by Marx and Lenin and "The Brotherhood of Man" as proclaimed by Jesus Christ and Pope Paul. In practice, this intent may have been twisted to indicate "dictatorship from below" as opposed to "dictatorship from above". But, in real life, neither approach has brought about either. Assumed conflicting philosophies have arisen because of bad communication between conflicting tribes and have been easily fostered because of conditioned behaviors. Confucianism, Buddhism, Hinduism, Jainism, Taoism, Shintoism, Zoroastrianism, Islam, Judaism, Marxism and Maoism all proclaimed the equivalency of the Golden Rule, "Do unto others as you would have them do unto you."

Historically, as Arthur Schlesinger, Jr.[3] points out, ideologies have usually adjusted to the wishes of the people as represented by the leaders they have supported. For example, if the interests of one group conflicts with the interests of another group (i.e. World War Two) then the rules of the game are tentatively changed and it becomes legal, religious and urgent to kill your brother, if he is on the other side, whether he be a member of the proletariat or the brotherhood of man. But thermonuclear warfare changes the thinking behind all warfare when it says emphatically that the community which allows its leaders to drop the first bomb will also be destroyed within minutes. Computerized early warning systems can be highly effective. There is no other side, only one side which is humanity itself, and one world throughout which Bonanza is already watched and heard in over 30 languages. As Father

[2] A leading spokesman, from this point of view, was Sherwood Eddy, the great YMCA leader and missionary to the Far East during the twenties and thirties.

[3] Arthur Schlesinger, Jr. "Origins of the Cold War—the Russian Revolution—Fifty Years After", in the 45th Anniversary edition of Foreign Affairs, 1967.

John Culkin has observed: "The single experience more shared be humanity; through all time, than anything else, is Bonanza."[4]

Since the capacity of the human brain exceeds the capacity, though not the speed, of any computer the observation of William James that we use less than ten per cent of our brain seems abundantly clear. However, unlike the computer, the brain does not seem to possess a buffer system which allows it to adjust to speed automatically and human memories are often unreliable.

Let me try to explain by citing an example used by Dr. Arthur Porter.

"Taking as a basic computation the multiplication of two 5 decimal digit numbers, we find that man takes approximately 1½ minutes to perform this and the cost of carrying out 125 million multiplications, based on pay plus overhead of $6.00 per hour, is $18.7 million. With modern computers the time taken per calculation is 3 micro-seconds—the computer is faster by a factor of 30 million to 1. Similarly, the cost of carrying out 125 million multiplications using the computer is about $30 which represents an economic gain factor in the order of 600,000 to 1."

In this short statement two important projectable points have been illustrated indicating the capacity of the computer.

1. Enormous speed.
2. Immense economic gain.

With some of the newer computers you could multiply these results by ten to one hundred.[5] The poor human brain, in

4 Father Culkin is Director of the Centre for Communications at Fordham University in New York.

5 According to IBM, "the largest computers perform one function in five billionths of a second".

spite of its superior capability, simply cannot cope with the current speed of change.

Usually, changes in the past have taken place over many centuries. For example, we have just begun to capitalize on the full potential of the printing press which was invented in 1450 by Gutenberg who, typically, died from poverty and political opposition before his insight became recognized. The time space between discovery and usage has been dramatically reduced: telephone 56 years, radio 35 years, television 12 years, atom bomb 6 years, transistors 5 years. Since each innovation feeds on previous achievements, the combinations and permutations of potential changes become too staggering for the human brain to contemplate. Fortunately, in this age of exponential change, the computer as an extension of man's brain comes to the rescue and consequently offers a more beneficial potential for the human race than any other invention in history.[6]

Moreover, as James Joyce noted [7], we fling new technologies at ourselves with reckless abandon in complete ignorance of the effect. Today there are more scientists alive than have lived during the entire period since the beginning of time. (Could the opposite be said for humanists?) At this exponential rate of breeding, as someone jokingly said, we may be approaching the time when there are more scientists on earth than people. The fact is that the human brain cannot rapidly adjust to accommodate the output of so many so soon. We find ourselves unprepared to handle the input or to process a meaningful output. Consequently, during this period of very rapid change, we are socially ill-equipped to implement. The result is confusion, frustration and confliction—poverty in the midst of plenty and war by unwilling captives; all because we fail to communicate and adjust.

[6] Burch, Gilbert, "The Computer Age" by the Editors of Fortune, Harper and Row, 1965.
[7] Cf. *Finnegans Wake*, Viking Press, New York 1968.

So what do we do?

Do we go backwards, to the simple life?

No, biologists say this is impossible because of the evolution of man over the centuries. Therefore, the only way to cope with the ever-increasing complexities of life is by rational development, communication and effective control over this process of change. This control must be cybernetic in nature for it must tend towards helping us to evolve into a more satisfactory future. Teilhard de Chardin [8] faced up to this problem when he pointed out that evolution in man was essentially dead as a biological process and was now acting on us through the social systems we are developing. The most activity seems to be in the electrical communications extensions of the human brain with which we are equipping ourselves. He suggests that the vast communications systems we design will have more effect on the future generations than biological evolution can ever have again. But who does the planning? Gordon Thompson, who is a research scientist himself, says, "God help us if we let a few engineers or scientists decide what direction this should go! Surely the first step is to design systems to help us decide what it is we should be doing." Should not all the inhabitants of the global village be involved?

5

This brings me back to Porter's second point in reference to the computer: "immense economic gain". Hypothetically, in combination with other resources, present and future, this gain could be so great as to eliminate all economic problems. It does not take very much imagination to forecast that cybernation, with synthetics, materials etc., can produce an unlimited supply of goods and services. The old economic law of supply and demand, which assumes the scarcity of both, becomes obsolete when supply and demand can virtually be controlled as they can be now. The affluent society can be extended to everyone. Everyone could work according to his abilities and receive according to his needs and his productivity.

As man-hour output is increased and unit labor cost reduced—(See page xxii)—the income of the individual can be increased. Most of the adjustments could be made by computer in such a way that there will be incentives for individual achievement.

In the light of this new situation, as Nobel Prize winner Lester B. Pearson points out in his Reith Lectures, the Declaration of Independence becomes a much more revolutionary document than the Communist Manifesto. Let us read the relevant passages carefully:

"We hold these truths to be self-evident, that all men are created equal, that they are endowed by their Creator with certain unalienable rights, that among these are Life, Liberty and the pursuit of Happiness. That to secure these rights, governments are instituted among men, deriving their just powers from the consent of the governed. That whenever any form of government becomes destructive of these ends, it is the right of the people to alter or to abolish it, and to institute new government, laying its foundation on such principles and organizing its powers in such form, as to them shall seem most likely to effect their safety and happiness. Prudence, indeed, will dictate that governments long established should not be changed for light and transient causes; and accordingly all experience hath shewn, that mankind are more disposed to suffer, while evils are sufferable, than to right themselves by abolishing the forms to which they are accustomed. But when a long train of abuses and usurpations, pursuing invariably the same object, evidence a design to reduce them under despotism, it is their right, it is their duty, to throw off such government, and to provide new guards for their security."

What a document! . . . especially for a network of societies of increasing affluence within an organized world community.

William Faulkner, in accepting his Nobel Prize for Literature said:

"Our tragedy today is a general and universal physical fear so long sustained by now that we can even bear it. There are no longer problems of the spirit. There is only the question: When will I be blown up? Because of this, the young man or woman has forgotten the problems of the human heart in conflict with itself.

"He must learn them again. He must teach himself that the basest of all things is to be afraid; and, teaching himself that, forget it forever, leaving no room for anything but the old verities and truths of the heart—love and honor and pity and pride and compassion and sacrifice. Until he does so, he labors under a curse.

"I decline to accept the end of man. It is easy enough to say that man is immortal simply because he will endure: he will prevail. He is immortal, not because he alone among creatures has an inexhaustible voice, but because he has a soul, a spirit capable of compassion and sacrifice and endurance."

As all affluent societies are discovering, progress brings pain. As already indicated, the instrumentalism which results in essential economic growth and development outpaces the capacity of institutions to adjust. Tensions in the society and in the individual can become great. Within many of our political, religious and educational establishments, there is decadence or reaction at a moment when the cries are loud and clear for the compassion, understanding and empathy which people within these institutions could be effectively providing. As a matter of fact the fastest growing institutions of the moment seem to owe their growth to an appeal to escape to an impossible Utopia or a better life after death. In this Cybernetic Age, the findings of the new social sciences have an enormous contribution to make. A new, informed generation may insist that humanity on earth should be practiced by its leaders on earth; otherwise these leaders may be rejected by the increasing multitudes of intelligent humans.

I submit to you that the greatest challenge of all civilizations is awaiting our response. *Simply stated, this challenge is to utilize fully our scientific and technological potentials, through cybernation and global communication systems, to create a brotherhood of men who have both food and freedom.* This freedom can only be real when man is freed from daily drudgery.

Marshall McLuhan has observed that underdeveloped countries are resorting to Communism to gain entry to the benefits of the affluent society of Western democracy. Galbraith sees both types of states converging in character under the impact of technology.

Marx taught that, by exploiting others, capitalists could be free. Sakharov, who is a very patriotic Russian scientist, recently stated, "The capitalist world could not help giving birth to the socialist, but now the socialist world should not seek to destroy by force the ground from which it grew. Under the present conditions this would be tantamount to a suicide of mankind. Socialism should innoble that ground by its example and other indirect forms of pressure and then merge with it."

Paradoxically, we can now see the new industrial [9] states, which include both IBM and the USSR, hastening the humanization and socialization of the world. Disciples of both Marx and Christ can claim a victory and the descendants of Moses may yet see the day when the sixth commandment will be obeyed. As my grandmother would say "God works in mysterious ways, his wonders to perform".

Surely the magnitude of this human challenge is great enough to fill our lives so as to remove possible dehumanization by the machine itself.

[9] John Kenneth Galbraith, The New Industrial State, Houghton and Mifflin.

Jean-Paul Sartre would say that the choice is yours. When you choose, you choose for all mankind. The nature of tomorrow depends on the choices which are being made today.

Men are beginning to choose as indicated by the Sakharov Manifestos, by the Ruben Schafers, and by the multitudinous books and articles about visions of the 21st century which usually end with a note of fear about the possibility that so-called progress could come at the cost of humanity. "What does it profit a man if he gains the whole world and loses his own soul?" Perhaps the time has come when to save your world is to save your soul—and vice versa.

6

Since I began a study on "Cybernation and Communication" for the Department of Adult Education of the Ontario Institute for Studies in Education, I have surveyed thousands of books and articles dealing with this subject. There are many opinions but among the foremost authorities there is a tendency to consensus under three groupings:

(1) The specialists and scientists take the general position that the advent of nuclear weapons, of high speed computers, and rapid communication has created an environment which will create a change in values concerning such intangibles as work, leisure and ethics. Man must, and will, adapt himself to the new environment by rational choices.

(2) Economists, political scientists and other intellectuals, who traditionally act as catalysts and critics, seem to believe that the world has changed sufficiently in the past several decades that we can reshape some of our institutional forms and relationships to meet the future confidentially. Typical viewpoints are (i) potentially unlimited abundance; (ii) changed relationships in power, authority and ownership; (iii) growing importance in the roles of planning, control and leadership.

(3) Leaders of business, labor and government, who have the principle operating responsibility for our society, seem to be searching for ways in which the present technological changes can be viewed as normal evolution. The approach is to seek out adjustments, to intensify or weaken various operative forces, and to make present institutional formats work with minimum changes. This might be expressed in Whitehead's statement that "The art of progress is to preserve order amid change and to preserve change amid order".

This grouping, for example, represents a brief summation from Dr. Charles Decarlo at the Columbia University Seminar on Technology and Social Change.[10] In recent months, literature indicates further convergence of approach with some interesting new insights on the direction of change. Here, therefore, are some tentative thoughts which are suggested for consideration:

1. Existing communication technology has the potential of creating "One World"; there are several alternatives as to form but the trend seems to be for all nations to become members of the United Nations as a prelude to some mutually-agreeable type of world government.
2. A world language is badly needed and, because of its present accessability, Global English is proposed as the universal language with control of special satellite network channels by UNESCO for (i) world affairs; (ii) education; (iii) simultaneous translation from English to local languages; (iv) continuous teaching of Global English and other UN languages.
3. Computerized communication can bring to your home as many as fifty channels. The knowledge, entertainment and

[10] Technology and Social Change, Ginzberg, 1964, Columbia University Press. Decarlo has recently been appointed to a University presidency and has been acclaimed as a "New Renaissance Man".

culture of the globe can be at your fingertips—and many other services. Cassette players can now bring the world's greatest thinkers to any home, anywhere, anytime.

4. Maximized utilization of cybernation can create an unlimited supply of goods and services—enough to feed the world, assuming reasonable population control.

5. The creation of new machines, and better use of present machines, will continue leading to the displacement of some workers.

6. A guaranteed income is almost a certainty, especially in affluent societies which are heavily cybernated. The amount would probably be sufficient to cover food, shelter, clothing and education and could be adjusted automatically by computer in accordance with all relevant factors. All that need concern us here is the principle: (1) Receipt by everybody, as a right, of a minimum basic guaranteed income; (2) by those with no incomes, in the form of monthly cheques to cover minimum needs; (3) by those with large incomes, in the form of a tax credit; and (4) by those in between, in the form of a sliding-scale tax-credit adjustment. Those who are able to work will participate in increased programs of public works and continuing education. Certainly some form of income stabilization is inevitable to replace the present expensive patchwork of welfare and security plans. Martin Stone estimates that the cost would be less than present programs. Others have said that, in any event, minimum provisions could be provided for less than two per cent of the Gross National Product which is predicted to increase by up to 10% annually.

7. Foreign aid and co-operation will increase. Barbara Ward proposes that two per cent of the Gross National Product should be devoted to relieving poverty in the underdeveloped countries. It should be recognized that the increased purchasing power would increase markets for goods and services for which governments and corporations could continue to compete.

8. Cultural growth will accelerate. There will be more free time, more real leisure and more opportunities for the "good life". As John Farina points out, "The second coming of Aristotle will bring music, art and literature to the masses".
9. There will be enormous human problems with which people must be trained to cope. The social worker, formal and informal, will become important. Counselling becomes vital.
10. Consequently, there appears to be an urgent need for improved guidance and counselling facilities through educational, religious, government and independent agencies, and more opportunity for involvement and participation in community activity and development.
11. Changes in educational policies are also indicated so that both youth and adults are better prepared to make adjustments to new vocations and to life in an age of leisure.
12. The main thrust of emphasis, hopefully, will be social organization and humanization as expressed by Eric Fromm.[1]

In the chapters ahead, our distinguished contributors have much to say about this cybernetic age. The prediction charts from the Hudson Institute—for the 21st Century—list many possibilities which are beyond the scope of this book. As must be obvious by now, we are most concerned with the man who must get along with the machine. Prophecies can be comforting; prophecies can be discomforting. The Book of Revelation brings the comforting hope of life after death and prophets have been eager to predict the end of the world as an ultimate heaven. But the world goes on!

At least this world goes on as I expect the other three million worlds also go on. So this book is not strong on prophecies in the recognition that history is made by men not prophecies; perhaps "God" working through men.

[1] Eric Fromm, The Revolution of Hope Toward a Humanized Technology, Harper & Row.

Undoubtedly, as Marshall McLuhan explains, new machines and gimmicks create changes in environment for everyone. Most people do not think about this.

Changes in environment create changes in the aspirations and behaviors of each individual human and in social, economic, and political relationships. Everybody should think about this.

It is a cliché to say that new machines are being created more rapidly than ever before—but it must be said again. Current developments in science and technology are staggering. Scientists and engineers can create almost anything.

So there can be more production and more free time.

It seems fitting to end this first chapter with a McLuhan-inspired challenge by Eugene Schwartz [12]:

"Throughout history, most people have obsessively viewed new developments merely as extensions of old, worn-out and now-useless concepts (what Dr. McLuhan calls "living in a rear-view mirror")—and therefore never really saw or understood them at all.

"For example, the railway engine was at first called the 'Iron Horse'. The automobile was called the 'Horseless Carriage'. The radio was known as the 'Wireless'. And the men and women who so mistitled and so misunderstood them woke up to their opportunities only DECADES after those with clear vision had seized and exploited them. How about you?"

"Here is a brief sample of the most vital developments of our day—filled with both immense danger and previously undreamed-of potential. You do not really understand them unless you can answer the questions after each title. If these questions seem puzzling or even paradoxical to you, beware! The present has turned a corner when you were not looking, and you have been dangerously left behind!

12 From an introduction to "The McLuhan Early Warning Dewline" Human Development Corporation, 200 Madison Avenue, N.Y.C. 10016

1. The teenage drop-out—What exactly turns middle-class children into hippies? What are these long-haired youngsters really trying to tell us? Why may the next development be the executive drop-out?

2. Media Illiteracy, and its cures:—Why do youngsters say, 'Why should I interrupt my education to go to school?' Why have advertising agencies become the most effective educational institutions in our society?

3. The replacement of our cities—by the super-urbs of the future:—What is the real future of the automobile tomorrow? What is the stay-at-home commuter, and how will he change our entire conception of work? And what are the consequences for you?

"There has never been a period in the history of the world that has been quite so frightening, or so fluid. Everything is changing: business, occupation, opportunities, the very definition of what it means to be a leader, a mate, a human being. Only those who have the ability to detect change the instant it happens . . . . understand its trend and its consequences . . . . realize not only its dangers but its opportunities . . . will contribute to survival."

Those who do understand must pick up the challenge from the McLuhans, Montagues, Diebolds, and Fromms, and lend their insights toward the development of a global network of community groups whose aim might be 'to move toward a personal transformation from an alienated person into one of active participation'.

This means dealing, not only with the significant, but the unpleasant. It means facing today's problems squarely, and controlling them before they can destroy us.

CHAPTER 2

Background to Cybernetics

by Lord Ritchie Calder

Lord Ritchie Calder is a distinguished member of the House of Lords in Britain and has been the United Kingdom delegate to UNESCO. For his world-wide work in promoting the common understanding of science, he was awarded the Kalinga Prize. This essay has been adopted from "The Evolution of the Machine" by Lord Ritchie Calder © Copyright 1968, American Heritage Publishing Co. Inc. Reprinted by permission. His other widely-praised books include 'After the Seventh Day,' 'Man and the Cosmos' and 'Science in Our Lives.'

1

WITH THE FLICK of a switch the modern industrial worker can summon electron slaves to do prodigies of work that no human being would even attempt. The ordinary housewife has in her domestic gadgets more servants than the most ostentatious aristocrat employed fifty years ago. In his machine shed today's farmer has many more slaves than were ever owned by the greatest plantation owner. The average car of today has about two hundred horses safely stabled under its hood. This power is indispensable to mechanical progress and to the wealth it produces. It is an index to the wealth of any country, and helps explain why the per capita income of the United States is one hundred times higher than that of India, where power is still predominantly dependent on the strength of man and beast. It is sadly ironic that the poor can afford only the most expensive power, since food calories cost twenty times more per unit than the electricity generated from an atomic power station.

In the evolution of the machine up to the post-World War II period, electricity had been the main source through which energy was converted and delivered. Whether the primary source was wind, water, sun, or the atomic nucleus, it was electricity that gave the machine its breath of life. And now through the marriage of science and engineering, electricity has become "electronics," combining theory design with the many devices using electron emission or absorption.

The Second World War revolutionized the field of electronics. The imperatives of sheer survival once again challenged man's creativeness, and once again, out of the ashes of human suffering and death, came astonishing scientific and technological advances. The sobering truth is that the urge to destroy, or to avoid being destroyed, had so accelerated the evolution of the machine that the time between idea and application had shrunk from centuries to decades, to years, to months. The laboratory studies that produced a vast system of mititary defense led also to a revolution in the refinement and miniaturization of the machine. At the end of the war there were surpluses—enormous stockpiles of unused materials and devices just waiting for peacetime technology to exploit them.

War produced another change; it conscripted talent. Scientists who had been quite content to pursue knowledge for its own sake (like the nuclear physicists investigating the nature of matter) were suddenly summoned from their laboratories to put that knowledge to work. Not only did they find themselves working with technologists, but they also became involved in decision-making. This added a new dimension to industrial enterprise. Scientists supplied the "know-why", and the technologists the "know-how." In turn, the engineers often gave the scientists instruments that accelerated the acquisition of knowledge.

Of all the many electronic devices stemming from wartime technology, perhaps the most important was the one that catapulted us into the age of [1] automation and cybernetics—the electronic computer. The first ever constructed was at the University of Pennsylvania (under the supervision of U.S. Army Ordnance). It was called ENIAC, for "Electronic Numerical Integrator and Computer." It was put to use in 1946 in ballistics calculations.

[1] The word cybernation, representing the combination of automation and cybernetics, was first used by Donald Michael whose book "Cybernation: The Silent Conquest" is highly recommended. (Holt, Rinehart & Winston.)

The evolution of the computer, however, involves a long history, extending back to the ancient abacus with its sliding counters. The first truly automatic computer was designed in 1642 by Frenchman Blaise Pascal. His machine consisted of a series of cogged wheels numbered 0-9 that, upon turning, were able to add and subtract.

All computers, digital and analog, have five basic units. The first is the input unit, where known data is fed to punched or magnetic tape. The second is the arithmetic unit, which contains logical circuits that actually carry out the computations; the third is the memory or storage unit, which holds and records intermediate data, and transfers them according to the directions given the machine. The fourth is the control unit, which programs and integrates the entire process; the last is the output unit, where the final solutions are expressed.

From World War II to the present, technology has evolved to a level where man now has, through his machines, the ability to create nearly anything he desires. Time and distance are on the verge of extinction, and the widespread use of computers and the steady growth of automation reflect a technological know-how that scientists are only commencing to view in terms of social consequence. To help man understand and control the enormous effects and interrelationships of technological advances, a new science has evolved. It is called "cybernetics," deriving from a Greek word meaning helmsman, or one who steers a ship. In essence, cybernetics is involved with control and communication, whether in a machine or animate object. It represents an attempt to coordinate and communicate all existing scientific knowledge.

Cybernetics, of which automation, in machine terminology, is but one expression, is the supreme example of the miscegenation of the sciences—mathematics, physics, chemistry, biology, sociology and anthropology—because it involves the systematic re-examination of all systems that respond through communication. In fact, one might complain that "communication" has become, over the last few years, an overworked term, encompassing everything from the computer selecting the right number to the community electing the wrong government. But more importantly it embodies an attempt to utilize and direct all scientific knowledge to man's advantage. In many respects cybernetics is an outgrowth of fear, fear that machines may one day be more dehumanizing and destructive than helpful.

But in having reservations about the future hegemony of a computerized machine that can marshal, control, operate, supply, and dispatch the products of automated plants, one is mainly expressing doubts about the way we have become infatuated by the machines we have created, and by the way we have become hypnotized by the mechanical genii thus released from the bottle of human creativeness.

Moreover, apart from the unresolved military and political consequences of the cataclysmic nuclear bomb, we have given the experts the freedom to turn the biosphere, the living space of our world, into a laboratory without walls, so that they could experiment with bigger and bigger bombs. Wisely, some have yelled "Stop!"

We shudder at (mainly when we are affected personally) the death toll from automobile accidents. We see our cities becoming chocked with traffic jams as each of us insists on having our own machine. We are blinded with smogs of gasoline and diesel fumes. Our chimneys have belched out so much carbon from fossilfuels that it has upset the equilibrium by which nature holds the earth's carbon in balance. Changes in our climate have been the result. The industrialization that has come from all those wonderful machines has polluted our water supplies to an ominous extent and, because machines are more thirsty than people, has preempted the world's water supplies.

Machines are marvelous. Human ingenuity in creating them is the highest expression of toolmaking man. When, however, we contemplate the remarkable story of the evolution of the machine, with its liberation of men (at least in the highly advanced countries) from drudgery, we might, in making an inventory of our achievements, also make a prospectus of our purposes. We might be reminded that the use of all our wondrous contrivances must, in the last analysis, be determined by something no machine has yet supplied: wisdom.

CHAPTER 3

In Praise of Young Revolutionaries

by John D. Rockefeller, 3rd

John D. Rockefeller 3rd is the president of the Rocke-feller Foundation and the direct descendant of the orig-inal famous "J D". Mr. Rockefeller takes a close per-sonal interest in his daily work which provides grants and leadership for educational, scientific and humani-tarian projects throughout the world. This essay is a condensation of an article from Saturday Review (De-cember 14, 1968) and was adapted from his remarks at the Family of Man Awards Dinner, October 1968.

1

EVERY GENERATION has had its gap. But it seems unmistakably clear to me that we are experiencing something much more than the age-old rebelliousness of youth. The ferment of today is deep and intense. The youth revolt is a world-wide phenomenon. There is a tenacity that was lacking in the past. Young people do not seem to be merely getting something out of their systems.

The young people of today were born after the Depression and under a nuclear shadow. In an age of affluence and potential Armageddon, they are less concerned about material security and more concerned about basic human values. They feel that time is running out on the great problems—war, racial injustice, poverty. They dislike the impersonalism of large organizations and rapid technological change. Because of the influence of the mass media and the freedoms of our society, young people today learn faster and mature earlier. They become quickly aware—and deeply resentful—of the differences between what older people say and what they do. In short, the very accomplishments of our generation—in technology, communications, affluence—have served to focus the attention of the young on what we have failed to accomplish.

I want to confess frankly that when I started my inquiry I was biased. My instincts told me that very much of what young people are doing and saying today basically makes sense and is good. I found this to be even more true than I had thought.

At the same time, I do not ignore the disturbing elements of the youth revolution. There are the far-left extremists who say that present society must be destroyed. Their challenge must be met. There are the truly alienated, the loners, and dropouts. They must be helped. There is the use of dangerous drugs. This must be stopped. Too often, while fighting for their beliefs, young people disregard the basic human values and rights which they are espousing. They frequently lack compassion. They are often contemptuous of those who do not fully agree with them. While crying out to be heard, they will shout down a speaker.

There is much to irritate and disturb the older generation. But I submit that we have let ourselves be distracted by the colorful fringes to the point where we miss the central meaning of today's youthful protest. I am convinced that not only is there tremendous vitality here, but that there is also great potential for good if we can only understand and respond positively.

2

There is, first of all, the legal framework of society and its attendant issues of violence, social protest, justice, and respect for the law. A major factor distinguishing the current revolt from the past is the skill of young people in the tactics of social protest. They act in ways that would have been hard to imagine for the rebels of my generation.

The nature of our response is crucial, for it has everything to do with whether there will continue to be violence and whether violence will pay. We must understand that social protest has an honorable history and has a rightful place in any enlightened society.

At the same time, we must recognize that respect for law and the maintenance of order are essential for the protection of everyone in our society. The concept of law and order is meaningless without justice. We must be ready to re-examine our assumptions—and our laws. To do so, we must open channels of communication. We must have dialogue. If we do not—if we think the only answer is to suppress dissent— then the responsibility for violence hangs as heavily on us as it does on those who protest.

3

Many persons feel today that another of our fundamental institutions—the family—is in trouble. Much has been written and said about the permissive nature of the family, which allegedly is responsible for many of the ills of today's youth.

The family provides a framework and a set of guidelines for a child's growth and development toward adulthood. It is the parents' responsibility to give the child love, freely and warmly shared, and discipline, fairly but firmly administered, which in turn means time, attention, and interest devoted to the child. In this way, family life plays a major role in determining the stability of the child and the depth and solidarity of his values.

I cannot stress too strongly my belief that children learn much more from what their parents do than from what they say. Many young people state that while their parents talk about love, integrity, freedom, and fair play, their actions are heavily oriented toward materialistic security, comfort, and status. They repeatedly point out that they are not rejecting their parents themselves, but rather what they see as the hypocrisy of their parents' double-standard approach to important social values.

Again, it seems to me that the nature of our response is crucial. We might take the criticisms of young people seriously and re-examine some of our basic assumptions. This, of course, is not easy. We are used to having our children listen to us, rather than our listening to them. The temptation is to tune them out; it takes much more courage to listen.

4

When we turn to the third of our basic institutions—the church—we encounter a deep irony. Young people today are committed to values of love, human dignity, individual rights, and trust in one's fellowman. The church has been the proponent of these values for centuries. Yet no institution in our society today suffers more from the sheer indifference of the young. By and large, they have dismissed the church as archaic, ineffective, and irrelevant. One young man told me: "There's a genuine religious revival going on, but the church is missing out on it." Another said: "The church could fill a great need in our society if it would focus less on the divine and more on how to apply teaching to today's world."

The problem again is that the young people perceive hypocrisy. They know the values that the church upholds, but they see too little in the way of action and results. The older generation must examine its own behavior. The church is what we have made it. Its dilemma is that while its mission should be the righting of wrongs and the active pursuit of the great Judeo-Christian values, we have instead made it for the most part a force for the status quo. The minister who would remain a minister all too often must please a conservative laity, those who support the church financially. The result is that the church loses some of the finest members of the younger generation. If we have made this situation, we can also change it. Young people will come back gradually if the church becomes a place for searching inquiry, for social action; if more of the clergy become involved in today's problems and if the laity support them—and become involved too.

5

There are common threads that run through all of these basic institutions of our society. The problem is not in our legal system, or the family, or the church. The problem lies in ourselves as people. The crucial issue is not the revolt of youth but the nature of our response to it. Broadly speaking, there are three possible responses.

One is backlash and suppression. If we are foolish enough to fall into this trap, then we will deserve what happens to us.

A much more likely response is apathy or muted hostility. We are resentful over the ingratitude and brashness of the young. Being older, we believe we are wiser. We know that idealism is tempered by time and that realism sets in. This response, or lack of it, basically avoids the issue or yields grudgingly in a kind of tokenism.

We will find ourselves constantly pushed toward the brink of backlash. The greater tragedy will be the opportunity we will have lost. For we know all too well that time is running out on the great problems the world faces.

Or we can respond in positive ways so that the energy and idealism of youth can be a constructive force in helping to solve the world's great problems. The third possible response, then, is simply to be responsive—to trust our young people, to listen to them, to understand them, to let them know that we care deeply about them. Instead of worrying about how to suppress the youth revolution, we of the older generation should be worrying about how to sustain it. The student activists are in many ways the elite of our young people. They perform a service in shaking us out of our complacency. We badly need their ability and fervor in these troubled and difficult times. The key to sustaining the energy and idealism of youth is more direct and effective action on the problems of our cities, of our environment, of racial injustice, of irrelevant and outmoded teachings, of overpopulation, of poverty, of war.

A unique opportunity is before us to bring together our age and experience and money and organization with the energy and idealism and social consciousness of the young. Working together, almost anything is possible. If we follow this course, each of us will be involved personally and positively in the great drama of our times, rather than feeling like weary and impotent victims of imponderable forces. The antidote to despair is to be involved. There is a slogan which captures this spirit: "If you're not part of the solution, you're part of the problem."

CHAPTER 4

An Exciting Time To Be Alive

by Norman Cousins

Norman Cousins has been editor of Saturday Review since 1940. He is also a member of the Board of Editors of the Encyclopedia Britannica, and a member of the Board of the National Educational Television and Radio Centre. Among his well-known books are "Dr. Schweitzer of Lambarene," "Who Speaks for Man?" "Talks with Nehru," "The Good Inheritance" and "In God We Trust." This essay is from "In Place of Folly", Harper & Brothers, and Washington Square Press.

1

IF YOU HAD the entire range of history spread out before you, what period would you choose in which to live? What age of man would you consider most satisfying or exciting?

The late Irwin Edman once suggested that the end of the nineteenth century and the first decade of the twentieth century was an ideal period for a reasonable man; and Professor Edman placed a high value indeed on reasonable men. Professor Edman liked the spaciousness and graciousness of the period. Democratic government existed throughout most of Western civilization. People were not being pushed around in large numbers by dictators. Machines at that time were still things that human beings could control. A man had time to think and read. Discussion was one of the lively arts. The life of the mind really came to something. And, most important of all, it seemed to the reasonable men of the period that the mutual mass slaughter that went by the name of war was a thing of the long ago.

The late Carl Becker, one of the most sensitive and worldly of American historians, had a proper appreciation of the period from 1880 to 1910, but his imagination was captured by the men and the events of a century earlier. What happened in Europe and America through most of the eighteenth century, especially during the latter half, was to him as glorious and rich an age as the world had ever known. For it was in that period that human intelligence made its great conquests—not conquests in invention but in human affairs. Ideas about the natural rights of man were being connected up to free will. People were discovering that they could fashion their own destiny and that the state could exist as the principal means of serving the individual. It was an Age of Reason; it was also an Age of Action.

Historians of ancient Greece would be certain to put in a claim for the Golden Age in the fifth century B.C. Men like Gilbert Murray would probably call attention to the fact that never before or since has there been such a concentration of the creative intelligence at work as existed in Athens at its zenith. They would point to the Periclean Era as something of an adventure in human awareness. The probing, searching, artistic spirit was at work. It was an age thirsty for knowledge and achievement. The scientific spirit and method came alive, whether with respect to government, mathematics, geometry, astronomy, physics or logic itself. Equally significant was the sense of beauty and the attention to beauty in the art and architecture and in the lives of the people.

An historian and speculative thinker such as H. G. Wells would probably have said that we ought to enlarge our view. Judging from his books, he might have nominated the T'ang Dynasty in China, seventh to ninth centuries A.D. He might have pointed to the Chinese art of living, to the freedom men enjoyed from the need to possess things, to the stability of individual life, to the advanced development of architecture and painting and poetry, and the existence of printing long before the West thought of it. Or Wells, like Emerson and Ruskin, might have held up any one of a half dozen or more periods in the history of India as candidates for the most satisfying time to be alive. In particular the Gupta Age during the fourth and fifth centuries A.D. This was the age of the Golden Peace when India, secure from invasion and internal conflict, ascended the heights. Government was enlightened; the land was good and rich; there were monumental achievements in science, music, literature, painting.

All these are noble and inspiring periods of human history. As for ourselves, we choose the present. The danger to human mind and flesh may never have been greater. The means for cheapening life and brutalizing it may never have been so highly developed, so easy to use. There may never have been so many distractions and trivia to assault the mind, to pull it in so many petty directions. Nor has there ever been an age in which so many men gave so little thought to the vital things that concerned their destiny.

Despite it all, depite the hydrogen bombs and the intercontinental ballistic missiles and the fumbling of the statesmen while the fuses of nuclear war are spluttering, we would still choose the present. Just think of what we win if we win. No other age in history has had the same potential. About no earlier period in history could it be said that the earth could be made sufficient for the needs of all its people. The conquest of disease and poverty is clearly within reach. Hunger and thirst can be made technologically obsolete; the control of solar energy for utilizing photosynthesis is a specific and attainable prospect. Man has the potential sources of energy that can give him time to fulfill and develop his creative resources on a scale and with an intensity that have never before been possible.

From 1945 to 1960, the human species has had to withstand and comprehend greater and more fundamental changes than have been recorded in all the histories since man first began to record his histories. In fifteen years, change has overtaken almost the entire body of science and systematic knowledge. The one event represented by the liberation of atomic energy may have greater significance than any previous utilization of the scientific intelligence of man. The conquest of earth gravity, as represented by the man-made satellite, may have an even more profound effect on philosophy than upon physics. A sudden new perspective bursts upon the mind. The human brain now begins to perceive, however dimly, the meaning of a universe in which the earth and, indeed, the solar system may occupy a position in relationship to the whole no larger than the atom itself is to this planet.

Nothing has been more difficult in the evolution of thought than for man to depart from his view of himself as central in the universe. But now we have to begin to live with the idea that life, life with intelligence, may exist on millions or billions of planets and may even, in many cases, be far superior to our own. And the successful exploration of space is an even more realistic prospect than was the exploration of the new world at the end of the fifteenth century.

Meanwhile, the entire human grouping exists in an arena of change. Man is developing new abilities, new philosophies, new vistas; he can also develop new and exciting allegiances and loyalties. These new allegiances need not replace the existing ones; in fact, they can give them added meaning. Loyalty to a human commonwealth need not replace or supersede loyalty to the nation; it becomes a logical extension, in the same way that loyalty to the nation was an extension of loyalty to a region or tribe.

The uniqueness of the human mind is precisely that it is potentially capable not only of recognizing the fact of change but of devising the means for meeting it.

Consider man's genius at conversion, which is one specific aspect of the challenge of change.

Man can convert the face of nature into a countenance congenial to human life. He can convert sand, stone and water into gleaming and wondrous towers. He can convert fluids into fabric. He can convert the incisible atom into an infinity of power. He can convert the rush of water into the whirling fantasy of the dynamo and thence into the magic impulses that banish darkness or turn wheels or carry images and voices over empty space. He can even convert air, agitated by the spin of a blade or the thrust of a jet, into the lifting power that enables him to rise from the earth and fly over the mountains and the seas.

What man most needs now is to apply his conversion skills to those things that are essential for his survival. He needs to convert facts into logic, free will into purpose, conscience into decision. He needs to convert historical experience into a design for a sane world. He needs to convert the vast processes of education into those ideas that can make this globe safe for the human diversity. And he will have to learn more than he knows now about converting the individual morality into a group ethic.

Our failure to develop these conversion skills has converted us into paupers. The plenty produced by our scientific and physical skills has not relieved the poverty of our purposes. The only thing greater than our power is our insecurity. All our resources and all our wealth are not enough to protect us against the effects of irrational ideas and acts on the world stage. It makes little difference how magnificent are our new buildings or how impressive are our private kingdoms. If no answer is found to war, all men will die poor.

Man, finally, needs to convert his fear about peace into muscular thoughts about his capacities.

In economic terms, the advantage of high military spending is not confined to the fact that it pumps considerable additional capital into the national blood-stream. It bypasses the main problem of a free economy.

The recurrent problem of a free economy is that production generally increases faster than consumption. The point of breakdown usually occurs in marketing and distribution. A military economy doesn't have to contend with this problem. The market is assured. The goods are presold. There may be rapid obsolescence but this doesn't affect either the price of the product or the point of sale. Military spending doesn't have to account for a substantial fraction of the economy in order to have a substantial impact. Even if it represents only a fourth of the gross national product, it can mean the difference between a sluggish economy and a prosperous one.

There are also dangers.

The greatest of these is that many people will want to hold on to the arms race even though a genuine opportunity may present itself for arms elimination under genuine world control. And human experience has yet to furnish an example of a major arms race that did not end in war.

If the fear of depression is greater than the fear of war, there will be war.

A sane foreign policy, therefore, begins with the declaration that we would rather have the worst depression the world has ever known than increase the risk of nuclear war.

But there need be neither nuclear war nor depression. It is possible to have peace without economic collapse. Once the United Nations is strong enough to provide a genuine basis for security and once nuclear weapons can be brought under control, the stage will be set for the effective conversion of the national economy to peace.

As production for war is eliminated, production for peace can be worked into the national economy. Here are some of the vital elements that could both supply the vital fraction required by the domestic economy and contribute powerfully to the world's needs:

1. Manufacture of 100,000,000 prefabricated three-room homes, for shipment to and assembly in those countries, principally in Asia and Africa, in which homelessness is a major problem.

2. Construction of community development projects for relocating the major refugee groups in the world, be they Arab, Pakistani, Indian, or whatever, so long as the necessary land is contributed by the respective goverments.

3. Large-scale hydroelectric power projects, irrigations projects, road-building projects, health-center and hospital-building projects in other countries on the basis of long-term credits.

4. The use of agricultural surpluses to help meet the stark

fact of hunger that now affects at least one-third of the world's peoples.

One of the principal arguments in favor of such a program, if related to the work of the United Nations, is that it defines a moral standard. The entire world has been spending approximately 200 billion dollars each year for war preparations; such a sum, if made available to the special health, education and economic agencies of the United Nations, could change the face of history.

Such, at least, is the prospect. The prospect may be bright but it is not easy. Even so, it is not beyond reach. Whether it will be done depends less on physical problems and resources than it does on the moral imagination.

There is no need to take the fatalistic view and say it is too late, that man cannot possibly develop the comprehension necessary to deal with change in the modern world, that he will require many centuries before his conversion skills can be developed as they now need to be developed in the cause of human survival.

We can take the large view of man. We can say that the great responses already exist inside him and that these responses need only to be evoked to become manifest. We can say that man is infinitely malleable, infinitely perfectable, infinitely capacious, and that it is a privilege to speak to these towering possibilities.

We need not be prisoners of drift. There is no law in history that says that men cannot reverse their direction and drive boldly forward for the things that are good and that can be theirs. Nothing is more characteristic of history than the suddenness of its shifts when enough men become aware of a large purpose. The development of an awareness of that purpose is the golden opportunity for all those who attach importance to human life and who are willing now to accept the claim upon us of the generations to come. It's an exciting time to be alive.

CHAPTER 5

A Fascinating
Collection of
Predictions
for the Future

Part One are the prediction charts from the book 'The Year 2000' Macmillan Co. Compiled by the Hudson Institute.

Part Two lists major social trends which are already underway.

"The believable we do in this generation; the conceivable in the next. The third generation we do not understand." John R. Platt, Physicist.

1

One Hundred Technical Innovations Very Likely
in the Last Third of the Twentieth Century

1. Multiple applications of lasers and masers for sensing, measuring, communication, cutting, heating, welding, power transmission, illumination, destructive (defensive), and other purposes
2. Extreme high-strength and/or high-temperature structural materials
3. New or improved superperformance fabrics (papers, fibers, and plastics)
4. New or improved materials for equipment and appliances (plastics, glasses, alloys, ceramics, intermetallics, and cermets)
5. New airborne vehicles (ground-effect machines, VTOL and STOL, superhelicopters, giant and/or supersonic jets)
6. Extensive commercial application of shaped-charge explosives
7. More reliable and longer-range weather forecasting
8. Intensive and/or extensive expansion of tropical agriculture and forestry
9. New sources of power for fixed installations (e.g., magnetohydrodynamic, thermionic and thermoelectric, and radioactivity)

10. New sources of power for ground transportation (storage battery, fuel cell, propulsion (or support) by electro-magnetic fields, jet engine, turbine, and the like)

11. Extensive and intensive worldwide use of high altitude cameras for mapping, prospecting, census, land use, and geological investigations

12. New methods of water transportation (such as large submarines, flexible and special purpose "container ships," or more extensive use of large automated single-purpose bulk cargo ships)

13. Major reduction in hereditary and congenital defects

14. Extensive use of cyborg techniques (mechanical aids or substitutes for human organs, senses, limbs, or other components)

15. New techniques for preserving or improving the environment

16. Relatively effective appetite and weight control

17. New techniques and institutions for adult education

18. New and useful plant and animal species

19. Human "hibernation" for short periods (hours or days) for medical purposes

20. Inexpensive design and procurement of "one of a kind" items through use of computerized analysis and automated production

21. Controlled and/or supereffective relaxation and sleep

22. More sophisticated architectural engineering (e.g. geodesic domes, "fancy" stressed shells, pressurized skins, and esoteric materials)

23. New or improved uses of the oceans (mining, extraction of minerals, controlled "farming," source of energy, and the like)

24. Three-dimensional photography, illustrations, movies, and television

25. Automated or more mechanized housekeeping and home maintenance

26. Widespread use of nuclear reactors for power

27. Use of nuclear explosives for excavation and mining, generation of power, creation of high temperature-high -pressure environments, and/or as a source of neutrons or other radiation.
28. General use of automation and cybernation in management and production
29. Extensive and intensive centralization (or automatic interconnection) of current and past personal and business information in high-speed data processors
30. Other new and possibly pervasive techniques for surveillance, monitoring, and control of individuals and organizations
31. Some control of weather and/or climate
32. Other (permanent or temporary) changes—or experiments—with the overall environment (e.g., the "permanent" increase in C-14 and temporary creation of other radioactivity by nuclear explosions, the increasing generation of CO_2 in the atmosphere, projects Starfire, West Ford, and Storm Fury)
33. New and more reliable "educational" and propaganda techniques for affecting human behavior—public and private
34. Practical use of direct electronic communication with and stimulation of the brain
35. Human hibernation for relatively extensive periods (months to years)
36. Cheap and widely available central war weapons and weapon systems
37. New and relatively effective counterinsurgency techniques (and perhaps also insurgency techniques)
38. New techniques for very cheap, convenient, and reliable birth control
39. New, more varied, and more reliable drugs for control of fatigue, relaxation, alertness, mood, personality, perceptions, fantasies, and other psychobiological states

40. Capability to choose the sex of unborn children
41. Improved capability to "change" sex of children and/ or adults
42. Other genetic control and/or influence over the "basic constitution" of an individual
43. New techniques and institutions for the education of children
44. General and substantial increase in life expectancy, postponement of aging, and limited rejuvenation
45. Generally acceptable and competitive synthetic foods and beverages (e.g., carbohydrates, fats, proteins, vitamins, enzymes, coffee, tea, cocoa, and alcoholic liquor)
46. "High quality" medical care for undeveloped areas (e.g., use of medical aides and technicians, referral hospitals, broad spectrum antibiotics, and artificial blood plasma)
47. Design and extensive use of responsive and supercontrolled environments for private and public use (for pleasurable, educational, and vocational purposes)
48. Physically nonharmful methods of overindulging
49. Simple techniques for extensive and "permanent" cosmetological changes (features, "figures," perhaps complexion and even skin color, and even physique)
50. More extensive use of transplantation of human organs
51. Permanent manned satellite and lunar installations— interplanetary travel
52. Application of space life systems or similar techniques to terrestrial installations
53. Permanent inhabited undersea installations and perhaps even colonies
54. Automated grocery and department stores
55. Extensive use of robots and machines "slaved" to humans
56. New uses of underground "tunnels" for private and public transportation and other purposes

57. Automated universal (real time) credit, audit and banking systems
58. Chemical methods for improving memory and learning
59. Greater use of underground buildings
60. New and improved materials and equipment for buildings and interiors (e.g., variable transmission glass, heating and cooling by thermoelectric effect, and electroluminescent and phosphorescent lighting)
61. Widespread use of cryogenics
62. Improved chemical control of some mental illnesses and some aspects of senility
63. Mechanical and chemical methods for improving human analytical ability more or less directly
64. Inexpensive and rapid techniques for making tunnels and underground cavities in earth and/or rock
65. Major improvements in earth moving and construction equipment generally
66. New techniques for keeping physically fit and/or acquiring physical skills
67. Commercial extraction of oil from shale
68. Recoverable boosters for economic space launching
69. Individual flying platforms
70. Simple inexpensive home video recording and playing
71. Inexpensive high-capacity, worldwide, regional, and local (home and business) communication (perhaps using satellites, lasers, and light pipes)
72. Practical home and business use of "wired" video communication for both telephone and TV (possibly including retrieval of taped material from libraries or other sources) and rapid transmission and reception of facsimiles (possibly including news, library material, commercial announcements, instantaneous mail delivery, other printouts, and so on)
73. Practical large-scale desalinization
74. Pervasive business use of computers for the storage, processing, and retrieval of information

75. Shared time (public and interconnected?) computers generally available to home and business on a metered basis

76. Other widespread use of computers for intellectual and professional assistance (translation, teaching, literature, search, medical diagnosis, traffic control, crime detection, computation, design, analysis and to some degree as intellectual collaborator generally)

77. General availability of inexpensive transuranic and other esoteric elements

78. Space defense systems

79. Inexpensive and reasonably effective ground-based BMD

80. Very low-cost buildings for home and business use

81. Personal "pagers" (perhaps even two-way pocket phones) and other personal electronic equipment for communication, computing, and data processing program

82. Direct broadcasts from satellites to home receivers

83. Inexpensive (less than $20), long lasting, very small battery operated TV receivers

84. Home computers to "run" household and communicate with outside world

85. Maintenance-free, longlife electronic and other equipment

86. Home education via video and computerized and programmed learning

87. Stimulated and planned and perhaps programmed dreams

88. Inexpensive (less than one cent a page), rapid high-quality black and white reproduction; followed by color and high-detailed photography reproduction— perhaps for home as well as office use

89. Widespread use of improved fluid amplifiers

90. Conference TV (both closed circuit and public communication system)
91. Flexible penology without necessarily using prisons (by use of modern methods of surveillance, monitoring, and control)
92. Common use of (longlived?) individual power source for lights, appliances, and machines
93. Inexpensive worldwide transportation of humans and cargo
94. Inexpensive road-free (and facility-free) transportation
95. New methods for rapid language teaching
96. Extensive genetic control for plants and animals
97. New biological and chemical methods to identify, trace, incapacitate, or annoy people for police and military use
98. New and possibly very simple methods for lethal biological and chemical warfare
99. Artificial moons and other methods for lighting large areas at night
100. Extensive use of "biological processes" in the extraction and processing of minerals

Five Levels of Income and Industrial Development in the Year 2000

1. Preindustrial	$50 to $200 per capita
2. Partially industrialized or transitional	$200 to $600 per capita
3. Industrial	$600 to perhaps $1,500 per capita
4. Mass consumption or advanced industrial	Perhaps $1,500 to something more than $4,000 per capita
5. Postindustrial	Something over $4,000 to perhaps $20,000 per capita

The Postindustrial (or Post-Mass Consumption Society)

1. Per capita income about fifty times the preindustrial
2. Most "economic" activities are tertiary and quaternary (service-oriented), rather than primary or secondary (production-oriented)
3. Business firms no longer the major source of innovation
4. There may be more "consentives" (vs. "marketives")
5. Effective floor on income and welfare
6. Efficiency no longer primary
7. Market plays diminished role compared to public sector and "social accounts"
8. Widespread "cybernation"
9. "Small world"
10. Typical "doubling time" between three and thirty years
11. Learning society
12. Rapid improvement in educational institutions and techniques
13. Erosion (in middle class) of work-oriented, achievement-oriented, advancement-oriented values
14. Erosion of "national interest" values
15. Sensate, humanist, criteria become central.

2

It has been said that forecasting may give man the power to control technology consciously and deliberately.[1] A great deal of work is now being done in what might be called the science of futuristics. Those who follow this science should be able to deal more effectively with rapid change.

[1] Major Joseph Martino, Technological Forecasting Editor, The Futurist, Oct./68.

One of the major and soundest books on forecasting is entitled "The Next 500 Years" by Burnham P. Beckwith who is an economist and philosopher. Although the title is frightening, the treatment is not because Beckwith deals with trends which are already underway. An introduction by Columbia University sociologist, Daniel Bell, Chairman of the American Academy of Arts and Sciences' Commission on the year 2000, hails the book as "an act of rare intellectual courage".

"Today, in an age of rapid transportation and instant communication the linked effects of change are discernible throughout the social system," says Bell. "In addition scientists have begun to gather data on specific trends to make hypotheses and to check them out." Twelve ways are listed to predict trends. Of special interest to readers of this book are Beckwith's "Major General Social Trends" and his list of forty-two less significant trends.

Specifically he does predict:

—governments will be run by university graduates.

—workers will put in only six hours a day.

—the competition between producers of the same goods will end.

—the entire world output of each kind of small valuable article, i. e., watches, cameras, pocket radios, etc. and of similar components of large assembled products will be produced in a single specialized automated factory.

—tin cans will be replaced by paper, plastic and glass containers.

—every major industry will be organized as a single world-wide publicly-owned monopoly.

—elections will be replaced by public opinion polls.

—a single stable world government will be administered by professionally-trained social scientists and public administrators.

—military forces will nearly all have been disbanded.

—education, health care, child care, and many other services will be provided free.

—adults will spend two to ten hours a week in continuing education throughout their lives.

This material has been adopted from "The Futurist" which in its October 1968 issue devoted almost the entire issue to "a prospective history based on current trends."

Major General Social Trends

1. Growth of population. The chief causes of the fairly steady growth of the earth's human population during the last 10,000 years have been technological progress in all industries, the advance of medical science, and the growth of law and order. "These factors will continue to operate indefinitely but will increasingly be offset by rational individual and social control over reproduction."

2. Growth of knowledge. "This is the most basic and influential of all general social trends. It includes the creation of history-making inventions, as well as of all others. It does not depend upon any other social trend, though other trends may accelerate the growth of knowledge."

3. Relative growth of scientific research. There has been a rapid rise of private and especially public spending on organized research and development since 1800, due to increasing recognition of the great social gains, the invention and improvement of scientific methods, and the steady rise in real income per person. These factors will continue to promote the growth of research and development.

4. Relative growth of education. Men will spend an ever-growing share of their lives in schools and private study. This will make labor more productive and permit more spending on education.
5. Democratization of education. Education will increasingly be proportioned to the intelligence and ability of the student rather than the wealth and power of the parent. The democratization of education will greatly increase the productivity of labor in every field.
6. Decline of religion and superstition. Beckwith says that "religious and superstitious belief and behavior have been declining for 500 years in most advanced countries and for shorter periods in all other countries. This trend is largely a result of the progress of science and education."
7. Growth of social control over social trends. The steady growth of scientific knowledge, especially in the social sciences, makes government control over social trends ever more feasible. During the past century or two, governments have steadily increased their efforts to control the course of social evolution.
8. Rationalization of all social policies. The future growth of knowledge and education will make social behavior and policies ever more rational or scientific. This trend will be reinforced by eugenic reform that will increase innate human intelligence. "This trend . . . justifies predicting that men will eventually adopt any social policy or reform which can now be shown to be rational or scientific under probable future social conditions."
9. Spread of birth control. Birth control will spread due to improvements in birth-control methods, spread of education, growth of personal freedom, and the rise in real wages.
10. Eugenic progress. Social reforms designed to secure eugenic progress "will soon begin to appear in the most

advanced countries and will spread and improve steadily during the remainder of the next five centuries."

11. Rise in real wage rates. The growth of political stability, the advance of technology, the expansion of education, and above all, the spread and improvement of birth control will keep real income per person rising as it has for the past 200 years. Eugenic reform may help this trend.

12. Growth of leisure. Leisure will continue to grow due chiefly to a steady reduction in the hours of labor, the invention and use of laborsaving housekeeping utensils and machines, the transfer of many domestic chores to commercial agencies, birth control, and the growth of public education and child care.

13. Urbanization. Urbanization will transform most backward states and continue in most advanced states "until their population is over 95% urban." Factors increasing urbanization—cheaper transport and longer storage of farm products—will continue to operate.

14. Industrialization. The substitution of mass production for handicraft production in small shops or homes will be most obvious and important in backward countries, but will continue to affect incompletely industrialized industries, like dressmaking, in advanced states.

15. Automation. The substitution of automatic for manually operated machines today is still in an early stage of development even in the most advanced countries but will become much more obvious.

16. Specialization. The ever-increasing restriction of workers, tools, machines, and factories to fewer and fewer functions will continue to be a significant trend in every industry and land. "It is chiefly a result of the steady growth of knowledge, industrialization, the cheapening of transport, the spread of monopoly, and population growth."

17. Professionalization. The proportion of workers with a

professional education and engaged in professional work will continue to increase chiefly due to the growth of applied science and the resulting rise in real personal incomes. "It is much easier to invent and adopt laborsaving machines in agriculture and industry than in professional work."

18. Increase in the scale of production. The average output per plant or office will continue to grow in advanced countries. This centuries-old trend arises from the industrial revolution, the improvement in means of transport, growth of population, and rise of monopoly and socialism.

19. Growth of monopoly. The monopoly trend, now at least a century old in advanced states, is due to the advantages of horizontal integration, the development of ever larger and costlier machines, the constant improvement of methods of large-scale management, and the fact that the creation of monopolies makes it much easier for governments to co-ordinate, regulate, rationalize, and stabilize economic activities.

20. Centralization of control. Centralization of political, economic, educational, medical, and other forms of control is a product of the numerous inventions which have cheapened and speeded transport and communication, facilitated military conquests, and improved the efficiency of bureaucracy. "The invention of nuclear weapons has recently made world conquest and rule possible and a world government inevitable."

21. Collectivization. The growing substitution of government ownership or control for private ownership or control is a product of the industrial revolution (which substitutes collective for individual work), ever-growing economic specialization and inter-dependence, the development of social science (most neoclassical economic theory is applicable only in a socialist economy), the

rapid increase in the efficiency of large-scale management and government, and the near universal human desire for economic security and relative equality.

22. Rise of meritocracy. There will be continued progress toward meritocracy—rule and management by the most able—because the growth of knowledge will make ability easier to recognize and experts ever more influential. Also contributing to the trend will be the inevitable democratization of professional education, the steady decline of private inheritance, the growth of general education, and the coming decline in personal-income differences.

23. Advance of feminism. By feminism, Beckwith means: "the steady increase in the influence and activities of women outside the home—in politics, business, the professions—and in their personal authority inside the home." Feminism has been promoted by the industrial revolution, urbanization, birth control, the growth of internal peace and order, education, and the invention of new household machines.

24. Decline in income differences. Differences in real income per person will continue to decline, as they have since 1900, due to the common human dislike of large income differences, the growth of birth control, the expansion of free education, political democratization, eugenic progress, and the development of social science.

25. Relative growth of free distribution. The proportion of consumers' goods and services distributed free of charge will continue to grow faster than national income for a century or two in advanced countries and for much longer in backward countries.

26. Reduction of all personal economic risks. The average personal risk of losing property or income through unemployment, sickness, accident, flood or other misfortune will be steadily reduced due to the growth of peace

and order, the rise of private and public insurance, improvement in medical care, the spread of monopoly, and the growth of free distribution.

27. Increase in paternalism. There will be an increase in legislation which protects relatively incompetent minorities against exploitation or their own poor judgment. Increasingly, laws will restrict fraud and false advertising; prohibit or curtail the sale of harmful goods and services: make insurance, medical care, and education free and compulsory. "Paternalism will grow indefinitely, for two major reasons. First, the inevitable progress of applied science will enable experts to give more and more valuable advice concerning many personal decisions now left to individuals. Vaccination became compulsory only after scientists discovered how beneficial it is . . . Second, the inevitable growth of education will make all governments more and more responsive to expert advice; hence they will increasingly adopt paternalistic measures advocated by experts."

28. Rise of humanitarianism. The movement from cruelty and brutality toward consideration and tenderness in the treatment of human beings has been obvious in the ever more humane treatment of defeated nations, prisoners of war, heretics and dissenters, delinquents, children, wives, the feeble-minded and insane, the poor, the sick, and all other potential victims of brutality. The rise of science, the growth of peace and order, the increase of wealth in all advanced countries will continue to promote growing humanitarianism.

29. Growth of intergroup relations. The beginning, multiplication, and elaboration of social relations between families, clans, tribes, city-states, nations, and empires will continue to grow during the coming centuries.

30. Cultural homogenization. There will be a standardization of all human beliefs and activities—political, eco-

nomic, educational, sexual, artistic, scientific, and recreational—due to the increase in travel, migration, communication, and freight transportation, which will prevent isolation of human groups. Furthermore, Beckwith adds: "As men become more rational and scientific, social customs and policies will become more uniform. The most significant homogenization trend will be the further Europeanization of all non-European countries . . . North America is, of course, a cultural colony of Europe, so Americanization is Europeanization. Backward Asiatic and African countries will adopt more and more European social customs and policies in order to improve their own standard of living. It is much easier to imitate successful methods than to devise new ones as good."

31. Growth of personal freedom. The opportunity to make and carry out uncoerced choices concerning one's own conduct will continue to grow, but Beckwith cautions: "The prediction does not imply that social or governmental regimentation or regulation of individuals will decline. The common belief that all regimentation restricts personal freedom is unjustified."

Less General and Less Significant Social Trends

Beckwith believes that these trends will probably continue well into or throughout the period 2500 to 3000:

1. Increasing relative study and prediction of social trends.
2. Increasing scientific social experimentation.
3. The decline of racialism, provincialism, and nationalism.
4. More artificial insemination.
5. More sterilization.
6. More use of psychological testing.

7. A steady rise in average I.Q.
8. Continued migration to more pleasant climatic areas.
9. Continued miscegenation.
10. A decline in international wage-rate differences.
11. A decline in average hours of labor.
12. Relative expansion of mail-order and phone-order buying.
13. More government control over consumption of harmful goods.
14. More standardization of goods.
15. More regional specialization in agriculture and manufacturing.
16. Relative increase in spending on continental landscaping.
17. Relative increase in spending on public gardens, parks, forests, etc.
18. Relative increase in spending on entertainment and recreation.
19. Centralization of accounting operations.
20. Ever-growing relative use of desalted water.
21. Domestication of more sea animals.
22. Growth of ocean agriculture.
23. Substitution of synthetic for natural foods.
24 Growth of interregional and intercontinental traffic.
25. Increase in proportion of planned one-project communities.
26. A decline in the number and use of minor languages.
27. Constant improvement of major surviving languages.
28. Ever greater relative investment in organizing and preserving knowledge.
29. More supervision of parental care of children.
30. Relative expansion of public pre-school child care.
31. Prolongation of pre-school and university full-time education.
32. Relative growth of adult education.
33. More individualization of all education.
34. More use of teaching machines.

35. More use of boarding schools.
36. Relative expansion of health care.
37. More professional aid in selecting mates.
38. More sexual intercourse from age 15 to age 80.
39. More government effort to promote personal friendship.
40. A decline in faith in ideologies.
41. Better exploitation of gifted persons.
42. A continued lengthening of average life and workspans.

BOOKS FOR FURTHER STUDY

The Next 500 Years: by Burnham P. Beckwith. Forward by Daniel Bell. Exposition University Book, 341 pages at $10.00—19 Coleman Place, Apt. 38, Menlo Park, California, 94025. Identifies many well-established trends and makes hundreds of predictions that may be either accepted or debated. Clear and concise. $10.00

The Year 2000: A Framework for Speculation on the Next Thirty-Three Years: by Herman Kohn and Anthony J. Wiener with contributions by other staff members of the Hudson Institute, 431 pages. Macmillan. "Though condemned in some circles for its links with the American military establishment, the Hudson Institute has been conducting some of the most sophisticated, systematic explorations of the future. This book, summarizing much of the Institute's thinking, can hardly fail to be of interest." $9.95

Towards the Year 2000: Work in Progress": the summer, 1967, issue of Daedalus, journal of the American Academy of Arts and Sciences. The volume summarizes the work of the Commission on the Year 2000. "Scholarly, often illuminating, sometimes turgid, this is a monumental effort and 'must' reading for serious futurists. Its ideas and insights will be mined for years to come. $3.00

Here Comes Tomorrow: Living and Working in the Year

2000: by the staff of the Wall Street Journal. Dow Jones Books, 196 pages. Based on interviews with various experts, the book looks at the future of population, food, computers, energy, air travel, space, communications, automobiles, cities, homes, medicine, education, and war. Very readable. For the general reader. Paperback. $1.85

The Future: by Theodore Gordon. St. Martin's, 184 pages. "A space systems engineer's briskly presented thoughts about the future, especially its technology. Some discussion of the Delphi Technique." $3.95

How Business Economists Forecast: Edited by William F. Butler and Robert A. Kavesh, 540 plus XIV pages. Prentice-Hall. "A collection of essays by top businessmen, this volume is a well-written introduction to economic forecasting and provides a wide survey of business forecasting methods. No previous knowledge of economic or statistical theory is required." $16.95

The Most Probable World: by Stuart Chase. Harper & Row, 239 pages. "A popular social science writer attempts to envision the most likely shape of the future." $5.95

Toward the Year 2018: A collection of essays marking the Foreign Policy Association's 50th anniversary. Cowles Education Corporation, 177 pages $5.95

Environment and Policy: The Next Fifty Years and *Environment and Change: The Next Fifty Years.* These two volumes, edited by William R. Ewald, Jr., and published by Indiana University Press, bring together the papers presented at the 1967 American Institute of Planners' Fiftieth Year Consultation in Washington. "A stupendous treasure-house of ideas about the future from some of the world's most original thinkers." Paperback. Each vol. $4.95

The Dynamics of Change: by Don Fabun. Prentice-Hall, 190 pages. This puts a hard cover around the 1966 Kaiser Aluminum News series on the next 20 years. "This is a lavishly illustrated book that will go nicely on a coffee table.

The text strings together quotations concerning land use, transportation, communications, computers, and problems of abundance. An attractive gift." $6.95

History and Futurology: by Ossip K. Flechtheim. Foreword by Robert Jungk. Verlag Anton Hain (Meisenheim am Glan, Germany), 126 pages. Paperback. A collection of essays written between 1941 and 1952, about equally divided between history and futurology. "A slim but scholarly work by a distinguished political scientist. The portion dealing with futurology is very readable and should interest most futurists." $3.35

Scientific Progress and Human Values: Edited by Edward and Elizabeth Hutchings. American Elsevier Publishing Company, 219 pages. Leading scientists discuss science's role in shaping the morality, ethics, and values of the future. "Thoughtful, informative, well-edited. The chapters by Robert Sinsheimer and Robert Morison are especially recommended." $7.50

The World of 1984: Edited by Nigel Calder. Penguin. Two volumes totaling 420 pages. Paperback. Brief forecasts by scientists for their specialities. Originally published in the British Journal "New Scientist". "A mixed bag. Some articles are overly technical and dull; others are well-written and stimulating. The collection impresses by its variety." Both volumes included in price. 1.90

The Next Generation: by Donald N. Michael. Vintage, 218 pages. Paperback. "Very sober, sincere attempt to foresee what young people will face during the next 20 years." $1.65

The Meaning of the 20th Century: by Kenneth E. Boulding. Harper & Row, 199 pages. "Boulding offers a stimulating though perhaps simplistic view of man's social evolution and the dangers (war, overpopulation, exhausting of raw materials, and entropy.) he faces." Paperback. $1.45

The Challenge of Man's Future: by Harrison Brown. Viking, 290 pages. "Dated (1954) but solid and still pertinent. Emphasizes population, food, energy sources." Paperback. $1.65

The Next Hundred Years: by Harrison Bround, James Bonner and John Weir. Viking, 193 pages. Caltech scientists discuss food, industrialization, technical manpower in prospects for coming decades. "Published in 1957, but the problems are still with us." Paperback. $1.45

The Step to Man: by John R. Platt. John Wiley, 216 pages. "Imaginative thoughtful essays. Exceptionally well written." $5.95

Dialogue on Education: edited by Richard Kean. Bobbs-Merrill, 144 pages. "Some of education's most future-oriented thinkers contribute essays to this stimulating volume." Paperback. $1.25

Education and Technology in the 21st Century: Proceedings of a symposium directed by Waldermar Johansen, chairman of San Francisco State College's School of Creative Arts. Published as a class project. Paperback, 102 pages. Includes some serious thinking by Arnold Barach, Ralph W. Gerard, Maxwell Goldberg, and other scholars." $3.50

Evolving Mankind's Future: by Julius Stulman. Describes "The World Institute: A Problem-Solving Methodology.", 95 pages. Paperback. $1.95

Designing the Future: The Role of Technological Forecasting: by Robert W. Prehoda. Chilton. "Lucid and to the point. The professional researcher can read it with profit, and the non-scientist will also find it both clear and interesting." $8.50

Automation and Economic Progress: edited by Howard R. Bowen and Garth Mangum. Sectrum. A variety of studies produced by Paul Armer, Joseph Spengler and other scholars for the Federal Government. "Well-edited. Meaty." 167 pages. Paperback. $1.95

Technology and Change: The New Heraclitus: by Donald

A. Schon. Dell. An investigation of how industry effects technological change. "Clear, concise, and perceptive." 248 pages. Paperback. $2.25

Dialogue on Technology: edited by Robert Theobald. Bobbs-Merrill, 109 pages. Impact of automation on human values. Paperback. $1.25

Beyond Tomorrow: The Next 50 Years in Space: by Dandridge Cole with space art by Roy Scarfo. Amherst Press (Wisconsin), 168 pages, 100 illustrations, including 54 in color. "Stimulating text by imaginative but solidly grounded scientist." $7.50

The Case for Going to the Moon: by Neil P. Ruzic. Putnam, 240 pages. "The editor of 'Industrial Research' presents the rich potential rewards of space exploration." $7.50

Environment for Man: The Next Fifty Years: edited by William R. Ewald, Jr. Papers presented at an American Institute of Planners meeting in Portland, Oregon, in 1966. Paperback. "Several illuminating essays plus some academic potboilers." $2.95

Some of these books may be available from your local book stores and libraries. They may all be ordered at the prices quoted from "The Futurist", World Future Society, P.O. Box 19285, Twentieth Street Station, Washington, D.C. 20036, U.S.A. Incidentally, any reader is entitled to join the society and receive "The Futurist" magazine regularly by paying a membership fee of $5.00. The above prices are quoted in U.S. Funds.

PART
TWO

NOW WE COME TO THE FIRST MAIN EVENT

CYBERNATION IS "automation and cybernetics" and, since most of our writers refer mainly to computerized automation, this section is really about cybernation and the word could, in most cases, be substituted for automation (as we have sometimes done.)

Historically, the word "automation" was originally coined by our first contributor John Diebold at the age of twenty-six—several years before Donald Michaels coined the word "cybernation". Words such as cybernetic and cybernation are relatively new and only the latest and best dictionaries and encyclopediae give meaningful definitions.

Diebold's statement (Chapter Six) is already a classic and is as timely today as at the time of delivery. It is basic and understandable since it was written—away back in 1963—before many of the new words had come into existence. Those wanting specific help can usually find it in one of Diebold's many books on specialized areas. He is one of the top cybernation consultants to government and industry in the world.

Charles Killingsworth (Chapter Seven) is another renowned leader in the field of cybernation with over twenty-five years of experience in labor relations as a university professor.

John Hayes (Chapter Eight) is one of the top union leaders of the age. He is highly qualified to speak for the unions and does so boldly and fairly.

The late John Snyder (Chapter Nine), with whom I was associated personally, gained fame for his leadership in the creation of a major conglomerate for the manufacturer and sale of automated equipment and as Co-Chairman, with John Hayes, of the American Foundation on Automation and Employment. He too was blunt and fair.

The late Norbert Weiner (Chapter 10) was, of course, the father of modern cybernetics. His name speaks for itself.

John Rose (Chapter Eleven) is the leading English spokesman on the entire subject. The focus of his message is toward the Management and Human Relations Aspects.

Finally, our distinguished collaborator Arthur Porter (Chapter Twelve) does a wrap-up which is crammed with proposals for action. But as Professor Porter says, "Most books on this subject automatically become obsolete between conception and publication."

We have tried to profit by the Porter advice by limiting comments to concepts which are basic, transferable and timeless. We hope this section will provide a solid philosophical base for advanced study and some guidelines which should remain valid for many years to come.

CHAPTER 6

The Magnitude of Automation

by John Diebold

John Diebold is President of the Diebold Group, Incorporated, who are leading consultants in the uses of technology to industry and government. This reading was first presented as a formal address at the Fifth Annual Salute to the Alumni of Columbia University, June 3rd, 1963. With minor changes it became the keynote address at the founding conference at the American Foundation on Automation and Employment. It appears as a Chapter in his book of speeches and articles "Beyond Automation"—McGraw-Hill. It has been widely reprinted and has become a classic. Our deletions have been minor.

1

WE HAVE YET TO PERCEIVE the magnitude and the true nature of the momentous change automation is effecting in our lives, our businesses, and our society. Both the potential and the problem are far greater and quite different than has yet been realized. The problem is grave and requires far more private, as well as public, action than has yet been proposed.

The speed of this technological change is so great that we must do far more than even yet proposed to ascertain: (1) the nature of the future that is cast for us by today's innovations; (2) the magnitude and character of the problems posed for mankind by automation; and (3) the alternatives open to us to cope adequately with the changes automation is making in our world.

Automation is perceived only as a manpower problem, involving changes in labor requirements, changes in skill as jobs change, retraining, and worker mobility. Managers and workers who have experienced automation in practice know that it is more than this—that it is introduced, more often than not, to make possible wholly new ways of performing a task, whether that task be controlling a business, a government agency, or passenger air traffic.

Automation is all of these things, but it is also much more.

Machines have always been important to us primarily in their role as agents for social change. We use the term Industrial Revolution not because of the revolutionary machines of James Watt and Richard Arkwright, but because they created a whole new environment for mankind, a whole new way of life. What Watt and Arkwright gave to history was much more than the steam engine and the cotton gin, the railway and the power loom. Their machines gave society a whole new tempo and outlook.

Today's machines are far more powerful agents for social change than those of the first Industrial Revolution. For they result from a new-found ability to build systems that process and communicate information, translate from one language to another, respond to the human voice, and devise their own routes to goals that are presented to them—systems, moreover, that improve their own performance as a result of encountering the environment. In other words, they are machines that learn, in the normal sense of the word, and deal with the very core of human society—with information, its communication and use. These are developments which augur far more for mankind than net changes in manpower or new ways of doing old tasks. Mankind will undertake new tasks, not merely perform old tasks in a new way. The technology of automation is a tool that vastly extends the range of human capability and that will fundamentally alter human society.

The very nature of this technology, its concern with the building blocks of human society, will, in the course of the lifetime of many of us, force us to reconsider our whole approach to work, to society, and to life itself.

Let us look, for example, at automation as perceived by the individual, by the manager, and by the makers of public policy.

The individual perceives automation as a job threat, or, if he is a mathematician, an engineer, or otherwise in a position to benefit, as a challenge and an opportunity. Yet automation is going to force the individual to reconsider his very concept of himself. As Professor Herbert A. Simon, of the Carnegie

Institute of Technology, states: "The definition of man's uniqueness has always formed the kernel of his cosmological and ethical systems. With Copernicus and Galileo, he ceased to be the species located at the center of the universe, attended by sun and stars. With Darwin, he ceased to be the species created and especially endowed by God with soul and reason. With Freud, he ceased to be the species whose behavior was—potentially—governable by rational mind. As we begin to produce mechanisms that think and learn, he has ceased to be the species uniquely capable of complex, intelligent manipulation of his environment."

2

Man will find a new way of describing his place in the universe. Machine systems certainly show no signs of many of the fundamental human qualities such as imagination, volition, purposefulness, compassion, or love. Yet man's ability to build machines which learn and which already possess so much of the quality we today call "intelligence" means that, in addition to the obvious increase in our leisure time— or, as Professor Peter Drucker so aptly calls it, discretionary time—our role as individual human beings is being inexorably changed by automation.

The manager, whether public administrator or private businessman, today perceives automation as a labor-saving device and as a means for exercising tighter control over his enterprise and making it more responsive to rapid change. The great theme in today's business literature is that automation represents an opportunity to do a better job of managing.

This is all well and good as far as it goes, but by itself it tells only a small part of the story. For the significance of automation to the manager is not so much the new methods it gives him for managing—the new kit of professional tools, so to speak—but the fact that the enterprise he manages will be totally changed due to the changes automation is effecting in our society.

As the goals, aspirations, needs, and wants of the individual shift again and again through the human social changes induced by automation, the economic realities that sustain the enterprise will change. This fact holds a far more profound meaning for the manager and businessman than the procedural revolution taking place today in management methods. For in their roles of serving human wants lies the entrepreneurial raison d'etre of business and government organizations alike.

Rapid and major social shifts mean an entirely new and more day-to-day role for strategic planning in guiding the enterprise. It is here that automation is making profound change and it is here that we must look for the essence of the managerial meaning of this new Industrial Revolution. The heart of enterprise lies in ascertaining and filling human needs, not in the techniques of management, however important they may be in today's giant and changing organizations. Vitality and survival are determined by the ability of the organization, whether private or public, to perceive and fulfill the now rapidly changing human needs.

Makers of public policy see automation as a problem of unemployment, change in manpower requirements, and retraining, which is altogether correct as far as it goes, and of critical importance. (The additional need for increased productivity occasionally produces in these officials a schizophrenic impression of calling, in effect, for "more technology —but slowly! ")

But the reality of the situation is that the problems of public policy are much greater than is yet realized by any but a very few. International political and economic forces will increasingly require us to press for world leadership in these new technologies, which are correctly visualized by the remainder of the world as the basis for the tomorrow in which they intend to live. This necessary drive for technological leadership—on which increasingly rests our economically privileged position—will sharpen and intensify the as yet largely unperceived social problems of automation.

3

We have no corner on this technology. We can look forward only to increasing pressure from all parts of the world to move ever more rapidly. The revolution of information technology is a revolution moved by human brains—and there is precious little built-in advantage to us, other than our educational system and our major institutions of research. We will feel increasing pressure to keep ahead with both.

The solution is the creation of an environment conducive to technological leadership and rapid change. The first step must be the removal of all reason for fear over individual harm due to technological change. But the problem cannot be solved backward. The proper role of public policy is to create the conditions necessary to leadership in the human use of this new technology.

The electronic computer—today's precursor of the machine systems automation is so rapidly bringing into existence —is important not nearly so much because of the things it does today, however much we have already come to rely on them in our daily lives, as because it represents a new-found human ability based upon the most powerful of theoretical insights into the nature of information and its uniquely important place in our lives. As this ability is expressed in machine systems that abstract and translate documents and help physicians to diagnose disease, lawyers to prepare briefs, and teachers to develop the capabilities of their students, the world will become a far different place from what it is today.

Major social innovation, as rapid and as great as the technological innovation, seems to me to be called for to cope with such changes. Last time we ignored the need for social innovation. One result was Karl Marx, whose ideas have had more to do with shaping the lives of all of us than we might care to believe.

The very magnitude and importance of the problem of social innovation mean that we should not look to government for the solution. It is a task which should involve all of us, our best minds and hearts. It is a problem to be solved by the private as well as the public sector.

Pope John XXIII made a notable contribution to showing what must be done by the private sector in his encyclical Mater et Magistra. Governments can do much to ameliorate the human toll of transition and to help create an environment that will encourage technological leadership. But the shape of tomorrow's world is surely a problem to which we all can usefully contribute as individuals and working through private organizations as well as through our governments. We have hardly yet begun to face up to these aspects of the problem.

For example, the foundations, nourished in large part by increasingly automated industries, have thus far been conspicuous in their lack of interest in what President Kennedy characterized as "the major domestic challenge of the sixties." The private foundation is an institution to which we might reasonably look for help and guidance as the private sector contemplates these critical problems.

Let me revert one last time to that upheaval of two centuries ago that we now call the Industrial Revolution. No one in eighteenth-century England, least of all Richard Arkwright or James Watt, thought that the new machines were changing civilization. Yet, for us, looking back, that is precisely what was revolutionary about them. They took men off the fields and out of small shops and put them for the first time into factories. Hence they gave us mass production, and through mass production the first civilization in history in which luxury was not confined to a few.

Like the pioneers of the Industrial Revolution of the eighteenth century, we face today a world in which only one thing is certain: change, fundamental change. But unlike those earlier pioneers, we live in an age with the greatest sense of social responsibility in all history. Our task today is to use wisely our technology, our knowledge of history, and our compassion to make the age of automation a golden Periclean age in which a society based on the work of the machine— not the human chattel—rises to the full heights of which the human spirit is capable.

CHAPTER 7

Machines, Manpower and Jobs

by Charles C. Killingsworth

Dr. Charles C. Killingsworth is professor of labor and industrial relations at Michigan State University. This reading includes statements made before the Sub-Committee on Employment and Manpower of the U.S. Committee on Labor and Public Welfare. He attained his Ph.d from the University of Wisconsin and is the author of various books and articles on cybernation and trade unionism.

1

Does automation create jobs or does it destroy them?

A GREAT MANY PEOPLE have the view that this question has been conclusively answered and that it is a waste of time to debate it any further. The only difficulty is that there is still disagreement as to what that conclusive answer is. I think it is fair to say that most professional economists have taken the position that there cannot be such a thing as permanent technological unemployment. One prominent economist said that anyone who challenges that proposition is challenging the mainstream of economics. On the other hand, Secretary of Labor Wirtz suggested that we cannot take it for granted any longer that automation does create jobs. Labor leaders and others can point to such concrete examples as the permanent elimination of tens of thousands of elevator-operator jobs in New York City as a concrete result of automation.

This sharp conflict between the excessively general assertion and the excessively specific example has seriously hampered our efforts to find some solutions to the problems of automation and employment.

There is a good deal of evidence to tell us the nature of the employment problems that grow out of automation. That evidence shows rather clearly that the truth of the matter in this area of automation and employment is a great deal more complex than the half-truths that many of us have been taking for granted.

I have organized my comments around three basic questions. First, what is automation? Second, how is automation different from earlier kinds of technological change? And finally, the third and biggest question, what are the effects of automation on jobs?

2

What is Automation?

One type is what is commonly known as "Detroit automation," one of those giant transfer machines, about a city block long, that have come to be commonplace around Detroit. It works like this. A raw cylinder block is put in at one end, and progresses automatically through the machine, with hundreds of operations being performed on it along the way. It comes out at the upper end a finished, completely machined cylinder block. This machine reduces by 90 percent the labor requirements for machining a cylinder block, even though it is a rather primitive form of automation. It is primitive because it is inflexible: if you want to shift from an eight-cylinder engine to a six-cylinder engine, say, you have to scrap the machine, or at least rebuild it extensively. Because the labor-saving potential is so great, however, this type of automation is widespread, and its use is still increasing.

The second major type of automation falls under the heading of computer technology. This is a world of its own, more sophisticated and with more promise for the future. Certain computer installations already approach the automatic factory.

This general technique of competely automatic operation under computer control is found in petroleum refining, in steel and a good many other industries. There are chemical plants that are completely under computer control, and some power plants have been run by computers for a period of years. So the idea of the automatic factory is no longer a myth.

Another kind of computer application comes under the heading of information processing. Let me give you a few illustrations out of a growing multitude of examples of the capabilities of this kind of equipment. Not very far from New York City, there is a computer which is programed to handle the complete payroll calculations for a factory of some 26,000 employees. This machine computes hourly rates, overtime rates, deductions, incentive payments—all the computations that need to be done—and takes only 25 minutes per week for the job.

Banks have installed electronic accounting systems that are almost completely automatic.

Among other interesting examples of computer applications are:

1. The computer which is able to prepare tape for the setting of type.

2. The Air Force computer which very rapidly translates Russian into English.

3. Computers for medical diagnosis, into which the medical history of the patient, plus his symptoms, are fed. These computers can diagnose an ailment about as accurately as could an experienced doctor.

4. The computers installed by TWA in its overseas lines, which, along with some radar gear, have completely displaced the navigators. The pilot tells a computer where he wants to go and what route he wants to follow; the computer keeps track all the way and tells the pilot whether he is on or off course, and how much of a correction is necessary.

5. The driverless bus tested by the City of Chicago, which has demonstrated its capability by steering its 108-inch width through an opening 110 inches wide.

6. Computers for decision-making. Many plants are relying on computers for rather important decisions about such things as inventory control, production planning—particularly in construction jobs—and even such matters as plant location.

It may be a grain of comfort to some of you to learn that we can even point to an example of a vice-president who has been displaced by a computer.

There are also experimental applications of computers that I think have a good deal of promise for the future. For example, a scientist taught a computer to play checkers. This is a routine kind of accomplishment, but the thing that is interesting about his experiment is that his computer is able to learn from experience: the more games it plays, the better it gets, because it remembers its mistakes and doesn't repeat them. Dr. Samuel reports that at first he was able to beat this computer most of the time. Now he rarely, if ever, is able to beat it.

The intellectual foundation for all these achievements of computer technology is cybernetics, the science of communication and control. Because it is a very complicated science, an understanding of cybernetics requires a mastery of mathematics, of some principles of physics, and of many other aspects of basic science.

But for purposes of discussion, the whole setup can be simply explained by analogy with the familiar wall thermostat. The thermostat is programed by setting it to the required temperature. Temperature is measured by a thermometer which is part of the thermostat. When it falls below the required level, the thermometer generates a signal, or input, which is sent to the thermostat. The thermostat then generates a signal, or output, which is then sent to the valve of your furnace or steam radiator and opens it. The room temperature then rises, until the desired level has been reached, when the thermometer informs the thermostat, which shuts off the valve on the furnace or the radiator.

If you can imagine a thermostat with 75,000 different instructions, you have in essence the automatic system exemplified by the refining unit.

It can be readily seen that there is a tremendous variety

in the possible inputs and outputs of this kind of automatic system. A paper tape from a newspaper reporter's typewriter can be turned by a computer into instructions for a type-casting machine. Radar pulses fed into a computer can result in readings on a gauge on an airplane dashboard. The input can be a medical history of the patient; the output, medical diagnosis. The input can be Russian; the output, English. So we have almost an infinity of possible applications of this general principle. The big trick lies in the programing of the computer. Most of them do exactly what you tell them to do; they never make a mistake. The computer people have developed a rather important little word, "GIGO," meaning "Garbage In—Garbage Out." This expression explains a good many of the well-advertised failures of this kind of automatic system. If you put garbage into a computer it will give you garbage back.

3

How is Automation Different from Earlier Forms of Technology?

It is important to distinguish cybernation from earlier kinds of mechanization, technological change, or economic change, although a great many people use all of these expressions interchangeably. Figure 1 illustrates the differences between these various concepts. The broadest one is "economic change," which includes such developments as the growth of the Common Market and the exhaustion of natural resources.

A subdivision of economic change is "technological change." I would include under this heading such things as chemical discoveries and the use of pure oxygen in the steel-making process. A still narrower concept, one particular type of technological change, is "mechanization." The use of the lever is one example of mechanization, the steam engine is another.

Figure 1. Nest of Change

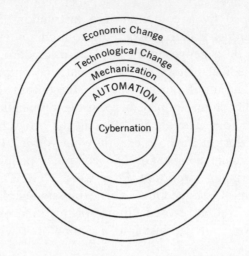

There is an element of automation in most kinds of mechanization, but some kinds of mechanization involve a good deal more automatic operation than others. At the rim of the inmost circle, which involves no element of automation, is located the cave man's lever. In the borderline area is found such a machine as the steam engine, which involves an element of automatic operation but is very far from an automatic factory. The automatic oil refinery, the completely automatic steel-rolling mill are, of course, at the core of the area marked "cybernation."

One fundamental difference is that the economic environment today is far different from what it was when the steam engine, electric power, the moving assembly line, and other major technological changes of the past appeared. Today we live in a fully developed mass-consumption society. This difference can be illustrated by the automobile industry.

Consider the situation when Henry Ford introduced the moving assembly line, at that time a very revolutionary idea. This took place in 1913. The population of automobiles in

1913 was about one million, or one automobile per hundred persons. In other words, the automobile industry was in its early adolescence. It was in a period of explosive growth, and had great potential for further expansion.

The assembly line greatly increased the productivity in Henry Ford's factory. Within a year after he had introduced it he had reduced by 90 percent the man-hours required for assembling a Model T Ford. His sales also increased enormously. The number of cars in existence increased tenfold, from a million to ten million, in the ten years following the introduction of Henry Ford's moving assembly lines. In that same period the automobile population increased from one car for every hundred people to one car for every ten people. So despite this enormous saving of labor, Henry Ford had to increase the number of his employees greatly during that period of time.

Let us compare this 1913 situation with the situation of the 1950's when "Detroit automation" started to come into general use in the automobile industry. We had an automobile population of close to fifty million in the 1950's, making one car for every four persons in the United States. In the fifties, the total number of automobile registrations continued to climb, but it went up only about 50 percent in the ten-year period from 1950 to 1960 as compared with an increase of 1,000 percent in the ten years following 1913.

This illustrates a point of fundamental importance in our consideration of the impact of automation. When a major labor-saving innovation is introduced into an industry in the rapid-growth stage—then that invention may very well spur further growth, resulting in a large increase in employment, as was the case in the automobile industry. This is the historical pattern that prompts a great many people to say that "machines make jobs." There are a number of examples in history which are similar to the situation in the automobile industry.

But the fact is—and this is something that a great many

people overlook—that when an industry has reached its period of maturity, when, for example, there already is one automobile for every three people in the country, then it is no longer possible to have further dramatic increases in sales. The improved productivity that is made possible by a 90-percent labor saving then makes it possible for the industry to supply the market while employing a smaller number of workers. This is about what happened in the automobile industry in the 1950's. And if you look across the whole range of consumer goods, I think you will see that our mass-consumption society has done a tremendous job of supplying consumer wants. Of the wired homes in this country, 99.5 percent already have electric refrigerators, 82 percent already have electric washing machines, 93 percent have TV sets. We have more radios than we have houses.

I want to mention in passing that a major reason for the booming prosperity in the countries of western Europe is the fact that they are in the early growth stages of the mass-consumption society that we in this country have had for about thirty years now. At the present rate of development, it will be perhaps twenty or thirty years before they reach the kind of problems that we are now facing.

I do not mean to suggest by the discussion above that consumers in the United States have had all of their wants satisfied and have about stopped spending money. This is not true. But a second major difference in the environment today is that the patterns of consumer spending are changing, and this is changing the patterns of employment.

I think it is entirely logical that the kind of shift from goods to services should be characteristic of the mature stage of the mass-consumption society. It is significant that the United States is the only country in the world where the jobs in service-producing industries outnumber the jobs in goods production.

Cybernation itself is different in important ways from these earlier technological changes.

One major difference is its much broader applicability than such revolutionary changes of the past as the moving assembly line and the steam engine.

A second difference is that cybernation seems to be spreading much more rapidly than most of the technological changes of the past.

A third difference is that automation is the product of a new source of invention—basic science. In 1913, Henry Ford invented the assembly line because consumer demand was pressing. It was proper to say, in that day, that necessity was the mother of invention. But today it is more often the other way around: Invention is the mother of necessity. Many of the sophisticated, highly complicated developments are direct outgrowths of the tremendous increase in our knowledge in basic science.

4

What Are the Effects of Automation on Jobs?

My first point is that automation, particularly in its more advanced forms, fundamentally changes the man-machine relationship. Of course, earlier technological changes also altered this relationship. For example, the assembly line created literally millions of very simple repetitive jobs that could be learned in just a few days. Anybody that had two hands, two eyes, and a capacity to endure monotony could do the work.

But today things are different. We have the electric eye, the iron hand, the tin ear, and the electronic brain. We also have the know-how to tie all of this hardware together into very complicated self-regulating systems that can perform an enormous variety of jobs.

This has two major results in the job market. The first is a great reduction in the number of simple, repetitive jobs, where all that is required is five senses and an untrained mind. The second is a great increase in the number of jobs that are concerned with designing, engineering, programing, and administering automatic production systems. We need a great many more scientists, engineers, mathematicians, and other highly trained people, and many less blue-collar workers.

Clearly, unemployment at the bottom of the educational scale is relatively unresponsive to general increases in the demand for labor, while there is very strong responsiveness at the top of the educational scale.

The most fundamental conclusion that emerges from my analysis is that cybernation and the changing pattern of consumer wants have greatly increased the importance of investment in human beings as a factor in economic growth. More investment in plant and equipment, without very large increases in our investment in human beings, seems certain to enlarge the surplus of underdeveloped manpower and to create a shortage of the highly developed manpower needed to design, install, and man modern production facilities.

As we have all heard over and over again, the outlook for high-school dropouts is bleak indeed. Exhortations, no matter how well meant, are not going to cure this problem. But here again dollars alone are not the answer. We need many more highly skilled teachers, counselors, and social workers. These, too, are in very short supply. Many other present shortages of highly trained manpower, in the private sector of the economy as well as in the public, could be cited. Unquestionably these shortages would be intensified and new ones would appear if we moved closer to full utilization of our economic potential.

To put a complex matter briefly, we must find a fundamentally new approach to the financing of at least this important part of the cost of higher education. We must make it as easy for an individual to finance his own investment in higher education as it is for him to finance the purchase of a home. I have proposed that we make provisions for loans to college students up to a maximum to $12,000, with a repayment period as long as 40 years, at a subsidized interest rate of 2 percent. Repayment should be on the basis of a flat percentage of income—a kind of social-security system in reverse. Others may think of better solutions; the means are less important than the end, which is to make higher education readily available to all who can benefit from it.

And we do not have all the time in the world. Human history has been described as a race between education and catastrophe. In the past, education has been falling behind in that race.

CHAPTER 8

Cybernation: Bomb to End Bombs

by A. J. Hayes

John Hayes has been president of the International Association of Machinists and Vice-President of the AFL-CIO. He is a top union leader who has won wide respect as Co-Chairman of the American Foundation on Automation and Employment and in various presidents' commissions in the labor field. He has served almost fifty years as a union officer and has already earned a place in history as a great interpreter of the times. This is an adaptation of an address before the Conference on Automation and Social Change sponsored by the Ontario Government in Toronto.

1

CYBERNATION PRESENTS a threat and a challenge second only
to the possibility of the hydrogen bomb. What I shall try to do
in this article is to define the nature of this threat, the nature
of the solution to it, and the nature of the people whose reaction to twentieth-century problems is to retreat behind a
Maginot Line of nineteenth-century ideas.

In the past there has been some tendency to underrate and
deprecate the seriousness of automation's implications for mankind. For many years, economists, industrialists, and government experts reassured one another that automation was just
a logical extension of mechanization and that, like mechanization, it would create more jobs, more work, more prosperity,
and more satisfaction for the human race. In fact, not so many
years ago, anyone who tried to warn that automation held as
much threat of human redundance as of material abundance
was likely to be ridiculed and even reviled. Today, however,
many people are finally beginning to realize that cybernation is
not just a new kind of mechanization—but a revolutionary force
capable of overturning our social order. Whereas mechanization made workers more efficient—and thus more valuable—
cybernation threatens to make them superfluous—and thus
without value.

The army of the unemployed—what we might call the
walking wounded in the onslaught of cybernation—is now
almost as great as the total population of Chicago and Los

Angeles. In Canada, total unemployment is greater than the total population of Vancouver.

In view of these trends and projections, it is obvious that we need not go on merely defining and analyzing the problem, or proving its existence. On the contrary, our need now—the need of industry, government, and labor—is to find answers to the very serious new questions that automation raises. These questions are of broad scope and infinite variety. The most immediate question, of course, is how to cushion the impact of technological advance on individuals and communities that are in automation's direct line of march.

Ultimately, we may be faced with even more difficult and fundamental problems. How, for example, shall we maintain human dignity and provide each man with the sense of personal worth that is necessary to all men in a technology that threatens to need very few men? And how, also, shall we ensure that every family will have enough purchasing power to meet its own needs, as well as the need of industry for consumers, if automated machines take the place of the worker and deprive him of his wages in mills, factories, mines, offices, banks, warehouses, farms, and stores?

Unfortunately, we have not yet reached a consensus on even the first and most immediate of these problems. The difficulty of reaching such a consensus has been compounded by the unwillingness of some industrial managers to accept responsibility for those whose livelihoods are destroyed by technological advance. In the leading journal of a major industry, for example, 76 percent of a group of corporate officials subscribed to the principle, as a basis for bargaining, that "The company is entitled to all of the savings resulting from the introduction of labor-saving equipment." Such a contention is, of course, patently absurd, first, because in the United States, technological achievement is rooted in a long-established system of public education. Without such an educational system, to which all the people contribute, there would be no technological progress. Second, because technological progress is generated by public support of scientific research and development programs in governmental, academic, and industrial laboratories. In fact, of the $12.5 billion spent annually for all research and development in the United States, more than $7 billion comes directly from tax moneys that are paid by all the people. And third, because our heritage of scientific knowledge has been handed down by succeeding generations of artisans and skilled workers and comes from the countless contributions that they have made. This heritage of skill and know-how belongs to the people as a whole and must be used in the national interest. If management successfully enforced a claim to all the benefits and savings made possible by cybernation, it would commit economic suicide in the process.

In dealing with cybernation, the fundamental economic principle from which we must proceed is that workers are consumers and that it is pointless to plan automatic factories capable of pouring out endless streams of goods without also planning an economy in which those goods can be distributed and consumed by human beings.

Fortunately an increasing number of employers and government officials are beginning to see the light. One of the most enlightened, and one of the first to blaze a trail, is John Snyder of U.S. Industries, Inc. His effort to get to the heart of this problem through the American Foundation on Automation and Employment is not only a humane approach but good economics as well. If more employers were as concerned with men as with machines, many of the bitter disputes between labor and management, including those that have taken place in the longshore, newspaper, and railroad industries, would never have occurred. It is freely acknowledged that these and many other expensive disputes have their roots in automation and fear of technological displacement. If nothing else, the spread and the threat of more such expensive and time-consuming disputes have at least forced industry and government to take a second and closer look at the implications of automation.

When a group from the Foundation on Automation and Employment met with David L. Morse, Director-General of the International Labor Office, he made it clear that this problem is a world problem. Even in the European Economic Community, he said, where there has been a boom and a labor shortage, the member countries have seen the handwriting on the wall; they are already establishing social safeguards designed to minimize the future impact of cybernation on people.

Since the extent, seriousness, and scope of the problem are now being recognized, the next question is, what, if anything, can be done about it? There are no easy answers, but certain trends are beginning to emerge. For example, in most union negotiations today it is generally expected that the contract will contain one or more provisions relating to advance notice and consultation, reduction of the work force by attrition, transfer rights (including moving expenses), retraining, employee-adjustment services, wage-rate retention, early retirement, and severance pay. To some extent, through such provisions, the union can and does protect the worker.

But what about the worker without a job, the youngster out of school, for example, who, because of automation and high rates of unemployment, cannot even get a foothold in the labor force? It is in this youthful group that we already have our largest proportion of unemployment and one of our highest potentials for social disintegration.

Obviously, no one yet knows what the full answers are in this area and I do not pretend to. But, in seeking to adjust to a situation where fewer and fewer people can turn out more and more goods in less and less time, it seems evident that one fundamental change we will have to make in our society is to reduce the number of hours an individual works—not merely in a day, a week, or a year, but in a lifetime. We need a shorter workweek—and we will have to learn to schedule and to use the additional leisure time provided by the shorter workweek by simultaneously providing more holidays, more long weekends, more vacations, and more sabbaticals for more people.

We must provide more and better educational opportunities for our youth. If the present trend continues, we can expect that eight out of every ten youngsters now in grade school will not complete college. Some will not have the inclination. Some will not have the ability. But some with both the inclination and the ability will simply not have the money. Yet it is painfully evident that a high-school diploma is not enough in a world of automated technology.

The fact that millions of untrained jobless youths can be found idle and aimless on thousands of street corners testifies to the need for schools specially designed to bridge the gap between high school and college. For some, such publicly supported schools would serve in lieu of junior colleges, providing basic training in the liberal arts. For others, they would serve as advanced technical institutions, providing kinds of formal training that are in short supply even today—training, for example, in data-processing, programing, computer mathematics, industrial electricity, and electronic theory.

Our present system of education simply dumps hordes of raw and unready youths upon a job market that neither needs nor wants them. The establishment of advanced technical institutions, comparable to junior colleges, offering at least two- and perhaps even four-year programs, would not only stem the early flood of unready job-seekers, but would provide our burgeoning technology with badly needed skills.

At the other end of the age and employment scale, we must make it possible for workers to retire on decent incomes at 60 or even 55 years of age.

Much of the sting of automation can be removed both for

individuals and for our society by providing adequate protections for those directly in the path of automation, and by reducing the total hours each individual works in his own lifetime.

The foregoing suggestions are defensive, but in this battle against the harmful effects of cybernation we can also take the offensive. The unused segment of the labor force can be put to work to meet the many obvious needs of our society by, for example, planning and building more and better housing, schools, hospitals, parks, playgrounds, recreational facilities, clinics, youth centers, roads, and airports. We must develop new industries, new products, and a more vigorous trade between nations. The future need not be entirely black. Cybernation has its perils, but it also has its promise.

From the dawn of human history, from the caves where men first huddled by their fires, the dream of mankind has been freedom from want. For thousands of years such freedom for the overwhelming majority was not possible. Even today, more than three-quarters of the world lives in almost hopeless poverty. But today something has changed. Man holds in his hands a set of keys with which it is possible to open one of two doors. The first leads to abundance through rational planning. The other to economic chaos. The question is, which door will he open? Unfortunately, even at this late date we do not know.

At times the outlook appears grim and the outcome seems uncertain. Yet, so long as we have men and governments with enough concern to plan for the future, we can hope that despite the challenge of cybernation we will succeed in conserving for future generations the key values of our society.

CHAPTER 9

Three Myths and an Early Warning System

by John I. Snyder, Jr.

The late John Snyder, Jr. organized with John Hayes
the Foundation on Automation and Employment to
deal with human problems—"to develop ways to ease
automation's impact on workers whom it displaces." He
also pioneered the development and sales of automated
equipment as President of U.S. Industries, Inc. This
reading is a composite from a statement before the
United States Committee on Labor and Public Welfare
and his proposal for an early warning system for automation in New York City. This model might be applicable to some extent in your community.

MY COMPANY designs and produces automation machinery; therefore, those of us in the management of the company feel a deep sense of responsibility toward those people whom such machines are adversely affecting. It is in the area of automation's effects on human beings that our Foundation is focusing its primary attention in the form of research and study programs.

Our efforts are dramatically limited, however, in relation to the growing dimensions of our national manpower problem. Neither our company nor the other automation-machinery manufacturers possesses the kind of resources that enable us to bear the full burden, to assume the full responsibility for all those affected in one way or another by our machines. This simply is not the kind of responsibility that can be delegated to any one company or even group of companies. It is too large, too all-encompassing, too serious a responsibility not to be everyone's.

Apart from the research and study efforts that I have mentioned, our major task at the Foundation is to tell the truth about automation—not an easy task. Too many people are willing to accept too many myths about what is going on around us in our factories and offices. Too few people accept the very few truthful facts that are being turned up by real experience and intelligent study. I have taken on the assignment of telling the truth—or at least what I consider the truth—about both the short- and long-range effects of automation and technological change.

2

Myths

The problems resulting from the efficiencies of the new machines are vast and complex. From a technological point of view automation is working; but the same thing cannot be said so confidently from the human point of view. The technologists have done and are doing their job. They have developed and are developing equipment that works miracles. But, as is too often the case in this age of the widening gap between scientific progress and man's ability to cope with it, we have failed to keep pace.

Much of this failure is due, I think, to the existence of a number of myths about automation, which, because they are so widely accepted, have had a tranquilizing effect on many who otherwise might make effective contributions toward solutions to the human problems created by automation. The most seductive of these myths is the claim that, for a number of reasons, automation is not going to eliminate many jobs. Personally, I think this is a gross underestimate of the real situation. Automation is a major factor in eliminating jobs in the United States at the rate of more than 40,000 a week, as previous estimates have put it. We must also keep in mind that automation is not only displacing people directly, but also indirectly through what are called "silent firings," through the elimination of jobs that workers would have been hired for, prior to automation.

A second myth is that automation will create jobs for workers not only in running the machines, but in maintaining and building them. The hard truth here is that modern automated equipment requires very little maintenance. If it did not, it would not pay to operate it; and if the equivalent number of workers replaced by automation were required to build the machines and systems, there would be no point in automating.

A third myth that needs to be laid to rest is the belief that those who lose their jobs to automation can be retrained and put into other jobs requiring higher skills and paying more money. As studies have shown, automation is more likely to reduce than to increase the demands for skills and aptitudes. Furthermore, many workers are just not retrainable, due to their levels of intelligence, education, and age.

Still another myth is that workers replaced by automation in one part of the country can find jobs in other areas. The truth is that the workers thrown out of jobs are usually just those who are least able to move. They are the lower paid, the older, the unskilled. Either they cannot afford to move from an economic standpoint or they are psychologically incapable of beginning a new life in a strange area.

These myths or misconceptions serve as palliatives for those who either cannot or will not come forward to grapple with the human problems caused by automation. It is much easier to look for proof that these problems do not exist than to admit their existence and move ahead toward a solution.

The general failure to face these problems, the attempt in many places to avoid them represents, to my way of thinking, a moral weakness in itself; and I further believe that it can be an indication of a common failure to judge and understand the severe nature and extent of the thrust of this technological revolution. In the coming months and years, if we are to survive we will need new sociological and economic ideas to solve the problems we face in this area. All of us, whether our desks are in offices or at union headquarters, must work together as never before to come up with such new ideas. We have a moral obligation to make a substantial contribution toward solving the problems that accompany rapid technological change. If we fail, we are handing our children an invitation to disaster, for our failure to perceive the gravity of the human problems we are facing will represent a moral breakdown of the gravest dimension. On the other hand, by meeting and overcoming the challenges that confront us, by acting in the common good, and by conquering ourselves as we have conquered the natural forces around us, we can gain the rich rewards of our scientific ingenuity for ourselves and for generations yet to come.

3

Early Warning Systems

Over a thousand years ago, a Greek philosopher had this to say about the greatness of a city: "Not houses finely roofed or the stones of walls well-built, nor canals nor dockyards make the city—but men able to use their opportunity." We have to find solutions to a great many problems that accompany technological change as it moves in, in its ponderous and inevitable way, on the plants and offices.

While we won't find all the solutions today, our very presence shows that we are at least taking steps in the right direction—possibly the most meaningful steps taken to date in coping with the problems of technological change. For in our discussions today we are simultaneously involving three vital primary forces—government, labor, and management—and in my opinion this is a highly significant achievement. As regards automation, these three forces have not worked together at all before. But as of today labor, management, and an alert city government have joined forces to deal constructively with all the problems of technological change as they affect this city.

For such a joining together of labor, management, and government, New York City is, in my opinion, the ideal laboratory for us to use as a model for every other urban center. We have a progressive, far-sighted, and interested Mayor; our labor leaders over the years have demonstrated their energy and capacity; and our management executives by and large possess a strong social conscience. To round out the picture, our city's population and her basic industries offer a very wide cross section in terms of both income and occupational interests—a broader cross section, I think, than that of any other city in the country. New York also offers an ideal range of services. The city is perfectly suited, in short, to become the nation's test tube in which to devise means of coping with technological change.

For all these reasons, we are in a position here in New York to launch a unique experiment which will benefit not only the city's millions, but the entire country as well. And this is exactly what I am proposing that we do, beginning here and now. A tremendous amount of fact-finding and analytical work is needed—fact-finding and analysis in depth, by industry and by population group—before we can effectively develop meaningful steps to deal with automation and change. Specifically, I think we have to go to work immediately in three basic areas.

First, we need to determine the exact dimensions of automation's impact on each individual basic industry. We need to find out exactly what technological advances are available to what industries, how fast these industries are adopting such gains, and what the likely effects of those gains will be in economic and human terms. In other words, we have to determine exactly where automation is already causing job displacement or is likely to cause displacement in the future. And we need to find out to what degree this is happening, and how fast.

At the same time we must be working in the second of our basic areas—that is, investigating new job opportunities. It seems clear that while we determine how many men and women are being displaced in our various industries by the introduction of automation, we must simultaneously proceed to find out how many new jobs are being created, if any. We must find out where the jobs are, what they involve, and, most important, how labor and management can best work together to facilitate change while protecting the interests of individual workers.

Answers to these questions will lead us into the third and final portion of our experiment; that is, to find out what efforts must be made by both groups and individuals to redeploy workers from automated industries into nonautomated industries. We must find out what kind of skills are needed, what training will be necessary to facilitate the changeover from job to job. We must even go beyond this and somehow provide the necessary training. Over the long haul, we have to determine what educational level must be attained by our children so that as adults they will be able to adjust rapidly to technological change. We have to investigate the employment problems peculiar to our minority groups.

And that, I submit, is the kind of three-pronged program we must launch: (1) to determine the exact dimensions of automation's impact; (2) to determine where new jobs are to be found; and (3) to determine what kind of training or retraining is needed to facilitate the switch from old job to new. Only when we know some of the answers in these three areas can we begin to create solutions to the problems of automation's impact. I further submit that our search for answers must be a fully cooperative venture, involving labor, management, and the government; that it must be free of all partisan overtones; and that our investigations must reach into all of the basic industries—food, apparel, electronics, services, and trades—on an industry-by industry basis.

What we will be attempting to formulate from all of this research is the "early warning system" which will tell us where automation is creating or is likely to create problems.

We can then implement sound plans to cope with the immediate short-run effects of this change. And remember: The short-run problems must be solved first if we are ever to enjoy the long-term gains of technological change.

At the present time, I think that people generally have some sort of vague feeling that people "somehow" are being put out of work "somewhere" by automation. But I do not believe anyone is really aware of the problem unless he has been directly and personally affected. The fact remains that automation's introduction has already resulted in some dramatic, even frightening, changes in our accustomed ways of doing things.

Leaders in business and the government community all have the continuing obligation to work—whether in our own offices or as part of a project—to find solutions to the fundamental human problems of a business society. The real thinking and decision-making, as it affects people, cannot be done by computers or robots. No machine can liberate us from our current obligation to study the problems and then to decide how best to cope with the enormous impact of technological change. The danger is that we might forget this obligation. As we all know, the human mind likes to believe that things will take care of themselves if allowed to run their course. We must not allow this to happen. We must remember that people in very large numbers are deeply and personally involved in our dramatic Cybernation Revolution.

CHAPTER 10

Cybernetics for Human Beings

by Norbert Weiner

Dr. Norbert Weiner was the famous mathematics professor at the Massachusetts Institute of Technology who created the science of "Cybernetics". Part one is from his introduction to "Cybernetics or Control and Communication in the Animal and the Machine" and Part two is from "The Human Use of Human Beings" Cybernetics and Society (Doubleday). I highly recommend that you read "Cybernetics Simplified" by Dr. Arthur Porter (English University Press).

1

IT HAS LONG been clear to me that the modern ultra-rapid computing machine was in principle an ideal central nervous system to an apparatus for automatic control; and that its input and output need not be in the form of numbers or diagrams but might very well be, respectively, the readings of artificial sense organs, such as photoelectric cells or thermometers, and the performance of motors or solenoids. With the aid of strain gauges or similar agencies to read the performance of these motor organs and to report, to "feed back," to the central control system as an artificial kinesthetic sense, we are already in a position to construct artificial machines of almost any degree of elaborateness of performance. Long before Nagasaki and the public awareness of the atomic bomb, it had occurred to me that we were here in the presence of another social potentiality of unheard of importance for good and for evil. The automatic factory and the assembly line without human agents are only so far ahead of us as is limited by our willingness to put such a degree of effort into their engineering as was spent, for example, in the development of the technique of radar in the Second World War.

I have said that this new development has unbounded possibilities for good and for evil. For one thing, it makes the metaphorical dominance of the machines, as imagined by Samuel Butler, a most immediate and non-metaphorical problem. It gives the human race a new and most effective collection of mechanical slaves to perform its labor. Such mechanical labor has most of the economic properties of slave labor, although, unlike slave labor, it does not involve the direct demoralizing effects of human cruelty. However, any labor that accepts the conditions of competition with slave labor accepts the conditions of slave labor, and is essentially slave labor. The key word of this statement is competition. It may very well be a good thing for humanity to have the machine remove from it the need of menial and disagreeable tasks, or it may not. I do not know. It cannot be good for these new potentialities to be assessed in the terms of the market, of the money they save; and it is precisely the terms of the open market, the "fifth freedom," that have become the shibboleth of the sector of opinion represented by the National Association of Manufacturers.

Perhaps I may clarify the historical background of the present situation if I say that the first industrial revolution, the revolution of the "dark satanic mills," was the devaluation of the human arm by the competition of machinery. There is no rate of pay at which a pick-and-shovel laborer can live which is low enough to compete with the work of a steam shovel as an excavator. The modern industrial revolution is similarly bound to devalue the human brain, at least in its simpler and more routine decisions. Of course, just as the skilled carpenter, the skilled mechanic, the skilled dressmaker have in some degree survived the first industrial revolution, so the skilled scientist and the skilled administrator may survive the second. However, taking the second revolution as accomplished, the average human being of mediocre attainments or less has nothing to sell that it is worth anyone's money to buy.

2

The answer, of course, is to have a society based on human values. To arrive at this society, we need a good deal of planning and a good deal of struggle, which, if the best comes to the best, may be on the plane of ideas, and otherwise—who knows? I thus felt it my duty to pass on my information and understanding of the position to those who have an active interest in the conditions and the future of labor, that is, to the labor unions. I did manage to make contact with one or two persons high up in the C.I.O., and from them I received a very intelligent and sympathetic hearing. Further than these individuals, neither I nor any of them was able to go. It was their opinion, as it had been my previous observation and information, both in the United States and in England, that the labor unions and the labor movement are in the hands of a highly limited personnel, thoroughly well trained in the specialized problems of shop stewardship and disputes concerning wages and conditions of work, and totally unprepared to enter into the larger political, technical, sociological, and economic questions which concern the very existence of labor. The reasons for this are easy enough to see: the labor union official generally comes from the exacting life of a workman into the exacting life of an administrator without any opportunity for a broader training; and for those who have this training, a union career is not generally inviting; nor, quite naturally, are the unions receptive to such people.

Those of us who have contributed to the new science of cybernetics thus stand in a moral position which is, to say the least, not very comfortable. We have contributed to the initiation of a new science which, as I have said, embraces technical developments with great possibilities for good and for evil. We can only hand it over into the world that exists about us. We do not even have the choice of suppressing these new technical developments. They belong to the age, and the most any of us can do by suppression is to put the development of the subject into the hands of the most irresponsible and most venal of our engineers. The best we can do is to see that a large public understands the trend and the bearing of the present work, and to confine our personal efforts to those fields, such as physiology and psychology, most remote from war and exploitation. As we have seen, there are those who hope that the good of a better understanding of man and society which is offered by this new field of work may anticipate and outweigh the incidental contribution we are making to the concentration of power (which is always concentrated, by its very conditions of existence, in the hands of the most unscrupulous). I write in 1947, and I am compelled to say that it is a very slight hope.

3

Now, thirteen years later, it seems appropriate to take stock of the present position with respect to both cybernetic technique and the social consequences of this technique.

As is now generally admitted, over a limited range of operation, machines act far more rapidly than human beings and are far more precise in performing the details of their operations. This being the case, even when machines do not in any way transcend man's intelligence, they very well may, and often do, transcend man in the performance of tasks. An intelligent understanding of their mode of performance may be delayed until long after the task which they have been set has been completed.

This means that though machines are theoretically subject to human criticism, such criticism may be ineffective until long after it is relevant. To be effective in warding off disastrous consequences, our understanding of our man-made machines should in general develop pari passu with the performance of the machine. By the very slowness of our human actions, our effective control of our machines may be nullified. By the time we are able to react to information conveyed by our senses and stop the car we are driving, it may already have run head on into a wall.

The human brain is a far more efficient control apparatus than is the intelligent machine when we come to the higher areas of logic. It is a self-organizing system which depends on its capacity to modify itself into a new machine rather than on ironclad accuracy and speed in problem-solving.

If we adhere simply to the creed of the scientist, that an incomplete knowledge of the world and of ourselves is better than no knowledge, we can still by no means always justify the naive assumption that the faster we rush ahead to employ the new powers for action which are opened up to us, the better it will be. We must always exert the full strength of our imagination to examine where the full use of our new modalities may lead us.

CHAPTER 11

Management and Social Planning for Cybernation

by John Rose

Dr. John Rose is Principal, Blackburn College of Technology & Design. He was general organizer of the International Congress of Cybernetics (September 1969) University of London. He is a contributor to a new book (Survey of Cybernetics) and author of "Automation & Man" (Penguin). Material for this chapter has been taken from his book "Automation: Its Uses & Consequences" (Oliver & Boyd, London).

1

"THE STOMACH is the only part of man which can be fully satisfied. The yearning of man's brain for new knowledge and experience and for pleasanter and more comfortable surroundings can never be completely met."

Thomas Edison

In general, people resist change because it strikes at their emotional security. They resist technological change particularly, since it involves actual or imaginary social upheavals. Workers do, however, accept new techniques when consulted in advance and allowed to participate in the operation; otherwise, they often use their ingenuity to outwit the planners and management. The workers must be convinced by actual demonstrations that they will share in the benefits obtained by improved techniques and greater effort. Automation may be seriously jeopardised unless management foresees the workers' attitude and forestalls its consequences. Genuine consultations are essential, not just vague commentaries and an abundance of pamphlets. The objects of consultation are to air grievances, seek suggestions from workers on production problems, and build up a sense of partnership and participation. The success of introducing automation depends greatly on management's ability to enlist the support of the employees concerned. This is particularly important when, concomitant with the introduction of automation, management re-evaluates technical, administrative, organizational and human problems, i.e. when it performs a complete system analysis. Advance planning and extensive consultations with workers, held a considerable time before automating the plant, greatly facilitate the transition as was found in a survey made by the U.S. Department of Labor; this, however, is rather rare. The actual transition to automation is facilitated by carrying out the operation at times of full employment if possible, and during a period of the company's growth, in order to absorb the redundant workers. It is also important to train effective supervisors, i.e. individuals with skills in the technical, administrative and human relations fields. Above all, it is vital to avoid acting arbitrarily and without warning, since this attitude generates fear and emotional insecurity, feelings which in some cases lead to sabotage and obstruction. In all this, trade unions and management have to play a vital part.

The preceding chapter dealt with problems which Cybernation creates for the mass of workers and for those who are unskilled, uneducated, old, infirm and members of minority groups. It is necessary now to consider the role management plays in creating these problems and taking remedial action in the general setting of automation, particularly in regard to the advances in information technology. After all, the essence of management is the achieving of objectives through people.

Automation creates new problems because of the increased complexity of production, greater output, heavier investment, greater integration of processes and reduced flexibility of plants and offices, and thus calls for more scientific planning and control. Another difficulty is the increasing avalanche of paper coupled with a corresponding rise in the number of administrative and clerical workers. For example, the number of such workers has risen in the last sixty years in the U.S.A. from 2½% to 15% of the total working population, and there are today two-thirds as many clerks as productive workers. This process may, however, be reversed by office automation, i.e. by the use of computers for storage, communication and manipulation of information, and by the extensive use of data processing, i.e. co-ordination of all major statistical and accounting functions of a firm. Computers not only perform routine office tasks, such as preparation of payrolls, cost accounting, inventory control, etc., but also may solve economic and management problems by integrating a number of operations, viz. planning, production, inventory and sales, and simulating the effect of external disturbances on the system.

2

The first question to be considered is that of the relation of manager and computer. For many managers a computer was like 'a viper in their bosom'; for others it was just another machine. Whatever their views, managers who do not understand the computer and its potentialities are, in the words of experts, the mastodons of industry and the innumerates of the industrial society. This is particularly serious, since the computer creates a whole series of new problems, principally those concerning the structure of the companies themselves. A new group of technologists are brought in, a breed of computer experts, who are, however, excluded from policy making at high levels, despite their enormous capabilities. In these conditions middle management may be restricted to passing information from these experts to top management, thus becoming progressively atrophied and ceasing to be a source of recruitment for top managers of the future. Indeed, top managers themselves are in danger of falling under the spell of these modern 'sorcerer's apprentices' with their jargon of cybernetics, operational research and operation simulation.

At the same time, the computer is being abused. While

Great Britain has still fewer computers per head of population than any country in Western Europe, the machines installed are being greatly misused in many sectors. Too many firms fail to make effective use of these experienced machines because they do not really understand what they can do.

The trouble is that some top managements regard the computer as yet another item of office equipment to do routine work on accounts and payrolls, but this is an area where computers are least efficient in terms of the return on their cost. The remedy consists of introducing planning and research before the installation of the computer, and regarding it as a creative tool of management, a tool which will provide a company with information that will speed the responses of management to changes in the business situation.

The introduction of a computer is much more than the installation of electronic calculators; it is a tool of management having a far-reaching and fundamental effect on the organization and philosophy of company control; the installation of the machine necessitates rethinking concepts of organization and objectives of systems processed, and creates a central point and information spread therefrom to various divisions of responsibility (May, 1965).

One must also consider the effect of the avalanche of data supplied by computers to managers, who are unable to cope with the information thus provided. In order to enable the manager to digest and evaluate the information, a variety of techniques are needed. One of these is known as 'management by exception' (Ziessow, 1965). This is a term used to define the concept of not printing reports describing business transactions that are considered normal; only abnormal performances are reported to the management, e.g. work behind schedule, stock on back orders, accounts due but not received, etc. Most successful results are obtained in practice because of the high speeds of a computer and its ability to make logical decisions.

Stafford Beer (1966) examined the problem of the misuse of computers. In his view the gross error consists of companies being trapped by their cost-management techniques into comparing existing procedures with their possible automated equivalents; the result is bound to be wrong, since the existing procedures were set up to solve problems in a computerless world. The question is not how can a company use a computer in its existing set-up, but what should be the set-up, now that computers exist. This question, however, can be answered only by an enlightened and progressive top management, which is willing to regard the computer as a creative tool, a weapon in the armory of information technology.

3

Information technology based on computers presents a clear challenge to management control, the entire area of which will have to be examined from a fresh point of view, since this is a field in which management has so far played a small part compared with that of technology. The managerial implications, as analysed by John Diebold (1965), are as follows:

Cost and profits. Considerable savings may result from reduced costs of running data-processing operations; from applications to production planning, sales forecasts, industrial management and other new sectors; and from improved automation in plants and offices.

Company organizations. Top management will exercise greater control over more people, since a manager will be able to supervise a greater number of subordinates; hence there will be a thinning out of the ranks in middle management and, in general, there will be fewer posts at intermediate levels, such as group executive vice-presidents in American companies.

The direct link between the system and top management will increase, the channels being manned by data-processing personnel; the data-processing and the communication functions will be merged.

Internal operating environment. The management information-systems function will be an important part of general management rather than a departmentalized or functionalised management position. The management information system can also be used as a carrot extended to attract potential customers. For instance, a fertilizer company may offer a consulting service to farmers, free of charge, the calculations of fertilizer mixes for a given farm being done free of charge on the computer.

External operating conditions. A number of centers have grown up in the U.S.A. for the purpose of supplying computer-produced information to customers of firms endowed with a computer information system; in fact, except in cases involving business secrecy, the company would make its 'know-how' available to subscribing customers and non-customers alike.

Decision-making. This concerns routine decisions, decisions in production planning, personnel type decisions, i.e. supervisory and behavioral, and policy decisions such as those concerning new products, diversification, etc. The first and third types will be based on computers, though the latter will be made primarily on the basis of value judgment. As regards the personnel type decisions—such as taking holidays or a rest—man will have to decide, though he will have better means of evaluating his answer if he does so with the aid of a computer.

Managerial tasks. The erroneous view is sometimes held that in the future computers will entirely replace man. Even the most automated system contains assumptions that have to be built into the program by man. For example, even in a routine decision-making task, such as purchase, man builds in assumptions concerning sales forecasts, cost of maintaining stocks etc., and these assumptions must be constantly re-examined by man. Under these conditions the role of manager is becoming more important, since he will be faced with a constantly changing environment and will have to use up-to-date information technology; he will also have to rely on his common sense and judgment.

Centralization of management. Computer economics make it advantageous to centralize the actual storing and processing of information, particularly since the obtaining and processing of information is now completely separate from line management structure. The collection of data may be decentralized by having peripherals in branch offices, but the central processing unit is preferably located at head office. All the tasks, e.g. production, marketing, finance, etc., will then be under the control of the data-processing manager, who will be able to provide whatever is needed for the functional manager.

Training. The rate of technological development and its potential uses are such that all levels of staff may have to be periodically retrained and even repeatedly change their jobs within the same firm. The development of industry will depend not on computer engineers, but on staff familiar with the 'software' and systems analysis and design. This is especially important, since there is no methodology of systems analysis at present, while the pace of advance of information technology is so rapid that it is very difficult to evaluate the resulting economic and social consequences. It is the task of the manager not only to be concerned with issues of employment or production schedules, but also with wider issues affecting society, since machines are agents for social change. Constant training and mounting awareness of the implications ot the engine created are the guarantees of the manager's progress and outlook.

In general, automation calls for management with mental

flexibility, improved communications, ability to redesign tasks to make use of machines and not vice versa, and for professionalism based on sound scientific foundations, broad vistas and creativeness. Automation imposed a need for tighter control, but also for delegation of responsibilities. A new class is emerging, a so-called 'diploma elite', concerned not with incentives to increase output or productivity, but with the maintenance and better utilization of the machines. Fewer, but more specialized, people will deal with complex problems, aided by computers and sound management education based on scientific principles.

The problem of supervisors is also of interest. Leavitt and Whisler in their study of management (1958) predict that in the next two decades middle management will be replaced by overall co-ordinators, systems analysts and programmers. New skills will have to be developed to cope with new and complex problems arising out of automation. Similar considerations apply to the supervisors, who will have to acquire a better knowledge of complex technical skills and an aptitude to handle subordinates under conditions vastly different from those obtaining today.

4

Management education.

It is clear that automation has created a host of new problems, including those of management at various levels. The use of new techniques, including electronic data-processing, systems analysis, operational research, etc., and a completely new outlook on management problems makes it imperative to develop an educational system capable of coping with the results of automation. Management education will have to deal with various areas of activity, e.g., administration and organization, economic activity, and market and non-market environments.

The first activity is that relating to the traditional structure of the firm combined with human relations.

The second activity of economic management involves production and the efficient combination of capital, labor, all other resources, raw materials, etc.; theory may be of considerable assistance in this field, particularly if combined with statistics, formal economics and stimulation.

The third type of activity is concerned with markets in a broad sense, i.e., the purchase of materials, acquisition of finance, hiring of labor and sale of products; here again, economic theory and behavioral science may be of value.

The final sphere of activity deals with other areas, such as political framework, legal foundations, the impact of technology and scientific advances, the climate of public opinion, and general economic and social problems. All these activities require suitable education, which can be adapted to changing needs. There is a great need for the development of systematic theories of management, based on a synthesis of economic and technological principles. As far as large and complex automated firms are concerned, it is more vital to subject their activities to a critical analysis in the context of the national economy and technological progress than to gather large volumes of data. The primary conditions for success are creativity, logical thinking, flexibility and, above all, receptiveness to new ideas. With all this must be combined a deep knowledge of economics and technologies, with barriers removed between technologies, and between science, technology and the 'humanities'. A combination of a social scientist, technologist and economist would probably constitute the best 'mix' under the revolutionary conditions caused by automation. The enlightened manager will have to deal not only with problems of individual workers, but also with their organizations and trade unions.

CHAPTER 12

Reflections on the Man-Machine Society

by Arthur Porter

Dr. Arthur Porter is head of the Department of Industrial Engineering, University of Toronto. He was the inventor of one of the first computers in the early thirties and is internationally recognized as a writer, lecturer and consultant. He has been a tower of inspiration in the creation of this source book. His book, Cybernetics Simplified, is, in my opinion, one of the best statements on the subject. In its foreword, McLuhan states, "This is a much needed book. It helps to build a bridge between the two cultures whose separation plagues C. P. Snow and many others." Professor Porter has been closely associated with the Institute of Culture and Technology.

1

MAN'S WORLD is essentially a man-machine world. It always has been. The primitive "hand-axes" in use 400,000 years ago were the remote ancestors of the sophisticated computers of today. At all times during man's evolution he has adapted to ever-changing environments. Innovation has been the prime requirement. Not much imagination is needed to speculate that during the next half-century massive scientific and technological researches will profoundly affect man as a social animal. The first objective of this paper is to try to put into perspective the interrelationship between man and his machines. The subject can be approached from the point of view of the optimist or from the point of view of the pessimist. I am an optimist. Only through an optimistic outlook can we anticipate a society worth striving for—there are, of course, sensitive and indeed dangerous situations confronting society and many more will arise during the next few decades but it is only through such crises that society can survive as a vital entity. Challenge spurs creativity.

As technology proliferates, so must the informed public's understanding and appreciation of it expand. The ultimate control of scientific and technological advance, certainly in a democracy, is in the hands of the electorate. It is important that the electorate is sufficiently well informed to steer man's technological effort in desirable directions. Some measure of control is essential—it can be achieved only through educational processes which recognize change and which are adapted continually to changing environments.

Although it is not my intention to attempt to delineate the key problems facing society today, notwithstanding the fact that these have arisen almost exclusively as a result of man's increasing mastery over his environment through the invention of ever more powerful machines and artefacts, it may nevertheless not be out of place at least to mention them in order to provide a backdrop to my subject. The problems might be listed as:

(a) How do we avoid a nuclear holocaust? Because a truly effective anti-ballistic missile is impossible for at least a decade (or more) and because, increasingly, victory in war is not possible, and because the recent confrontation between the Soviet Union and Communist China provides evidence of changing attitudes and particularly a trend towards liberalism in the Soviet Union (recognizing that although the communistic experiment worked in some respects, it failed in others as any patterned society is bound to fail), we conclude that the possibility of nuclear war is diminishing. But efforts towards nuclear containment must continue.

(b) How do we handle the population explosion, especially in developing countries, and how do we cope with the associated problems of widespread hunger and poverty on earth? This is perhaps the key problem facing society—a multidisciplinary attack on it is essential. These are problems beyond my competence to discuss.

(c) Associated with problem (b) is that of a rapid expansion of world education to handle the 40% of the world's population who are illiterate. Throughout man's history transitions from one form of society to another, e.g. agrarian to industrial, frequently accompanied by war and revolution, have caused acceleration of the educational process. Much of the world's society is at present in the throes of transition and hence of uncertainty and unrest. And again, almost paradoxically, uncertainty and unrest and conflict are necessary states for evolution. Education is the mechanism which keeps them within reasonable bounds.

(d) How do we keep technology and applied science under close review and almost certainly under increasing control? An associated problem is that of dealing with the information explosion which is already threatening to fragment still further the very fragmented worlds of scholar, scientist, doctor, lawyer, engineer, etc. Maintenance of effective dialogue between disciplines is central to the problem, and the universities have a tremendous responsibility in this respect.

2

The brain is the key to man's greatness—it synthesizes all our perception of the external world and our inner experiences and it may be regarded as the fountainhead of all imagery and all creativity. During the whole of our lifetime the brain receives information through our senses, structures it and provides us with an extraordinarily complex picture of the external world. Unlike all other animals, man is born with very few primitive behavior patterns but with fantastic brain potential. In the biological sense, man's culture is continually being recreated by succeeding generations.

The associated powers of speech and of tool-making have probably been central to man's cultural evolution and indeed to his survival. Germain Bazin, Chief Curator of the Louvre, has even gone so far as to suggest that man's artistic talents in the arts, the drama and the dance, originally arose essentially as a result of his tool-making ability and particularly as a result of his recognizing the concept of "action at a distance"—the indirect force analogous to the behavior of his forearm. Culture and civilization have evolved largely through the production of tools and machines—the human person has become what he is as a result of these tools.

Undoubtedly, also, man's creative powers were stimulated by the uncertainty and hostility of his environment, and this continues to be the case. It has given rise to his great learning potential and to his urge to discover and to create in order to cope with conflict situations of increasing complexity. He has devised means to enhance and to stimulate his processes of thought. In this regard perhaps the key inventions up to, say, one thousand years ago were speech, writing and poetry. Poetry facilitated memory and the vitally significant process of associating one event with another, or one phenomenon with another, etc. Throughout his history, all man's thought processes in the scholarly, scientific and technological disciplines have been based on the association of ideas. The metaphor in poetry, the icon in the arts, and the model in the sciences are manifestations of this fact.

During periods of great uncertainty, such as the present, man's innate creativity increases. During his transition from hunter to farmer, and more recently from farmer to industrial worker, we find periods of great cultural evolution as well as periods of great mental and physical violence and strife. Weapons of war have throughout history exemplified the most advanced technology of the times and this is one reason why war may be regarded as a state of accelerated education.

But the truly great inventions have arisen because of man's innate urge to communicate and to store knowledge. Such inventions as speech, writing, printing and, very recently, automatic computing are essentially inventions in the field of communication. And since communication embodies the concept of time perhaps even the clock, which has had probably a greater impact on man's evolution than the steam engine, comes into the same category. In this connection, Lewis Mumford has suggested that it was

"The collective Christian desire to provide for the welfare of souls in eternity by regular prayers and devotions which probably gave rise to the temporal order which has governed men's lives ever since."

The clock, ubiquitous and elegant, is a central machine in our modern industrial society.

It was, moreover, the Gutenberg press which originally pointed the way towards the modern techniques of mass production—the invention of interchangeable movable type anticipated the mass production line.

In a review of man's cultural evolution, however brief, it is important to note that machines have progressively replaced man and animal as hewers of wood and drawers of water and, during the past decade or so, man is being displaced as a processor of "low-level" information. The first industrial revolution was concerned largely with eliminating man as a manual slave and replacing him by, for example, the steam engine—it should be noted that this was economically an attractive development. The first industrial revolution was essentially non-scientifically based and resulted from the inventions by, in some cases, illiterate craftsmen of important machines and energy transducers. In contradistinction, the second industrial revolution, in which we find ourselves at present, is highly scientifically based and is to a large extent predicated on extending man's central nervous system and his sensory organs through the communication media and the new techniques for storing and manipulating data, often by means of computers. Basically it has been scientific knowledge which has given rise to the tremendous proliferation of technology and, in particular, the empirical methods of science, combined with man's urge to discover, have resulted in "critical-mass" being reached and explosive growth triggered off. Although scientific research is incomprehensible to the vast majority of mankind, its implications for the future of society are tremendous.

Let us examine briefly the nature of our modern machines and their limitations. Machines control and direct energy and process information. It is noteworthy that the amount of energy available to man appears to be increasing exponentially, and the capacity of machines to handle energy must likewise. Similarly, man's ability to process information, as exemplified by the modern computer, also shows exponential growth—a new generation of computers has emerged approximately every five years since the birth of computers and each generation is approximately ten times faster and has ten times the capacity of its predecessor. In contrast the problem of increasing the world's food supplies by a factor of only four times before the end of this century is one of great complexity. Man's major problem will be to ensure that his machines are utilized rationally and for the benefit of society as a whole.

At present the major limitations of machines result from economic considerations, on the one hand, and to the fact that their operation is intrinsically clumsy and their behavior only lends itself to learning at very low levels (by human standards) on the other. Furthermore, technology can only be utilized optimally for man's benefit when man himself understands the basic principles of technology. This is clearly a challenge for the educators.

It is also interesting to reflect on the implications of Parkinson's first Law in an increasingly technological environment. It will be recalled that the Law can be stated as "Work expands so as to fill the time available for its completion". The modern machine, especially the computer, provides us with an admirable example of how the Law works. However large the computer, perhaps installed in a university, the work it is required to do expands rapidly until the system is saturated. This fact may have a profound influence on future society. Computers cause the proliferation of paperwork for the reason mentioned above and the paper so created creates more paper and the bloodless battle between Cybernation and Parkinson's first Law wages merrily. Indeed this battle is already constituting a safety valve for advanced industrial societies because it seems to act essentially as a self-regulating process which helps to preserve comparatively low unemployment levels. Perhaps, also, it is one answer to the problem of leisure.

3

The views of the experts concerning the impact of automation (symbolic of modern technology) are mixed. Some experts fear that automation is not being introduced sufficiently rapidly to cope with the problem of world poverty and with the associated low levels of education, while others take the stand that Cybernation is coming too quickly and, as a result, an increasing number of workers are unable to learn the new skills—the result would be increasing obsolescence.

What are the facts? During the past twenty-five years the productivity of the "average man" throughout the western world has doubled and so has his purchasing power. It is perhaps encouraging to note that in the late 1940's some economists were freely predicting that within a decade or two widespread unemployment, due to mechanization and automation, would be unavoidable. How far wrong their predictions were can be judged by the fact that in spite of the greatly increased introduction of mechanization and automation, of recent years, more workers are engaged today in manufacturing industries than were so engaged in 1950.

Furthermore, in the U.S.A., where technology has reached higher levels than in any other country, it has been shown that technological change has created more jobs than it has destroyed—the work force in 1965 was 9 million in excess of that in 1955.

The primary sociological effects of modern technology have been:

(a) To change the nature of the labor force and in particular to increase greatly the numbers of white-collar occupations and jobs at the expense of blue-collar occupations. Noteworthy is the fact that the numbers of agricultural workers are rapidly declining.

(b) Largely as a result of computer technology it is now possible to produce goods and services which would otherwise have been impossible—the major impact of man's capacity to handle information in massive quantities at ultrarapid speeds has been in the fields of education, the health services, space technology, and communication science.

(c) The role of the manager in all walks of life is changing. It is now imperative that managers have some understanding of the advanced tools of management, especially the computer, and some knowledge of the behavioral sciences.

(d) It is almost a truism that although the long-term effects of technological change will be beneficial, the short-term effects will probably lead to hardships among a minority of the working population. There is already a reduction in demand for poorly educated workers and a noticeable increase in demand for highly educated workers. The educational implications of this trend are of profound significance and will be considered in a little detail subsequently.

It is interesting to speculate on how the changing patterns of work, already in evidence, may affect the structure of the work force by the end of the present century—it would be foolhardy to attempt to predict much further ahead than this.

Recently Professor Dennis Gabor of Imperial College, London, has studied the problem of changing patterns of work and his conclusions are summarized in the table given below. It relates the minimum I.Q. requirements with specific professional and work areas and compares the percentages of manpower requirements in these areas today and in 2000 A.D.

Nature of Work	I.Q.	Present Percentage	Percentage in 2000 A.D.
Arts, science and learned professions	120 and up	4%	6%
Higher administration	113 and up	5%	4%
Education (below university level)	104 and up	5%	16%
Clerical	91 and up	20%	10%
Technician	91 and up	4%	6%
Production work	73 and up	40%	20%
Service operations	73 and up	17%	33%

The main features to note in the above predictions are, first, the fact that the number of people involved in education may increase three-fold and in consequence one person in five is likely to be involved in education by 2000 A.D.; second, the number of clerical workers expressed as a percentage is likely to be halved; third, the percentage of production workers is likely to drop from 40% to 20% of the working population, while people working in the service industries and utilities will constitute one in three of the working population by 2000 A.D. The prediction also reveals that automation will release perhaps half of the people in the I.Q. range 104 to 120 from existing classes of employment and large numbers will enter school teaching, the service industries, and educational and health service work in general.

Before leaving this brief reference to the social implications of technology, it may not be out of place to comment on how well society is adapting to change. There is undoubtedly a danger that the leaders of society, in all walks of life, will continue to cling to 19th century philosophies and try to fit 1960 technology to them. Man has a tendency to cling to the past and to forestall any attempt to undermine his vested interests. Marshall McLuhan has suggested that the effect of a major technological change upon a society is to cause it to become "numb". This numbness takes the form of rejection, refusal to admit the existence of the change, ridicule and frequently outright opposition. All innovation is subject to the same sort of reception by society. There is another danger also and that is the continuing dichotomy between the humanities and social sciences, on the one hand, and the sciences and applied sciences on the other. In a confrontation between the American poet, Robert Frost, and a former President of M.I.T., for example, the poet is said to have "pounded the table" and said:

> "Let the scientists and technologists take care of their own affairs which are going badly enough; let them play with their hardware, but let them leave the important problems of this world to us, to the poets and the philosophers."

Frost was by no means alone in his fear and, let us face it, contempt for the works of modern science. But science cannot be isolated from the rest of human affairs and it is impossible to understand trends in modern art and literature without an adequate awareness and perception of trends in scientific thought.

For my own part, I am happy to have been associated with the Centre for Culture and Technology, directed by Marshall McLuhan, at the University of Toronto because the Centre provides a meeting place for scholars, and scientists and professionals. The sort of dialogues in which we indulge may have an increasing influence on man's affairs. And by far the most important "affair" is the problem of education which I now examine briefly.

4

The impact of technological change on education cannot be over-emphasized. Indeed, perhaps at no other time in man's history has a single technological event, i.e. the launching of Sputnik I by the U.S.S.R. in 1957, had such amazing educational repercussions—I refer to its effect on the educational programs in the United States. The problem of gearing education to the changing environment is one of great complexity.

Perhaps one of the first questions to be studied is the design of the learning environment itself. Today, we live in a world of learning environments which are not restricted to the formal environments of the school and the university. But for the most part we pay little attention to the creation of new intellectual environments largely because the problem is inter-disciplinary and, as I have already mentioned, inter-disciplinary dialogue is not easy to stimulate.

To expedite the learning process we must utilize when appropriate the new communication media, new concepts in space utilization, and by no means least, computer and information retrieval systems, perhaps based increasingly on a national communications network.

Many people are obliged to live in environments which tend to inhibit intelligence and indeed consciousness of change. The level of curiosity and consciousness of a person appears to be related to that person's information handling capacity. If the environment in which he works is not conducive to activating his information processing system, his intelligence potential is likely to decline.

The first important requirement is for man to learn much more about the learning process. The importance of the behavioral sciences in "learning research" is at present being emphasized more and more especially in the universities. This is a highly encouraging trend which will pay great dividends in the future. But the results of learning studies must be communicated to the architect and to the engineer who will continue to be responsible for the design of the physical environments in which the learning process operates. Marshall McLuhan has stressed that the environment itself is a teaching machine. And, of course, man is the supreme "learning machine"—what we must seek, therefore, are environments which facilitate man's total involvement. Some form of conflict is central to learning because it induces motivation and the "game" provides the traditional "conflict situation"—that is, of course, if we eliminate war in which victory is no longer possible. Games are characterized by uncertainty and usually by unpredictability and hence their importance in learning situations. The learning environments we create in the future must embody adequate degrees of uncertainty in order that the urge to discover is always central in the student's activity or indeed in the worker's activity because industrial, church, and home environments are, by their very nature, learning environments.

Modern technology, and more especially the computer, is having a profound impact on mathematics and science as taught in the public schools and high schools. For example, the introduction of the "new mathematics", with its emphasis on set theory and logic, was probably expedited by the increasing influence of computer science in education. The "new mathematics" stresses the high significance of language. It is providing a bridge between natural language and mathematical symbolism. For instance, it is not possible to state a problem symbolically before it has been stated succinctly and logically in natural language. Furthermore, the elements of set theory and logic (i.e., "new mathematics") emphasize the importance of pattern and structure and here again we must thank the computer for expediting, at a comparatively early age in a student's education, the introduction of this new approach to mathematics. It cannot but enhance both the mathematical and the verbal aptitudes of the student.

Another encouraging sign in the teaching of science in high schools is the increasing emphasis on the empirical method. The "new science" as taught in the schools is predicted on observation and measurement, so of course is the "old science" but not for the most part, as taught in the schools. We must thank Dr. Zacharias and his Committee for the "breakthrough" in science teaching. Special emphasis is put on the process of learning through discovery. The technique is essentially multi-sensory and hence involving. Indeed the well-designed science laboratory constitutes an almost perfect learning environment. It was the feedback from science and technology into the schools which focused on the importance of the new methods, and their introduction was considerably facilitated when Sputnik I was launched.

Nor should we forget that man's evolution has been predicted on freedom. He has generally followed those paths which led naturally to liberty of thought and action. A learning environment should enlarge man's freedom in two specific ways. First, it should give him the choice of making new things and evolving new ideas and concepts, and second, it should open up new applications of the things he makes and new creations and discoveries from the thoughts he thinks.

The importance of assuring a measure of randomness in the environment has already been mentioned. It is particularly important in the design of learning environments.

It is worth noting, moreover, that randomness and uncertainty in the environment can be described as "noise"—not only auditory noise but all forms of distortion and "anti-information". But noise is also essential to life because it implies lack of predictability and hence encourages the adaptation of a species to its environment. To emphasize the great importance of "noise" in the learning and living process I have coined the phrase "the noise is the message" to stress the fact that it is sometimes the "deviation from the line" which provides the message rather than the line itself.

The technological environment is itself essentially "noisy" because we find it increasingly difficult to seek out patterns of behavior which will give clues to future developments.

While individual man possesses fantastically complex innate filters to reject unwanted information, society as a whole has only limited protective devices to handle the "noise". The universities traditionally have been charged with the task. But, while it is generally recognized that interplay and interaction between disciplines is increasingly essential, the "information explosion" poses a distinct threat to our being able to evolve the inter-disciplinary patterns so urgently needed. This is one of the central problems in the universities today. It is epitomized by modern art in which form and content are often very obscure and their discovery is only possible through deep involvement on the part of the viewer. I believe the message which the arts are presenting to society as a whole is the need to re-evaluate society's goals and values and in so doing to restructure its philosophies.

And it is important to raise the question again and again— can our formal traditional institutions, notably the universities, which, through their research laboratories and libraries, have promoted and encouraged change, be held responsible for controlling the acceleration of change? Can our educational environments withstand the "tidal wave of innovation" that threatens to engulf them or must new institutions be built to deal with this problem? It has been suggested by the historian Taggart that "the great advances of mankind have been due, not to the mere aggregation, assemblage or acquisition of disparate ideas, but to the emergence of a certain type of mental activity which is set up by the opposition of different ideas systems". In other words, some control of rampaging technology may be obtained through accelerating the degree of interaction between disciplines. This is a challenge for the designers of the learning environments of tomorrow.

5

No discourse on man-machine society would be complete without some reference to the changing relationships between man and the machines he has devised. This subject is today frequently referred to as man-machine dialogue or the man-machine interface. It is important because man must learn to live with his machines and above all to keep them in their place.

As would be expected man-machine relationships have changed immeasureably during the past few centuries. Until comparatively recently the tools man devised were truly extensions of himself and a close rapport existed between man and tool. Indeed, in the not too remote past, the tool was almost regarded as a God and sacrificial weapons were venerated. But with the advent of more sophisticated machines, especially electronically-controlled machines, the attitude is changing. The tool or machine is still an extension of man although it no longer requires, in many cases, the skill of man's hands to operate it. Perhaps we may be starving the faculty of touch—the "haptic sense". This is reflected to some extent in educational programs where we find, except in special vocational schools, that the role of tactility in the educational process is becoming minimal. This, in spite of the fact that multi-sensory stimulation is known to induce more excitement and hence a higher level of consciousness in the student. In many processes the interaction between man and machine is programmed and this means that the role of the operator is merely to monitor the behavior of the machine—no wonder he becomes remote from the machine's output! Such working environments cannot be regarded as learning environments because programmed and patterned behavior, being repetitious, does not provide the degree of uncertainty required to stimulate man's high level learning attributes. This is a problem in human factors engineering which will require close attention in the future. The problem has been recognized in, for example, the design of expressways where long straight stretches of roadway are avoided in favor of environmental variety (at increased cost, of course) in order to maintain an adequate level of consciousness on the part of the driver.

At the other end of the spectrum of man-machine interaction we find computers being used to facilitate complex decision-making processes. In such cases, the computer is usually used, for experimental studies, as a simulator of a real situation. This is man-machine interaction at a high level. For example, the computer simulation technique is at present being used widely in industrial operations and more recently in the planning of complex educational systems and hospital systems. In this utilization of machines we find educators, sociologists, and scientists in a real sense "playing" with the computer and establishing the close communion with it which a child establishes with a toy.

And the new machines will increasingly emphasize the importance of a continuing review of educational philosophy. The new educational environments involving new teaching techniques, new "anti-environments", and new tools must be studied on an inter-disciplinary basis.

Man-machine dialogue may well be undertaken at its highest level in connection with the teaching and learning process. During the past five years, it has been demonstrated that computer-aided instruction has enormous potential in the educational field—it is applicable not only in formal education systems but may well prove to be of universal applicability in industry, government, business and even, eventually, the home.

Although at first sight the idea of a computer acting as a teacher produces horrific responses from many people, it is nevertheless a logical step. The first point to remember is that computers will deal only with the more didactic parts of the curriculum and will thereby relieve teachers of that formidable part of their task which is oriented around rote learning and which the born teacher often finds boring. But this aspect of education cannot be ignored because it is the basis of mental discipline. It is expected that computer-dialogues in which the operation is essentially "question and answer" will be comparable to the Socratic mode of teaching—a close communion between teacher and pupil on an individual basis. Furthermore, the interaction is multi-sensory and hence almost by definition involving. The computer acts as an anti-environment and in so doing minimizes boredom even when learning procedures necessitate many repetitions.

I predict, moreover, that the increasing use of computer-aided instruction first in the schools and universities, far from ushering in the demise of the human teacher, will in fact elevate the status of teacher to that of a stimulator of creativity rather than, as is so often the case at present, a purveyor of facts. It may attract into the teaching profession the best intellects and capabilities and this is as it should be because the future evolution of society rests upon it.

6

Predictions:

(i) Technology has always been central in man's evolution and, with the accelerated developments of recent years, it is essential that society must study the implications especially from the standpoint of changing human values and human nature.

(ii) The key to human greatness is human learning potential —the need to evolve new learning environments capitalizing on technological change is mandatory. In particular, the respective significance of "pattern" and "noise" in learning, epitomized by the computer coping with patterned teaching and man coping with creative teaching, requires study in depth.

(iii) The machine is not a threat to society—in the words of Aristotle—"When looms weave by themselves, man's slavery will end".

In the future, the machine will create more leisure, for a large sector of society, and this must be welcomed because, hopefully, man will be educated to utilize leisure.

A fitting conclusion can be found in the Book of Ecclesiasticus:

> "The wisdom of the scribe cometh by opportunity of leisure and he that hath little business will become wise".

BOOKS FOR FURTHER STUDY

Amber, George H. & Paul, S. *Anatomy of Automation,* Prentice Hall, Englewood Cliffs, N.J., 1962.

Anschutz, Herbert. *Purposive Systems,* Spartan Books, N.Y., 1968.

Apter, M. J. *Cybernetics and Development,* Pergamon Press N.J., 1966.

Arnstein, George E. *Automation: The New Industrial Revolution,* American Industrial Arts Association, Washington, D.C., 1964.

Ashby, W. R. *Introduction to Cybernetics,* Chapman-Hall, London, 1956.

Bagrit, Sir Leon. *The Age of Automation,* Mentor Books, N.Y., 1963.

Beer, Stafford. *Cybernetics and Management,* English University Press, London, 1959.

Bell, David Arthur. *Intelligent Machines: An Introduction to Cybernetics,* Ginn & Co., Boston, 1964.

Berkeley, E. C. *The Computer Revolution,* Doubleday, N.Y., 1962.

Bernstein, J. *The Analytical Engine; Computers Past, Present and Future,* Random House, N.Y., 1964.

Brady, Robert A. *Organization, Automation and Society,* University of California Press, 1961.

Brown, John A. *Computers and Automation,* Arco, N.Y., 1967.

Buckingham, Walter. *Automation,* Harper and Row, N.Y., 1961.

Buckingham, Walter. *Automation: Its Impact on Business and People,* Harper and Row, N.Y., 1963.

Burck, Gilbert. *The Computer Age,* Harper and Row, N.Y., 1965.

Bushnell, Don D. & Allen, Dwight W. (Eds.). *The Computer in Adult Education,* Wiley, N.Y., 1967.

Calder, Ritchie. *The Evolution of the Machine,* American Heritage, N.Y., 1968.

Collins, N. R. & Mitchie, D. (Eds.). *Machine Intelligence,* # 1, Oliver and Boyd, Edinburgh, 1967.

Dale, E. & Mitchie, D. (Eds.). *Machine Intelligence,* #2 Oliver and Boyd, Edinburgh, 1968.

Diebold, John. *Automation,* Van Nostrand, Princeton, N.J., 1957.

Diebold, John. *Man and the Computer,* Frederick A. Praeger, N.Y., 1969.

Drecher, Carl. *Automation. What It Is, How It Works and Who Can Use it.* Norton, N.Y., 1957.

Ellul, Jacques. *The Technological Order,* trans. by John Wilkinson, Alfred A. Knopf, N.Y., 1964.

Forrester, J. *Industrial Dynamics,* M.I.T. Press, Cambridge, Mass., 1961.

Francois, W. *Automation,* Collier-Macmillan, N.Y., 1964.

Friedmann, George. *The Industrial Society: The Emergence of the Human Problems of Automation,* Free Press, N.Y., 1955.

George, F. H. *Automation, Cybernetics and Society,* Leonard Hill, London, 1960.

Goodman, L. L. *Man and Automation,* Pelican Books, N.Y., 1957.

Grabble, E. M. *Automation in Business and Industry,* Wiley, N.Y., 1957.

Hall, J. A. P. (Ed.). *Computers in Education,* Pergamon Press, Oxford, 1962.

Hosèlitz, Bert F. & Moore, W. E. *Industrialization and Society,* UNESCO, 1963.

Jacobson, H. B. & Roucek, J. S. (Eds.). *Automation and Society,* Philosophical Library, N.Y., 1959.

Laird, Donald A. & Eleanor C. *How to Get Along with Automation,* McGraw-Hill, N.Y., 1964.

Lewis, Arthur O. Jr. (Ed.). *Of Men and Machines,* E. P. Dutton, N.Y., 1963.

Libstrew, Atis & Reed, Kenneth A. *Transition to Automation,* University of Colorado Press, Colorado, 1964.

Michael, Donald N. *Cybernation: The Silent Conquest,* Center for the Study of Democratic Institutions, Santa Barbara, California, 1962.

Morrison, P. & Morrison E. (Eds.). *Charles Babbage and his Calculating Engines,* Dover, N.Y., 1961.

Mumford, Lewis. *The Myth of the Machine,* Harcourt Brace & World, N.Y., 1966.

National Manpower Council. *Education and Manpower,* Columbia University Press, N.Y., 1960.

Porter, Arthur. *Cybernetics Simplified,* English University Press, London, 1969.

Rose, John. *Automation: Its Anatomy and Physiology,* Oliver and Boyd, Edinburgh, 1967.

Rose, John. *Automation: Its Anatomy and Physiology,* Oliver and Boyd, Edinburgh, 1967.

Rose, John. *Automation and Man,* Penguin, London, 1970.

Sackman, Harold. *Computer System Science and Evolving Society,* Wiley, N.Y. 1967.

Schultz, T. W. *The Economic Value of Education,* Columbia University Press, N.Y., 1963.

Silverman, Charles & the Editors of Fortune. *Myths of Automation,* Harper Bros., 1966.

Simon, Herbert A. *The Shape of Automation for Men and Management,* Harper & Row, N.Y., 1965.

Sluckin, W. *Minds and Machines,* Pelican Books, 1954.

Smith, Karl Ulrich & Margaret Foltz. *Cybernetics and Principles of Learning and Educational Design,* Holt, Rhinehart and Winston, N.Y., 1966.

Soule, G. *What Automation Does to Human Beings,* Sidgwick and Jackson, London, 1957.

Stieber, J. (Ed.). *Employment Problems in Automation and Advanced Technology.* Macmillan, London, 1966.

Weeks, R. P. (Ed.). *Machines and the Man: A Sourcebook on Automation,* Appleton-Century-Crofts, N.Y., 1961.

Weiner, Norbert. *Cybernetics,* Cambridge: Massachusetts Institute of Technology Press, 1961.

Weiner, Norbert. *Cybernetics: Or Control and Communication in the Animal and the Machine,* John Wiley & Sons, N.Y., 1961.

Weiner, Norbert. *The Human Use of Human Beings,* Anchor Books, N.Y., 1956.

Weiner, Norbert. *God and Golem, Inc.,* M.I.T. Press, Cambridge, Mass., 1964.

PART THREE

A BABY CRIES! A dog barks! A girl winks! All are communicating; a message is sent, a message is received.

In the world of men and machines, millions of messages are sent and received each moment. If the receiver understands exactly the message as intended by the sender, effective communication has taken place.

The plural for communication (the message) is "communications". But "communications" is also used in reference to the hardware (the medium). For example, the telephone network is a communications system; the computer is a communications system, etc. To further complicate the connotation, as McLuhan emphasizes, "the medium is the message". In other words, the style of a society is a function of that society's structured communications environment.

Moreover, people who write about communication, or communications, may not communicate with you. The reason is simple. Communication involves input, symbols, processing and output. If the receiver does not understand the symbols, or is incapable of processing, there is no communication. For example, a retarded English child could not be expected to understand a speech about cybernetics in Russian. This is why it is not unusual for someone to remark cynically that some specialists in communications fail to communicate.

Dr. Colin Cherry (Chapter 13) is one of the world's foremost authorities on the newly-evolved combined field of cybernetics information theory (linguistics-mathematics-phonetics-psychology-semantics). In its advanced forms, this involves prerequisites at the university level in mathematics and information theory. However, his philosophical approach should be comprehensible and helpful to the average reader. His book "On Human Communication" is highly recommended for the would-be experts and should be helpful to any professional in the physical and social sciences.

Dr. Marshall McLuhan (Chapter 14) is entirely different. He likes to describe himself, modestly, as an explorer, or prober, without a fixed point of view. Once you accept this definition, you can neither disagree with him nor avoid him. The New York Herald Tribune described him as the most important thinker since Newton, Darwin, Freud and Pavlov. Life Magazine called him "the Oracle of the Electric Age". "The New Republic" states, "it is extremely difficult to make sense out of much of the contemporary world without McLuhan's perspectives". If you would profit from his insights, read him meditatively as you would read an important poem. His message is profound and the content of his provocations is all around for us to see, if only we had his vision.

Gordon B. Thompson (Chapter 15) is the senior member of the scientific staff of the Research and Development Division of the Northern Electric Company, Limited, in Ottawa whose function is to serve as a "one-man think-tank" in exploring the usage and potentials of communication devices in relationship to the needs of society and, consequently, the market for advanced devices. This R & D department is unique in the world and its findings are universally recognized. His chapter speaks for itself.

Dr. Henry Cassirer (Chapter 16) has a major responsibility in extending the power of effective communications systems to the entire world through UNESCO. He is a member of a team who are constantly seeking ways and means of creating better communication among the people of "the good earth" who still use thousands of different languages ("symbols"), if indeed they are literate enough to use any. United Nations attempts to facilitate understanding by officially using five languages but most of the output is in English which, in spite of its complicated nature, appears to be the emerging global language.

Satora Takatsuka (Chapter 17) offers an interesting case study of an actual communications system in the exciting state of Japan. Japan is a world leader in the invention and application of technology and the result is reflected in figures on productivity and cost which might well become a model for the world. The output per man hour is the highest in the world in spite of the fact that unit labor costs remain low and constant. There is virtually no labor problem because wages have continued to rise in relationship to output per man hour—but never in excess, as has been the case in too many countries where unions have been allowed to boycott technology.

Finally, the statement from UNESCO on the application of mass media (Chapter 18) offers some concrete proposals which are worthy of consideration by every leader in the world. The emphasis is on adult education in the hope that, among these adults, wise leaders will rapidly come forth to form a network of understanding and cooperation in the elimination of war, violence and poverty.

CHAPTER 13

What Is Communication?

by Colin Cherry

Dr. Colin Cherry is the Henry Mark Pease Professor of Telecommunication, Imperial College University of London. This chapter is taken from his book "On Human Communication" (M I T Press) which was created under a grant from the Center for International Studies, Massachusetts Institute of Technology. The entire book is strongly recommended for those who wish to study communication in depth.

1

COMMUNICATION IS essentially a social affair. Man has evolved a host of different systems of communication which render his social life possible—social life not in the sense of living in packs for hunting or for making war, but in a sense unknown to animals. Most prominent among all these systems of communication is, of course, human speech and language.

Inasmuch as the words we use disclose the true nature of things, as truth is to each one of us, the various words relating to personal communication are most revealing. The word "communicate" means "share," and inasmuch as you and I are communicating at this moment, we are one. Not so much a union as a unity. Inasmuch as we agree, we say that we are of one mind, or, again, that we understand one another. This one another is the unity. A group of people, a society, a culture, I would define as "people in communication." They may be thought of as "sharing rules" of language, custom, of habit; but who wrote these rules? These have evolved out of those people themselves—rules of conformity. Inasmuch as conformity is the greater or the less, so is the unity. The degree of communication, the sharing, the conformity, is a measure of one-mindedness. After all, what we share, we can not each have as our own possession, and no single person in this world has ever been born and bred in utter isolation. "No man is an island, entire of itself."

2

Perhaps we may be permitted to comment upon a definition of communication, as given by a leading psychologist. "Communication is the discriminatory response of an organism to a stimulus." The same writer emphasizes that a definition broad enough to embrace all that the word "communication" means to different people may risk finding itself dissipated in generalities. We would agree; such definitions or descriptions serve as little more than foci for discussion. But there are two points we wish to make concerning this psychologist's definition. First, communication is not the response itself but is essentially the relationship set up by the transmission of stimuli and the evocation of responses. Second, it will be well to expand somewhat upon the notion of a stimulus; we shall need to distinguish between human language and the communicative signs of animals, between languages, codes, and logical sign systems, at least.

The study of the signs used in communication, and of the rules operating upon them and upon their users, forms the core of the study of communication. There is no communication without a system of signs—but there are many kinds of "signs".

The whole broad study of language and sign systems has been called, by Charles Morris, the theory of signs, and owes much to the earlier philosophy of Charles Peirce. Morris distinguishes three types of rule operating upon signs, (a) syntactic rules (rules of syntax; relations between signs); (b) semantic rules (relations between signs and the things, actions, relationships, qualities—designata); (c) pragmatic rules (relations between signs and their users).

3

Physically, we transmit signals or signs—audible, visual, tactual. But the mere transmission and reception of a physical signal does not constitute communication. A sign, if it is perceived by the recipient, has the potential for selecting responses in him.

The possibility of communication with a distant planet provides a currently popular example of communication that is initially one way. What can be assumed to exist in common between Earth and the planet that can serve as signs and rules, for a start, to build up a common language? We have no knowledge, if living creatures exist there, of their intelligence level, their sense organs, their basic concepts. For the concepts we each of us possess, and for which we have signs, depend upon our individual experiences. The concepts held by people of one culture may differ from those of another culture, depending upon chance of history or geography.

Man's life is a continuity of experience. It does not remain static but benefits from previous happenings; it advances now here, now there, and steadily grows in social scale. By contrast, animal life is relatively static, a here-now world, the animal living each moment as it comes. The very simplest creatures show little or no power of learning and benefiting from past experience. They do not have continued thoughts and do not readily form abstract concepts. They have no language in the sense that we have, and no system of organized thoughts, but use sign systems which are comparatively rigid and incapable of development. A man may change his method of expression, invoke new ideas; he can shift his line of argument, refer to past occasions, and hold out promise for the future. He can co-operate with his companions by changing his language to suit their reactions, and so achieve his goal more readily.

It has become a cliché to refer to man as "the communicating animal." Of all his functions, that of building up systems of communication of infinite variety and purpose is one of the most characteristic. Of all living creatures he has the most complex and adaptable systems of language; he is the most widely observant of his physical environment and the most responsive in his adjustment to it. He has organized ethical, political, and economic systems of varied kinds; he has the greatest subtlety of expressing his feelings and emotions, sympathy, awe, humor, hate—all the thousand facets of his personality. He is self-conscious and responsible; he has evolved spiritual, aesthetic, and moral sensibilities.

A man is not an isolated being in a void; he is essentially integrated into society. The various aspects of man's behavior —his means of livelihood, his language and all forms of self-expression, his systems of economics and law, his religious ritual, all of which involve him in acts of communication— are inherently related.

CHAPTER 14

Communication in the Global Village

by Marshall McLuhan

Dr. Marshall McLuhan is Director of the Institute of Culture and Technology, University of Toronto, and is known around the world for his books, "The Gutenburg Galaxy", "Understanding Media", "The Medium is the Massage", "War and Peace in the Global Village" and many others. Life Magazine has called him "the oracle of the electric age" and the New York Herald Tribune has recognized him as "the most important thinker since Newton, Darwin, Freud, Einstein and Pavlov."

1

LITERATE, VISUAL MAN lives by classification and detached bureaucratic indifference. Literacy creates the organization man and the hardware services of advanced countries.

Literacy via printing produces hardware, Gutenberg fathered all assembly lines.

By 1840, for example, England had developed many hardware environmental services such as book, press, rail, post, highways, markets and mechanical industry to the point of virtual "communism". In other words, the hardware services available to the ordinary person were far beyond the means of the greatest wealth to provide for itself.

Marx came later. The Communist Manifesto was written in 1848. Like Edward Bellamy, Marx was looking backward, not forward. All Utopias from Plato's "Republic" to Orwell's "1984", are rear-view mirror images.

Marx was thus aware of the tribal communism of primitive peoples, but not of the new communism of his own environment.

2

Phonetic literacy is the only de-tribalizing technology known to man. But radio, talkies and TV, on the other hand, do not create this detachment, classification and civilization. Instead, they create software information environments. They create total involvement and tribalism. (Tribal man lives by ear, by involvement. The German word for "cloud" is "volk"—the tribe, the all-enveloping group dream.) This image of the family group and corporate consciousness evokes total participation.

Now twenty-five hundred years of literate hardware service and organization of civilized, specialized man are encountering the electric extension of our own nervous system (the new software service environments). The predictable dynamics of this encounter of the old hardware and the new software is manifest in every phase of our lives today.

At the same time that the Negro is being asked to detribalize and allow himself to be drawn into our centralized society, the new electric speed of information movement is resulting in a kind of decentralization of that society as a whole. Two articles in The New York Times for May 28, 1968, point up this irony. The first is apropos the switch from 4 to 36 phone books in London:

IN LONDON
A PHONE BOOK CRISIS
By Alvin Shuster

Special to The New York Times, London, May 27—The Books are the four telephone directories in use in the London area. Word leaked out a few days ago that the Government planned to replace the four with 36 neighborhood directories.

This alone might not have caused the public uproar that followed, except for one fact. The Government said that residents would get only the slim directory covering their own neighborhood. The assumption apparently was that persons in one neighborhood of London never called persons in another.

Once again, it is this kind of decentralization into tribal pockets that results from electric speed of information movement. (New York City is one extreme example of such tribal nucleation of spatial arrangement. The global village is another.)

The editorial page of the same paper carried an essay on the "Decentralization Shambles". It began:

"The worst failure of the State Legislature in the disasterous session just ended was on the critical issue of school decentralization". The lawmakers caved in ignominiously under the irresponsible pressures of vested interest groups led by the United Federation of Teachers. Brushed aside were the carefully considered proposals of expert investigators and the precise prescriptions of the state's own education authorities. What emerged instead was a watered-down version that bordered on a mandate for inaction.

Foot-dragging on decentralization involves a flirtation with disaster. It would sabotage the reform of the education of all children: ghetto frustrations would be aggravated with attendant chaos in the predominantly Negro areas.

The UFT is a typically centralized and literate organization, now incompatible with the new software environment and the new Identity Image fostered by that software.

3

Today, for example, the non-literate backward countries, and the non-literate individuals within our own society get the new software technology before they get the old hardware of the nineteenth century. Nigeria and Tanzania get radio before motor cars or ice boxes. The Negro got TV before he got cars or corn flakes.

Thus software creates in the Orient or in Mississippi a billion dollar service environment, a Barinecide feast of inviting goodies, before there is anything to eat. This is the gripe of the Columbia students as much as the kids in Watts. The latter declined to interrupt their education to go to school.

The TV child wallows in a software environment of Images before he acquires the literacy that relates him to the producer-consumer hardware. The TV generation is thus naturally a Peter Pan generation of mystics, that sees "maturity" and responsibilities as linked to a ruthless and archaic hardware.

4

When this TV generation arrives at the job plateau in the next three or four years, it will abolish all of the old hardware. The Columbia students are a mild foretaste of the drive towards primal, integral inwardness.

That is why the Negro question is a red herring. To the post-literate TV generation there are no Negroes. There are only people. The detribalized American Negro will find an overwhelming ally in the younger portion of the retribalized American middle class. Indians and Eskimos and Biafrans have the empathetic support of Canadian youth; Russian youth identify with the Czechs . . . and so on.

The immediate dilemma of the underprivileged minority groups is the need to acquire literacy in order to find a "job" in the old hardware service environment. But to get literate and to detribalize and specialize himself just when the white society is retribalizing, is a debilitating irony. (An irony felt by all white teenagers too.)

As for the individual within these groups, he is now confronting semi-literate unions and politicians, whose scant visual culture gives them a frantic grip on the antiquated hardware and the specialized skills and classifications of the pre-TV age. The danger of civil war will come from these ethnically dominated unions, for whom literacy and its hardware technology are still a novelty, still status symbols, still marks of achievement.

The old visual world of literacy could tolerate such collision of multitudes of private points of view, because of the certitude that these collisions took place within a permanently fixed frame. The collisions engendered by a ballot box guaranteed a faithful image of the general will. Monadology could go no further.

Radio ended the efficacy of the ballot box, as it ended melodic structure. Even when radio was new in the 1920's, it erased the old identity of groups and individuals alike.

> The first radio "broadcast" in the world occurred from Dublin post-office in 1916. The anti-British rebels tinkered with an old ship-to-shore Navy radio, until they put it into a diffusion pattern and proclaimed their new image to the world.

> At first, before this, radio had been used only as a substitute for the telegraph. The breakdown of this telegraph function yielded the breakthrough of broadcasting.

> (In a similar way, it was the "breakdown" of telegraph that led Edison accidently to discover the telephone. He heard voices on the telegraph wire, and set out to correct this defect. Thus is born—bassackwards— progress.)

It was the American Negro, in fact, who made the only creative response to the new software environment of radio. (The English limey or slum kids—the Beatles—made the only creative response to TV.) The New Orleans Negroes merged traditional hymns and English speech rhythms to create a syncopated new art form. ("Jaser", New Orleans French for "to yatter".)

Jazz is based on discontinuity: not on connection. On the tactile space of the interval, not on the visual continuum of the melody, (melody hodos, the song road.)

Jazz was in spatial terms the mosaic of the telegraph press, as much as the cubist multi-faceted world of Picasso. (When Le Corbusier first saw New York, he said, "It is le jazz hot en pierre.")

The syncopated and discontinuous character of jazz has been as much misunderstood as "Finnegans Wake". Touch, or contact, does not create continuity or connectedness. Quite the reverse. It creates the interval, as beat creates rhythm. (The Japanese housewife never reproves her husband: she rearranges the spaces between flowers to express her "blues".)

This is in direct contrast with the effect of the old literate, visual environment, which creates the illusion of an absolute "continuous" "Rational" space as a cosmic fact. In the May, 1968, issue of the "Scientific American", Frederick C. Kreiling contrasts the world of Leibniz and of Newton. The world of Leibniz, "inspired by Plato" assumed "the changing nature of true reality". "What is important to realize is that to Leibniz . . . Newton's theories seemed a regression to medieval notions that had been dispelled with great effort." For those who had come to see every force as the effect of the motion of material particles, they admitted of no way for bodies to affect one another except through the force of impact exerted when they came into contact."

The invisible pull of gravitational environment was incompatible with this view of change.

Today, the Leibnizians are those who think it is the "content" of media when it contacts the viewer or recipient that causes change. The Newtonians see the change upon the perceptions.

6

Jazz was accepted at once in all the world capitals, and still reigns in Tokyo, Berlin, Paris and New York. Thus the American Negro integrated the world while a few whites pondered the need to "integrate" white and black.

Jazz was a tribal, acoustic response adjusted to the global village created by radio. With this new medium, the tribal image returned in show business and in politics alike. The new showman in both had to "put on" his audience and become a corporate image—like Mussolini or Hitler or FDR or Jack Kennedy. These men were therefore tribal chieftans or Emperors on a scale unknown before in the world.

These men were quite blind, however, to their new environment. All environments are imperceptible to their inhabitants, as water is to a fish. That is why, as Trevor-Roper observes:

"Any society, as long as it is, or feels itself to be, a working society, tends to invest in itself: a military society tends to become more military, a bureaucratic society more bureaucratic, a commercial society more commercial, as the status and profits of war or office or commerce are enhanced by success, and institutions are framed to forward it. Therefore, when such a society is hit by a general crisis, it finds itself partially paralysed by the structured weight of increased social investment. The dominant military or official or commercial classes cannot easily change their orientation; and their social dominance, and the institutions through which it is exercised, prevent other classes from securing power or changing policy."

The matter of tribal violence, therefore, is no different from any other kind of violence, psychic or social, private or corporate, military, commercial or educational. (Even the Kingdom of Heaven can only be entered by violence—i.e., violence to our mundane image or identity.)

Wherever a gap or interval occurs, there is an area of new friction, ferment, interface and change. Thus, all violence is making, not matching. It has no target or goal so much as the creation of a new image, as in an ad "campaign". The Negro has no target or goal in his violence. Just as when he created jazz, he had no goals beyond making a form of participation and involvement.

The Newtonians (not to mention Planck, Einstein or Heisenberg) were more aware of the bias and physical distortion introduced into all frameworks by the mere act of perception. They knew that seeking was making, not matching. Artistic representation by matching, for example, was as much a product of literacy as representative government.

"It is above all that you may *see*", said Joseph Conrad in summing up his work. The violence is a probe of the contours of reality, much as new media like new biological species create new dimensions of space and time.

7

No society in history has ever known enough about the forces that shape and transform it to take action to control and direct new technologies as they extend and transform man. But today, change proceeds so instantaneously through the new media that it may be possible to institute a global education program that will enable us to seize the reins of our destiny—but to do this we must first recognize the kind of therapy that's needed for the effects of the new media. In such an effort, indignation against those who perceive the nature of those effects is no substitute for awareness and insight.

The extensions of man's consciousness induced by the electric media could conceivably usher in the millennium, but it also holds the potential for realizing the Anti-Christ. Cataclysmic environmental changes such as these are, of themselves, morally neutral; it is how we perceive them and react to them that will determine their ultimate psychic and social consequences. If we refuse to see them at all, we will become their servants. It's inevitable that the world-pool of electronic information movement will toss us all about like corks on a stormy sea, but if we keep our cool during the descent into the maelstrom, studying the process as it affects us, and learning to program and control it, we can come through.

CHAPTER 15

The Revolution in Communication Technology

by Gordon B. Thompson

Gordon B. Thompson has been described as "Canada's one-man think tank". He is an engineer and scientist who has specialized in communications. As a senior member of the scientific staff of the Research and Development Department of Northern Electric Co. Ltd., his papers and articles have been widely read by specialists. This chapter is an original essay which was specially created for "This Cybernetic Age". He is currently writing a major book which is still unnamed.

CYBERNETICS AND COMMUNICATIONS. By bringing together these two concepts, what new resources can we create? Can we invent systems growing from this combination that will be truly beneficial?

The concepts of cybernetics and automation have been used to a great degree in achieving the communications advances we now have. However, the effort has been one of using the cybernetic concepts to attain ends that were conceived in pre-cybernetic terms. Without the automation and cybernation concepts we now have, the launching and operation of a communications satellite would be impossible. However, these concepts form only a part of this satellite component of the larger global communications system. The concepts of cybernation and automation play little part in the overall goals of this hyper system. In the following pages, we shall examine the limitations of some of our popular communications miracles, and then go on to consider the implications of a fuller interaction between the concepts of communications and cybernation.

Are satellites a new medium, or are they just extensions of other more familiar techniques? Will the checkless society be a great society? What of the wired city? Shopping by 'phone'? To what extent will these systems and others like them change our lives, and has the research been done to assure that the change is for the better?

It can be categorically stated that we just don't know, for the research has not been done. It has not even been adequately defined. There seems a need to do more things scientifically rather than a need to do more scientific things, for the problems underlying our ignorance seem to lie in an area that has yet to be classified as scientific. Communications research today is more concerned with the niceties of a new Pulse Code Modulation system to haul signals than with the total effects of communications media on their host societies. The compartmentalization of science into rigid disciplines has severely limited the capability of the scientific community to make a meaningful contribution to the solution of these very real problems. The scientist today is a staunch member of the establishment, and is no longer pursued by a society because of his heretical beliefs. Science is not a socially dangerous occupation, but rather is quite as respectable as the priesthood.

In all honesty, it must be noted that there is a very widespread attention to trivia, a lack of the truly creative response to stress, and in general, a wide acceptance of the mediocre in our society. Surely that is what the "254 Pieces of 3/8 inch felt", a mere pile of felt cuttings, is trying to say from its corner in the National Art Gallery in Ottawa.

Let us return to an analysis of the more popular communications developments, and then after having set a more critical mood, attempt a synthesis between the concepts of cybernation and communications. This synthesis must be examined in the light of our lack of knowledge of the social implications of what we are proposing, and so must result in proposals with limited risks associated with their implementation.

Satellites have attracted a good deal of public attention, even to the oversubscription of the financing of the American COMSAT Corporation. It is hardly likely that any large government will act to control any really new situation. The fact that satellite hearings have been held to determine who should own, operate, and control them indicates that even the government knows what they are. We must have used analogues or paradigms from our previous experience to supply this knowledge; hence we have implicitly decided that satellites are an extension of the systems that developed these paradigms, the conventional radio transmission systems. Whether or not this is what satellites really are is beside the point, for we have collectively behaved as if this is what they are. Perhaps the territorial instincts exhibited at these same hearings are indicative of the way our productivity has outstripped our creativity. If we were really all that creative, surely we could invent sufficient channel capacity for all, whether to own, or to use, be it satellites or some other alternative. One suspects that the *satellite game* is more significant than the *satellite* itself!

Certainly the total channel capacity of all synchronous satellites is finitely limited, for to be stationary in the heavens above the earth the satellite's orbit must lie over the earth's equator. It will drift north and south throughout the year if it is off the equitorial plane. All synchronous satellites must lie in this single belt some 23,000 miles out in space, directly over the equator. This forces a limit to the number of useable parking places. Many of these places are useless because of their location vis-a-vis the earth itself. Regardless of whether the upper limit of synchronous satellite parking places is one hundred, or two hundred, or even three hundred, the number is obviously limited.

Coincidentally, we have a mushrooming demand, a demand that for the foreseeable future is merely hardware limited, and not limited in any fundamental way. For example, to equip the rest of the Ottawa schools with a television retrieval system, such as is now operating in some 130 teaching areas in the western part of that city, would require about 100 television channels for that city alone. Now, what about neighbouring Hull, Vanier City and Carleton County? There is just no way using synchronous satellites.

The rich seamless web that the switched telephone network creates is helped only in its longest paths by satellite technology, and even this contribution is somewhat limited due to the diminishing size of the window of acceptable times during which calls can be made as distance increases. A Quebec-France satellite would build a peak between 9:00 a.m. and 1:00 p.m. for these delimit the common hours of business. Extending the service another couple of time zones, would further reduce this window to a mere hour or so. Real time communications over distances that approach half the way around the globe carry very severe limitations, limitations that may make the use of Telex or other switched message services more prominent in the future. Admittedly they do not provide interaction, but there is a lot going for them, as any Telex customer will testify. Again, the effects of time, storage, and our unfamiliarity with these things in a creative way, indicates a possible lessening of forecast requirements for the real time satellite channels.

Satellites certainly have their role to play. They are the most mobile big time communications facility ever devised. Long haul, heavy route facilities of prime quality can be dropped off anywhere a ground station can be set up. The value of this to the development of the North, and other areas of inhospitable terrain is indisputable. It means anywhere on earth that can see an equitorial synchronous orbit (not the poles, for instance) can be part of the urban world. It is a limited resource, however and to the extent we more affluent nations might use it to substitute for slightly less economic ground facilities, we will limit the potential of underdeveloped areas that could make temporary use of satellite facilities to stimulate their own internal growth until such time as they can afford proper networks of their own. Our own Northland is much this way. Good communications will speed the development, but eventually the pressure to build proper commercial supply lines into the area and so connect it in a meaningful way to the southern regions will cause us to provide facilities that can move a pair of shoes cheaply into the North, and to bring back the products of its economy for our use. The physical plant required for this kind of communication needs only some minor additions and the needs of the more etherial kind of communication are easily met. If you build a road, it is not much more effort to put a string of radio towers every 30 miles along it, or bury a coaxial cable under it. Since the problem starts as a point to point communications problem, and usually involves limited resources, satellites offer a neat solution. Eventually, as economic development progresses the problem becomes one of providing a mesh-like network, with many cross links, for not only messages, but packages, people and bulk materials as well. The satellite can serve only the message part of this later stage, suggesting that it might be time to move it along to some other developing area.

The satellite's ability to bring interesting events throughout the world right into our homes via television is also important. But, this just allows television to achieve its rightful role. In this regard, the satellite is little more important than the development of the 416 vacuum tube by the Bell Telephone Laboratories which permitted the first coast to coast microwave system, without which first rate national television would not have been possible. Both are merely sequential steps to adequate transmission facilities.

It seems reasonable then, to say that the satellite is an extension of older communications media. It has caused no really fundamental quantum change. Now that we see this emperor in his real clothes, how are some of his companions clad?

To the extent that electrical banking reduces the odious parts of the banking routines, we have a valuable service; providing we can use the energies released in a more creative way than to chop up computers, or blow up stock exchanges. Money is already a sort of communications system. It communicates to the manufacturers how many Mustangs to build, and how much bread to make. It is an exquisite system in

174 / THIS CYBERNETIC AGE

this regard compared to the hopelessly more ponderous one that directs our largest industry, the Government. Surely, if given the choice between further sophist complication of the conventional world of money and a creative improvement to our political machinery to make it more responsive and competent we would choose the latter. If communications technology can contribute to each, then surely we should know more about the possibilities inherent in the latter suggestion. The expenditure of capital to achieve a checkless society may in fact deny the alternative. Unfortunately, we have been rather uncreative here, and produced more cuttings of felt rather than a meaningful expression of the fuller spirit of man. Hence, as a cost or effort reduction program, fine, but as an end in itself, the checkless society has little to offer.

The home shopping console may well be removing the one last major social experience too many people have, an opportunity to escape into a world of fantasy, that is tactile, olefactory, and generally quite sensually rewarding. Have we the right to turn this experience into one of those form-completing drudgeries?

These examples have been rather trivial compared to the picturephone concept, but since only conjecture can be used at this time, there seems little point in engaging in a discussion of the alternatives, and their pros and cons. To think that this work has never been adequately done at any level other than the classically technical level is appalling. More felt. Unfortunately, we will be the ones who will have 'felt' the effects, both socially and financially. We will reap the harvest of problems from over attention to the technical details of the automobile, to use an analogy, rather than attending to the problems of parking, congestion and pollution, the solution of which may involve the replacement of the automobile.

It seems as if the future offers us too many mediocre opportunities, too much felt, and not enough real substance. We seem to lack a way of identifying what good ideas there might be, and we certainly have no really effective means of arriving at a consensus about the future that uses competence and imagination as its prime ingredients, and significantly involves a large part of our population.

If the combination of cybernetics and communications is to be a great communications revolution, then the result of this synthesis might be expected to have some of the common characteristics that attended the past great revolutionary developments in communications. A glance back at a collection of those outstanding events, such as the invention of language, writing, the phonetic alphabet, papyrus, moveable type, mechanized transport, telegraph, telephone, etc., brings out the point that they each in turn made stored human experience more easily accessible. The telephone made it easier to get hold of an expert. The book made stored information very much more accessible. It would seem reasonable to suggest that this might be a characteristic of any truly significant synthesis of cybernation and communications. It is important to give emphasis to the idea of making this accessing of stored human experience easier, for there are dangers in just increasing the information flow.

The so-called information overload we are experiencing today tends to force us into a speeded up inductive reasoning process, where newly emergent patterns become generalized and seem too quickly to gain believers before adequate tests can be designed. Again, maybe our low level of creative response limits our approaches to the testing, resulting in premature rejection or adoption without the final steps of the inductive reasoning process being competently and creatively carried out. With complexity on the increase, we must find a way of coping more adequately with these problems, for unless we can learn to deal with the increasingly complex problems that face us with increasing ease, we will be hindering the natural processes of evolution that begin with primitive randomness and move towards ordered complexity. Today's complexity becomes tomorrow's routine.

It would seem that the only out is in the direction of an

interactive communications environment that widely embraces the society it serves, and which acts as a significant means of assisting that society in discovering its nascent consensi. Such a system would have to take account of the problem of generalization outlined above, but in overcoming this problem, would still have to be stimulating enough to make its use enjoyable and rewarding for the citizens of the society.

In his book, "The Age of Discontinuity", Peter Drucker talks of the way a corporation must operate, and espouses the notion that within the organization, an obedient posture must be taken by the employee if the aims of the organization are to be met. However, in an era where the content of more and more jobs is think-type activity, as opposed to labor-type activity, creativity becomes inhibited in the end by such a posture, for eventually the creative outpourings of the employees will cause the corporation to change.

Consider a research lab, where individuals are asked to make creative thrusts out into the unknown, and to design new products for the corporation to sell. At the beginning, it is possible to lay down a corporate policy to direct these searches, but sooner or later, the research activity must burst out of this limitation, for invention will alter the form of the corporation, or else it is not fulfilling its role as the prime wealth producer we know of. When this happens, either the corporation changes drastically (3M, Texas Instruments, IBM) or it remains staunch, and changes only superficially (AT&T). Size, age and activity area enter into this as well, but in general, methods of dealing with the pressures generated by this situation are unchanged from those the Roman Government used two thousand years ago, and are just not adequate to cope with the complexities present today.

Therefore, as more and more jobs become based upon competent think-type activities, it becomes increasingly important to tap these competences and use them in the highest activities of the organization, that is the determination of its objectives. That we don't in fact know how to do this very well is quite obvious to anyone in a large corporation of the think-type.

The technically competent worker is less likely to be in a position where his input is significant in the larger corporation. There is almost a ghetto of competence, which is cut off from the ruling class. They speak different languages, cherish different experiences, and have very little in common. The parallel with urban problems is quite interesting, if one reads sensual awareness for intellectual awareness.

Government is a think-type industry, by and large, and here the tale is no better. Much of the insensitivity, and ineffectiveness Peter Drucker complains of is probably due to our failure to evolve mechanisms or communications techniques to help the competences of the think-type employees to contribute interactively to the determination of policies in government.

Communications systems have, in the past, played an important role in helping societies develop their nascent consensi. The Greek amphitheatre where the citizens met is an example. The technology involved in the acoustic design of this communications system is quite respectable, even by today's standards. Unfortunately the system could not be extended beyond several hundred participants, so limiting the size of the group that could get involved.

Television today shows only that which its operators think is popular. If they are wrong, their listeners choose another channel. The mere showing of these things increases their popularity, and so for better or worse, television tends to build consensus by making that that is popular even more popular. Positive feedback. The artistic element enters the process in the determination of things that are becoming popular. In this respect, the Beatles are superb artists, and are now recognized as significant artists in the more usual sense. By having just the right amount of lead time, in combination with the right material, they managed to use television and radio to produce a complete revolution in music, with a very quickly established consensus that was in no way imposed by any large or powerful organization. Their revolution was so successful that they have become the new Establishment.

One wonders if the mere speed of today's communications systems doesn't contribute to a sort of consensus favoring mediocrity. If one could imagine a race track equipped with the fastest communications possible, one could conceive of bets being accepted up to a second or so before the horses crossed the finish line. In so far as the communications are concerned, this is possible, but the game is destroyed, for everyone would be a most mediocre winner. Similarly, a new idea today gets assessed, and dismissed or espoused long before the creator has had time to live with it. One wonders if the day of the great inventor isn't past. Did Alexander Graham Bell invent the machine that virtually killed his breed?

A closer inspection of the last two examples shows the role of cybernetics in this consensus process. In the case of the consensus developed by television, there was positive feedback present, for that that was becoming popular was shown, and so encouraged to become ever more popular. If the television station failed to choose correctly, its listening audience shrank, and so its effectiveness diminished, and this is an example of a negative feedback process controlling the growth potential achievable with the positive loop. Recalling a bit of cybernetics, we remember that a positive feedback condition causes growth or increase while a negative feedback process tends to control or reduce the output of the whole process, controlling it to meet given conditions. In our television example, the consensus will grow under the influence of the positive feedback of showing that which is already becoming popular, while the dimensional size of this consensus is controlled by the negative feedback involved in the assessment by the audience of the station's acuity in selecting material.

The horse race is pure negative feedback, where correcting information is available at all times, to lessen the chance of error. Nothing exciting ever happens with negative feedback, it just works well, and does a completely predictable job. Very good communication between the established experts and the creative newcomers to a field may in fact operate the same way, and provide an environment of negative feedback that enhances mediocrity and safety rather than risk change. These are examples of how the concepts of cybernation combine with communications. The combination in the television example is a neat balance between positive and negative feedback loops, but unfortunately the negative loop is so limited in information capacity that the sample used to exert this control becomes statistically trivial. We can do better.

It has been observed that the Egyptian withdrawal of papyrus contributed very significantly to the demise of the Roman Empire. Papyrus was the vehicle through which the authority of Rome was conveyed to the outposts of the Empire. Cut the lines of communications, and the whole fabric falls; there is no longer any viable consensus amongst the people, and so no more Empire.

Simple biological needs act as a consensus forming environment, causing men to agree on a course of common action long before they would in the absence of that need. War is another consensus producing element. Our recent disenchantment with authoritarianism probably stems from the dual causes of an increase in overall competence and the inability of the mere biological needs to meet its share of the consensus producing requirements of our increasingly affluent society. The falling off of this polarizing element in our environment is perhaps one of the significant causes of today's chaos. Can we invent a communications system to do the consensus forming that want and need performed previously?

One might observe that when the consensus forming systems within a society are effective and widely embracing, then that society is, almost by definition, a great society. A large corporation, and a government department are both a species of sub-society, and so offer a real testing ground for such systems before they are applied to the larger questions that involve the total of a society.

The design of such systems for a society at large is just too complex and risky a proposition to even contemplate, but the mini-states known as corporations provide an adequate design and testing environment of limited size and risk.

The complex problems faced in a large corporation are rather simpler models of the larger issues present in a society. However, in the commercial world, the need for a system to really work is present, and the effectiveness of the system can be measured in terms of how a corporation using the system fares in relation to one using some other technique of arriving at consensus amongst its members or employees. As more and more automation is incorporated into business, the chief problem is what futurable should the corporation embrace, and how should this be decided? In general there is a surplus of talent, and a shortage of agreement. In trying to utilize our increased opportunity for creative and individual contribution, we must develop better means of making the overall effect as satisfactory as when each contributor did his piece of labor, rather than his piece of invention, as it is now becoming. Invention is a lot harder to direct than labor! And this is the main challenge to the kind of system we are considering here.

In this mini-state manifestation, these systems would take on many of the characteristics associated with information retrieval systems, computers, and other current catch words of the future-ologist. The significant point here is to combine all the components into a meaningful system that can give the host society a quantum step increase in consensus forming capability. To have only a wired city without the over-riding system aims could be courting disaster. It is rather like sending a youngster into the munitions factory with a match.

Just as our grandparents were experience limited in letting

the horse influence the naming of its replacement, in both the case of the automobile and the railroad, so one could expect us to be limited to our past experience in relation to the role of the technology we now refer to as 'computers'. Surely this device is more than a mere computing engine, surely it is more than a manipulator of files, it is more than a step-and-fetch-it type of dumb servant. All these are ideas out of our past, with about as much creativity in them as the 254 pieces of 3/8 inch felt, (note that 'felt' is a four letter word too). Restrictive or controlling legislation has yet to be conceived of for computers, and no great series of coast to coast hearings have been held either. This is a new element in our communications arsenal.

One might make some tentative statements about a consensus forming system of this new kind. It would most likely involve some sort of Computer Assisted Instruction capability similar to that being researched for use in our schools now. In addition, one would expect the program to accept free language responses rather than the limited range of responses currently allowable in these systems. Research into this specific area is well along in at least two organizations in Canada. Furthermore, the system would have to be a learning system in that when it encounters a user who knows more about a particular phase of the material, it enters into a dialogue with that user to collect what it can, and assess and test this new data against what stored data and human expertise it can muster. This kind of thing has been done in game playing situations, so the essential principles are known vis-a-vis the learning part, however, the complexities of free language have so far inhibited any breakthrough in the broader aspects of the problem. For the time being, in the limited size models we are discussing, we can profitably use human insight. It would also be a very large system, involving many users.

Project Delphi provides a rather vivid example of how a

communications routine can be established to cause an inherent consensus to firm up. In this exercise, a questionnaire was mailed out to experts throughout the United States, asking when they thought milestones of future achievement, listed in a form, would be achieved. The answers were collected, and a plot of the distribution of the answers made for each milestone. The questionnaires were again mailed out, but this time, the statistical analysis of the previous results was included in the mailing. Positive Feedback. The results this time showed a considerable decrease in statistical spread. Some consensus had been generated. Generated from nothing but carefully refined information, and the interaction of that refined information with each man's wealth of experience.

Clearly the rules used in the refining process are delicate, vital and controlling. They must be thoroughly researched and adequately understood. But, it is after all this refining process that helps against the information overload syndrome. Having accepted the information absorbing nature of this process, let us observe that the Delphi project might act as a very simple model for our system. Note that the technique involved a large population in an apolitical mode, where each individual was reacting only to the system and the data being presented, not to the people who made the statements, for this identification is part of the information absorbed (used up) in the process and not relayed to the subsequent users.

So far we have turned our attention to the system in the large, concerning ourselves with those characteristics that would seem essential to help a society create an almost tribal type of informational environment. What about the actual terminal devices with which the users would interact? These would have to be the subject of a very competent analysis of the user's sensory characteristics in order to assure a stimulating and effective coupling.

Presumably, some user classes would be better suited to an alpha-numeric type terminal that relies heavily upon the phonetic alphabet, while other classes of users would benefit from a more iconic style of presentation, resembling a cartoon format perhaps. The role of the sound component should also be a programmable thing, again depending upon the user's needs. The design of the terminal equipment would be easily as important as the design of the overall system, for the users perceive the system through these terminal devices, and so here is where the message is formed. The competences for this chore have yet to be turned into what we might term engineering skills.

In conclusion, one might put forth a task statement describing a system that would interact with the members of a particular corporate mini-state in a meaningful and almost fun-like way, that would so raise their competences as to permit them to deal with the complexities of their interrelationships in a more rational and productive manner. Within this kind of environment, the tasks of learning, working and teaching smear into one, and if we really succeed, to this trio we may even dare to add entertaining! If this is what the wired city of tomorrow is, then let's get on with it. However, one can't be sure at this time that any given piece of hardware is relevant to these broader aims. Should computers fit, then fine. If satellites are needed to make this work, then they will have a great future. What we must not do is plan our future in terms of hardware bricks, but rather in terms of architectural statements that may totally depend on bricks, but in their conception were not limited by brick-type thinking. Alternatively, the thinking must be well done and the inductive portions that need testing must be well researched. Unfortunately the communications theory being taught today is of too little help in dealing with these problems. Perhaps the first application of systems of this nature would be in that most unassailable mini-state, the university itself. If interacting with a system of this type in any organization wouldn't in fact be a university, then we have missed the whole point of the exercise.

CHAPTER 16

Mass Media for Human Development

by Henry R. Cassirer

Dr. Henry Cassirer is Director of the Department of
Mass Communications for UNESCO (United Nations).
Consequently, he is widely informed on global matters.
This chapter is adapted from a paper in "Convergence"
which is the International Journal of Adult Education
edited by Dr. J. Roby Kidd, Head of the Department of
Adult Education, Ontario Institute for Studies in Edu-
cation.

1

ADULT EDUCATION, the development of human resources, is faced with a revolutionary situation due to rapid economic, social, and political developments throughout the world. This situation calls for new approaches to the objectives and methods of education, as well as to the uses of mass media. Media of mass communication—radio, television, film, and the press—have a key role to play in this adaptation to changing needs, although they too are limited in their spread and educational impact, and require new approaches to their use.

2

The Systems Approach

In most development plans, education systems and communication systems are treated separately. However, the systems approach envisages an institutional framework within each country to enable the varied machinery of education, including mass media, to be integrated components, operating in a single system. So that investment in this approach may be fully productive, it is essential for developing and advanced nations alike to devise new strategies which establish national priorities in the light of major needs and for which resources are allocated.

Traditional approaches consider media of communication merely as "audio-visual aids" to the instructor.

The media are not merely aids to the adult educator, but educational agents in their own right. Like other forms of education, they have their specific limitations (one-way communication, centralized production, need for technical infra-structure for distribution and reception, etc.) Their full effectiveness depends therefore upon integration into a comprehensive method of adult education.

Since people respond directly to and learn from images and sounds (radio, television, cinema, photographs, posters, etc.) it is important to appreciate that audio-visual media are not merely preparing people to use print: they can and should be employed in their own right for their educational value, as part of systems, or independently.

3

On the one hand, there is a trend toward ever wider dissemination. In developing areas, radio is beginning to cover an entire country, while television gradually ceases to be a largely urban phenomenon. Thanks to communication satellites, vast new perspectives are opened for the national and international distribution of many kinds of informational and educational messages (by means of radio, television, information data, still pictures, electronic blackboards).

On the other hand, there is a distinct trend to localization and individualization of communications. In developing areas, national radio broadcasting is being supplemented by local radio stations whose programs are better adapted to the social, economic, and linguistic conditions of the people living within the area of their coverage. Similarly, local low-cost newspapers are springing up, and both open and closed circuit television is being used to meet the specific needs of individual communities of institutions. This trend toward localization may be noted also in highly developed societies. Moreover, the wide choice of channels now becoming available permits individual study of mass media productions in libraries and homes (dial access to recorded materials, Electronic Video Recording, 8 mm. cassettes, and so on).

Although the massive dissemination of educational and informational messages has distinct values, it poses the danger of too much centralization and of lack of adaptation to the needs of local communities and individuals. The trend toward localization and individualization offers an opportunity to compensate for such centralization.

Ways have to be found to co-ordinate fragmented field agencies to facilitate the integration of mass media into their activities; they will then be equipped to extend the impact of adult education to areas and sections hitherto not served, and to infuse new content and new methods into their work.

It is evident that centralization introduces the danger of adults being restricted in their freedom of choice—choice of subjects to be studied, of careers to be chosen, and of leisure-time activities to be pursued.

4

The mass media are valuable whenever their programs are designed to reach a large or widely dispersed public.

The Meeting on Broadcasting in the Service of Education and Development in Asia, convened by UNESCO at Bangkok in 1966 stated:

Broadcasting should be considered part of the country's

188 / THIS CYBERNETIC AGE

basic facilities, like harbors, roads, electricity, for the provision of which funds are invested not merely for immediate and identifiable results, but which are rightly believed to promote a long-term increase in national production. As with investment in education, broadcasting resources should be expected to yield results in the form of an informed, motivated and skilled people, leading to the increased availability of productive manpower, whether in urban or rural areas.

The pioneers of the integrated use of mass media should have a fresh outlook, be familiar with the assets and limitations of the media, and take note of the results of research in this field.

Co-ordination should take place first at the government level, so that different ministries or national media organizations can pool their resources. But co-ordination will have to be continued with equal effectiveness in the production of programs and in their utilization on the local or reception level. Various forms of machinery were suggested: an interministerial council; a special cabinet department; or perhaps an independent trust or corporation outside the existing administrative structure, and thus more in a position to bring about agreement by all. On a lower level, co-ordination can be promoted by advisory councils of mass media organizations, through the establishment of educational mass media services, and directly through programs utilized by teachers, adult educators, group leaders, and the viewing groups themselves. What is needed is a communications strategy rather than a media-oriented strategy.

It is evident that there are few fields of adult education which cannot benefit from media of mass communication. Yet priority should obviously be given to broad educational needs rather than to specialized services of value to a limited number of individuals.

Education of children can be successful only if fully supported by parents. In rural areas, parents frequently resist schooling of children who are needed on the land; active parental support for the school program can, on the other hand, influence the work and learning of children in a positive manner. The role of mass media in this instance, then, is to help "to contribute to education in schools, colleges and other institutions through the enlightenment of the public in general and stimulation of co-operation by parents in particular." Another example of such broad effectiveness is the use of the media "to stimulate participation in public life and action on community problems at community level." By reporting on civic activities and raising issues of community interest to audiences grouped for reception, discussion, and action, the radio, television, and film can do more than merely inform the public: they can elicit the kind of awareness that leads to active participation in civic life and to a feeling of belonging to a broader community.

"Mass media may effectively serve the traditional aims of adult education . . . to enable men and women with fuller access to leisure time to revalue the purposes of leisure, to foster the growth in them of new intellectual, aesthetic, moral and physical interests, to teach them new leisure skills."

CHAPTER 17

Japanese Systems--
A Case History

by Satoru Takatsuka

Satoru Takatsuka is with the Japanese Broadcasting System (NHK). Because of the Japanese contribution to leadership in Communication Technology we are especially grateful for permission to reprint, in part, his article from the June 1969 edition of "Convergence." This magazine is the International Journal of Adult Education, contains articles in four major languages, and is available at $4.00 per year from Dr. Roby Kidd, Editor, Department of Adult Education, Ontario Institute for Studies in Education, 102 Bloor Street, Toronto, Ontario.

1

AFTER WORLD WAR II, the political structure of Japan was broadly democratized. In the field of education, equal opportunity for all, coeducation, and the scholarship system were legally guaranteed. Also, since 1955, restructuring of thought on the subject of extramural education has taken place, although this has been slow in developing.

The following may be advanced as an explanation for such a change in the concept of education: the rapid economic growth and the technological innovations that supported such growth necessitated a high-quality labor force. This need, in turn, made industrial circles demand that education be focused on the development of individual ability. They also demanded more substantial adult education. Thus, pressure was applied to change educational policies.

In 1962, Prime Minister Hayato Ikeda requested his own advisory organ, the Economic Council, to submit a report discussing the "basic direction of policies on the improvement of human capabilities for meeting future technological progress and fluctuations in the supply and demand of labor forces."

Meanwhile, technological innovations promoted economic growth, increased national income, and modernized living conditions. More free time available to the people stimulated leisure industries and caused a boom in that field. The increased national income raised the ratio of those going on to higher schools. This situation further stimulated enrollment in colleges and universities, so that now, college education for most persons is a matter of course, instead of being reserved for the elite, as in former days.

2

A review of the education system on the basis of conditions prevailing in 1968 reveals the following problems that require solutions:

1. How should education and training be provided to ensure a labor force prepared to meet technological innovations?
2. How should post-secondary education be provided?
3. How can the individual be educated to utilize leisure to enrich his life?
4. How can vocational retraining programs be organized?

Adult education through radio and television is to provide an answer for the four questions cited above.

The shortage of skilled workers to meet the requirements of technological innovations constantly runs to over a million, and has been in a chronic state since 1961. Especially notable is the lack of workers capable of leadership, and possessing special skills, for example: machine operators, automobile drivers, sewing machine operators, carpenters, and machine assembly workers.

In short, (a) administrative knowledge and ability have become necessary; (b) skills have diversified; (c) but, a higher degree of skill in certain single functions is required (d) and, on the other hand, types of occupations requiring no special skill are beginning to appear.

Under these circumstances, we must consider:

1. What roles can radio and television play under such changing labor conditions; and how can they take part in the training of skilled workers?

2. What would be the objectives of skill-training programs?

As far as the latter question is concerned, the answers are: one objective would be the training of leaders; and the second would be the development of a successful program for training skilled workers.

3

Students from industry acquire most of their vocational training through television programs. In such cases, the broadcasts offer scientific experiments as well as lectures by television instructors. This eliminates some of the difficulties arising from the students' inability to attend school in person. Education through television requires the collaboration of the teacher and the television instructor: therefore, teamwork has been stimulated among the television instructors and school teachers.

A beginning has also been made in broadcasting college level curricula for the general public. This represents a notable advance.

Besides organized adult education through broadcasts, there are many cases of selective utilization by individuals. In such cases, it is up to the broadcaster to stimulate the learning activity of the viewers and to report some kind of feedback.

Acquiring knowledge while staying at home, through radio and television courses, appears to be a system of education for the twenty-first century. Professor Bantaro Kido, a well-known Japanese educator, has said, "General education in colleges and universities should utilize audiovisual methods more widely in the future, and instead of increasing the number of colleges and universities with misqualified instructors, it would often be more effective to let people view educational broadcasts presented by better qualified ones."

CHAPTER 18

Application of
Mass Media

This is a UNESCO statement which emerged from the meeting on broadcasting in the service of Education Development convened by UNESCO at Bangkok in 1969.

Suggested Fields For Application of Mass Media to
Adult Education

I. General Educational Needs

Mass media in combination with various forms of adult education can help:
1. To create societies with equal educational opportunities for all sectors of the population;
2. To pursue the struggle against ignorance and superstition;
3. To promote understanding of mental and physical health;
4. To help the handicapped assume a more positive place in society;
5. To combat illiteracy—that is, by creating functional literacy among key sectors of the economy in developing countries; by creating literacy among significant minorities of disadvantaged adults in more advanced countries;
6. To contribute to education in schools, colleges, and other institutions through the enlightenment of the public in general and stimulation of co-operation by parents in particular.

II. Life in the Community

Mass media applied to adult education can help in a number

of ways to create new communities or to revitalize old ones; and to give national issues local significance. They may serve:

7. To stimulate participation in public life, and action on community problems at community level;
8. To provide live coverage of national and civic meetings (for example, representative assemblies, local councils, and so on), the content of whose deliberations and debates is educative;
9. To improve the effectiveness of voluntary organizations by providing training for lay leaders and workers in social work agencies, cultural societies, political associations, and the like;
10. To help people preserve their identity in the face of rapid social change and the disruption of traditional communities;
11. To combat intergroup prejudice, and thus contribute to increased international and interracial understanding.

III. Economy and Work

In this vital field, there are important tasks to be performed through mass media:

12. To contribute to the improvement of living standards by promoting technological and economic advance through improved agriculture and administration of rural institutions, increased industrial output, greater mobility of professional and productive workers, and other similar means;
13. To bring the knowledge and skill of key professions and occupations up to date, maintaining the efficiency of workers and others affected by technological change and advances in scholarship;
14. To update the professional expertise of teachers and auxiliary teaching personnel (such as the lay "monitors" used in some literacy programs);

15. To make maximum use of the short supply of skilled and experienced teachers.

IV. Personal and Family Life

Mass media may effectively serve the traditional aims of adult education:

16. To provide lifelong opportunities to enable adults to repair deficiencies in the earlier phases of their education;
17. To provide lifelong opportunities for the continuing education of adults;
18. To promote satisfactory family life (including education for family planning where necessary) and to foster mutual awareness and understanding between the different generations;
19. To enable men and women with fuller access to leisure time to revalue the purposes of leisure; through the growth of new intellectual, aesthetic, moral, and physical interests, to teach these men and women new leisure skills.

BOOKS FOR FURTHER STUDY

Aarons, Leon & May, Mark A. *Television and Human Behavior,* Appleton-Century-Crofts, N.Y., 1963.

Aipwell. *Teaching Adults by Television,* University College of Rhodesia, 1966.

Berelson, B. & Janowitz, M. (Eds.). *Public Opinion and Communication,* 2nd. edition, Collier-Macmillan, Toronto, 1966.

Campbell, J. H. & Hepler, H. W. (Eds.). *Dimensions in Communication,* Wadsworth Publishing, Belmont, California, 1965.

Carpenter, Edmund & McLuhan, M. (Eds.). *Explorations in Communication*, Boston Beacon Press, 1960.

Cherry, Colin. *On Human Communication*, Wiley, New York, 1957.

Dance, Frank E. (Ed.). *Human Communication Theory*, H.R.W., N.Y., 1967.

DeFleur, Melvin L. *Theories of Mass Communication*, McKay, N.Y., 1966.

Dexter, L. A. & White, David M. (Eds.). *People, Society and Mass Communication*, Collier Macmillan Ltd., Toronto, 1964.

Ellul, Jacques. *Propaganda: The Formation of Men's Attitudes*, Alfred H. Knopf, N.Y., 1966.

Eisenson, et al. (Eds.). *The Psychology of Communication*, Appleton, N.Y., 1963.

Gordon, Donald R. *Language, Logic & the Mass Media*, H. R. & Winston, Toronto, 1966.

Halloran, J. D. *The Effects of Mass Communication*, Leicester University Press, Leicester, 1964.

Havelock, Eric. *Preface to Plato*, Harvard University Press, Cambridge, Mass., 1963.

Innes, Harold A. *The Bias of Communication*, University of Toronto Press, 1951.

Jacobs, Norman (Ed.). *Culture for the Millions*, Beacon Press, Boston, 1964.

Klapper, Joseph T. *The Effects of Mass Communication*, N.Y. Free Press, 1960.

Lang, Kurt & Gladys E. Lang. *Politics and Television Quadrangle*, Chicago, 1968.

McLuhan, Marshall. *The Gutenberg Galaxy*, University of Toronto Press, Toronto, 1962.

McLuhan, Marshall & Quentin Fiore. *The Medium is the Massage*, Bantam Books, New York, 1967.

McLuhan, Marshall. *Understanding Media*, McGraw Hill, N.Y., 1966.

McLuhan, Marshall & Parker, Harley. *Through the Vanishing Point,* Harper and Row, N.Y., 1968.

Oliver, Robert T. *Culture and Communication,* Charles C. Thomas, Springfield, Ill., 1962.

Ohliger, John. *Listening Groups—Mass Media in Adult Education,* Boston University, Boston, 1967.

Pye, Lucian W. (Ed.). *Communications and Political Development,* Princeton, 1963.

Rossi, Peter H. & Biddle, Bruce (Eds.). *The New Media and Education,* Aldine, Chicago, 1966.

Smith, Alfred G. *Communication and Culture,* H. R. Winston, N.Y., 1966.

Smith, J. *Great Ideas in Information Theory, Language and Cybernetics,* Dover, N.Y., 1966.

Steinberg, Charles S. (Ed.). *Mass Media and Communication,* Hastings, 1965.

Sutherland, I. E. *Sketchpad: A Man-Machine Graphical Communication System,* Spartan Books, Baltimore, 1963.

Thayer, L. (Ed.). *Communication,* Charles C. Thomas, Springfield, Ill., 1967.

Thayer, L. (Ed.). *Communication Concepts & Perspectives* Spartan Books, Wash. D.C., 1961.

UNESCO, *Communications in the Space Age,* 1968.

PART
FOUR

There are those who maintain that there will be twice as many human beings on earth before the year 2000. As Lord C. P. Snow has observed, "This flood is already making us more callous about human life: the rapidity and completeness of human communications are constantly presenting us with the sight of famine, suffering, violent death."

Over half of the world's population live at or below subsistence level while rice is rotting in Japan and wheat in Canada. Yet, through such organizations as the Rockefeller and Ford Foundations, the wheat harvests in India and Pakistan have reached record highs. (The population of these two countries is greater than that of Africa and South America combined). A high-yielding, disease-resisting strain of rice has been produced through the International Rice Research Institute in the Phillipines, which has been exported to Asia and South America.

Many wonderful things are happening. New machines are being promoted by multi-national companies, new medicines by socially-minded scientists—and the list could go on.

Lady Jackson, better known as Barbara Ward, (Chapter 19) is recognized around the world as an economist with a conscience. She takes a candid look at the problems of world poverty and presents a three-point program for action. But she would be one of the first to agree that actions by individuals and groups should be coordinated under a planned program in which all nations are participating in the processes of communication, distribution and government.

Therefore, the Right Honourable Lester B. Pearson (Chapter 20) is bold enough to speak candidly about the possibility of the United States of the World. As his record reveals, Mr. Pearson has been a long-time participant in the resolving of problems at the international level. During his active relationship with the United Nations, he became known and loved as a mediator who could recognize various points of view and come up with plans which became acceptable to nations whose interests had seemed to be in conflict. His semantics may be unfortunate because "United States of the World" may be misinterpreted. On second reading, you will note that he did not discriminate between the United States of America, the United States of Soviet Republics or the United States of Europe. He said, "The United States of the World".

This leads directly into a definitive statement on world government (Chapter 21) by a man who spends his life earning money in order to be able to devote time to promoting this important concept. Reuben Schafer clearly enunciates the need for world government and steps which should be taken to make it a reality. I like his message because he has neither vested interests nor political axes to grind. He simply believes in world government. I suggest that a few dozen men of such dedication in each country in the world could achieve this objective which would go a long way toward solving the major problems of war and poverty.

Robert McNamara (Chapter 22) makes it clear that the resources through the World Bank are available to handle the financial matters.

The question which remains unsettled in my mind is why has not the United Nations been strengthened and supported to the extent that Viet Nam, for instance, might have been avoided. Of one thing I am certain, the youth of this generation will never allow a reoccurrence of a catastrophe of this magnitude. If, as it seems, two-thirds of the student population (to use the Japanese figure) are in favor of some kind of "communism", it is mainly because they are against any form of imperialist aggression, especially by a political institution in which they have not been allowed to participate. In Russia, according to Harrison Salisbury, the attitude of youth is "revolutionary" but they laugh when you mention "communism". To them, Russia is another imperialist power that must protect itself against other imperialist powers; equality for the masses in the birthplace of communism has become a meaningless myth but, like the Czechs, there are multitudes who are calling for humanitarianism. Indeed, it seems that everyone in the world is calling for humanization and groping, each in his own way, for a place to start. Hopefully, this book may assist in providing a starting point. Again it may be only a matter of semantics and bad communication.

CHAPTER 19

An Economist Looks at World Poverty

by Barbara Ward

Lady Jackson is the wife of a member of the British House of Lords who under her professional name of Barbara Ward is recognized throughout the world as an outstanding economist with a keen social conscience. She is presently a visiting professor at Columbia University. This article is an adaptation from a keynote address which she gave before an assembly of the World Council of Churches as published by the United Church Observer.

1

THIS WORLDWIDE economic system was created for economic and political reasons, not moral ones. It is not surprising then to find that it is a very much nicer system for the 20% of us who command 80% of the world's wealth than it is for the others.

Now that this lopsidedness exists, must we assume that it must continue? I want to give you two main reasons for believing that this imbalance between the poor and the 20% of the rich who own 80% of the trade is not necessary, need not last, and can be corrected, and that the world created by this correction would be a much more comfortable place for everyone to live in.

The first reason is that we have now been in the development business for nearly 20 years. You will find in most of the responsible developing countries—and that is the very large part of them—that the emphasis on modernizing agriculture, the realization that industrial processes must match local resources and needs, are now about 100% more sophisticated than they were 15 years ago.

In addition to this, we may be on the verge of an immense technological and economic breakthrough in world development. I mean, of course, the research into agricultural productivity which is beginning to spread around the world. The new hybrid grains, along with fertilizer and water, at this moment in India are producing crops up to 500% more than two years ago. If this possibility is pursued, it is perfectly possible that for the first time in many decades we shall see food supplies ahead of population. It is at this point, when children survive and living standards begin to edge upwards, that policies for extending family planning begin to work. This is one great reason why this is not a time for despair.

But I think the second reason is even more important. That is that we have been here before. We do know something about the lopsidedness of an economy which once seemed virtually incurable. It is only 100 years since Disraeli described Britain as a nation of the rich and a nation of the poor. Why has the situation in developed countries changed so sharply over the last 100 years? I suggest it is because we no longer accept the rule of the unrestrained market. We no longer assume that the economic system will, by itself, take us all on to wealth and felicity.

2

This has been one of the critical political changes of our time. We have made this change by at least three reforms which amount to virtual revolution in how we deal with our economic life. The first is a very straight-forward one, which we all know with more or less grief, and that is taxation. When Oliver Wendell Holmes said, "With my taxes I buy civilization," he meant precisely that. One reason why in America some of the most rapid advances took place was that it was the first country to put public money into public education. The beginning of opportunity to which education was the key began with the acceptance of public responsibility through taxes for that opportunity.

The second follows from the first. If we invest in the opportunities and skills of people, at the same time we increase their strength in bargaining and their ability to enter into proper relationships with the economic system of their day. This means collective bargaining, fringe benefits, pensions, profit-sharing—all the means whereby through the market we distribute more purchasing power to the mass of the people.

The third change, still new, is the policy of full employment. This policy, as practiced in North Atlantic countries, simply is the recognition that governments have the responsibility to see that employment expands, that resources are used, that the income of the people goes up.

These three changes have not destroyed the market. On the contrary, they are the only conditions within which the market will actually work. The change from the unbridled economic system to a system with moral, social and political restraints has been one of the critical factors in the developed world in the last 100 years. People who talk of the technical and industrial advance of these countries should never forget that none of this would have been possible without these moral and social reforms.

3

We have, within our society, made these changes. Why should we not make them in the international economy which our drive for trade and our colonial system have created?

There is no intellectual reason why not. Apparently without much strain we do spend 150 billion dollars a year on arms, and this very odd way of maintaining the demand for our products is something we carry almost without noticing it.

The objection always is that we can't afford it—that is if we, with 80% of our wealth, shifted our domestic reforms to the world level we would be ruined. I consider that argument so silly I'm not going to waste time on it. In fact, we grow by about three percent a year. America grows by 50 billion dollars a year. Canada grows by three billion. That is the addition of goods and services that we make every year. So please don't talk about not affording things. And let us tuck away in one corner of our memory the fact that the English- and French-speaking members of the Atlantic world spend 50 billion dollars a year on drink and tobacco. I'm not against either—but it does give us a certain margin.

So why can it not be done? You know why it can't be done. It's not for any economic reason. In essence, it can't be done for one reason only, and that is that we do not consider that the great obligations of society, which have been to some extent successful inside our nations, go beyond our frontiers. It's as simple as that. We are operating our world economy in the way the Victorians used to operate their economy between classes.

4

We have a clear possibility for action. First, we can invest one percent of our gross national product for a start. This is not more than a third of our annual increase in wealth. It just means getting richer more slowly.

Second, we can re-negotiate prices. Would we be all that worse off if we paid five cents more for a cup of coffee? And yet that might make it possible for African and Latin American countries to have development programs.

Third, would we really be worse off if some of the vast, vast sum spent on arms—only ten percent:—15 billions—went from the works of destruction to the works of peace? No. There is no intellectual difficulty here. One just comes back to the fact that we cannot see.

This to me is an utter tragedy. If ever there were an

apocalyptic moment, it is surely now. This is the time when, unless we go completely crazy, science and technology have made it possible to recreate the face of the earth, to make five grains grow where one grew before, to turn this vast affluence to the purposes of peace.

This is the spirit in which we can possibly make something new. Otherwise we haven't got a chance.

CHAPTER 20

The United States of the World

by Lester B. Pearson

The Right Honourable Lester B. Pearson is the former Prime Minister of Canada and made his reputation in world affairs as the popular long-time Canadian delegate to the United Nations. He is now taking a leadership role in the establishment of the International Development Center. This chapter has been adapted from his Reith lectures for the British Broadcasting Corporation under the theme, "Peace in the Family of Man."

1

NATIONALISM CAN BE a fine and noble thing: the love of a man for his own country and what it means to him. But political nationalism, the absolute sovereignty of the nation-state, can also be the strongest obstacle in the way of building world order, and in the way of the realization of the world community. The first reaction of millions of people today to any proposals for more effective international institutions, for international control of anything, is: "This means that foreigners will be taking charge of our affairs."

Turning from a hypothetical future to an actual past, the most subversive anti-national document of modern times—far more subversive than Karl Marx's Communist Manifesto—was the Declaration of Independence by the fathers of the American Revolution. In the eighteenth century, the idea that the colonies could not only defy the mother country, but form a federal society of their own was considered not only revolutionary but quite impossible. When the colonies declared their independence in 1776, each became a separate sovereign state. It was realized, however, though there was strong support for the narrower, separatist idea, that there had to be a broader basis for viable freedom than this. It was James Madison, who later became President himself, who said: "If that were all that was achieved" (sovereign status for each colony), "it would have been worthless." To him, it would have been sovereign fragmentation without any United States—the kind of thing we are told in some quarters today, that must persist in the world.

2

Things could easily have gone the separatist sovereign way in North America in the 18th century. The British colonies were on the Atlantic seaboard. The French were in Quebec to the north, and in Louisiana down south. The Spanish were moving up from Mexico, and the Russians were moving down from Alaska. French victory at the Battle of the Plains of Abraham could have changed the history of the continent and of the world.

If Great Britain had then acquiesced in French domination of the northern half of the continent, the two French settlements would have joined hands in the Mississippi Valley and there would have been a French ring around the American states. There would have been a Spanish-speaking state in the northwest. Our continent would have become a microcosm of today's world.

It may well be, therefore, that Wolfe's victory at Quebec not only made Canada safe for the British, for a time, but Quebec made the world safe for the American Revolution and the establishment of what another American president, John Quincy Adams, called a "compound nation," the United States of America.

Adams added: "The war taught our fathers that they had infinitely more to do than merely achieve their independence: that they must form their compact upon principles never before attempted on earth, including the principle where the political communities now free could unite into a union under one government."

We have now to extend that idea of a union of free political communities into a far wider international area than was ever considered at the time of the American Revolution, so that such national communities throughout the world will one day become part of a larger international community.

The problem today is not the creation of new free states, but subordinating the sovereign freedom of all states to the necessity of peace, security and progress. There could be no more difficult, or essential, task. Even the mention of it seems to take us into the outer space of unreality.

The Americans, after all, reached their goal of federation only after a long, hard fight; and after one of the bloodiest of all civil wars 75 years later. Yet this was a union between states which began with many strong bonds between them. The process will certainly be infinitely more difficult for states in the world of today. But the need is infinitely greater. . . .

The establishment of our international rule of law cannot depend on force. We have to do it by agreement; we have to do it step by step through international institutions. And we have years, perhaps, not centuries, in which to succeed, and only the tentative first steps have already been taken. . . .

In our country, if we tried to impose the melting pot theory of national development of all Canadians, we would not unify our country, we would destroy it.

If we cannot maintain the existing political federations of people with unity on essential matters, while at the same time recognizing their differences of culture and tradition and language—and even special constitutional rights—what chance is there in the future of building up a wider international community where these separate racial, national and even political differences can be merged, not submerged but merged, in the community as a whole?

From my own experience I believe that cultural and social differences inside sovereign states, as well as cultural influences on them from outside, can and should strengthen rather than weaken a political society in our modern world; political unity, in other words, does not have to mean either cultural or social uniformity.

It would be foolish and futile to insist that such differences should be eliminated in the interests of single, sovereign unity. It would be equally futile and foolish . . . in the international field to insist on the complete obliteration of national differences in the interests of international unity.

Nationalism is an especially strong, appealing, and noble emotion when it becomes part of the struggle of unfree peoples to be free. During that struggle, the new feeling of national unity can be stronger even than the older tribal feeling. It is only after freedom is achieved that the more restricted loyalties become strong again. . . .

It was only a few years ago that we thought of Nigeria, the most populous of the new African states, as an example of what could be done to reconcile development. It was a set piece which was working well so we thought; and then the whole thing collapsed. . . .

The hopes we had for Nigeria were so high that our present distress over what is happening must be that much greater. And yet, if we do not have some kind of federal society in these new continents, what chance is there for them surviving as free peoples at all; because the fragmentation will go on and on until some tyrant ends it and brings about a forced and despotic unity. . . .

There have been divisions between nations inside the Commonwealth, as bitter as anything in the UN. On more than one occasion in recent years, the Commonwealth might easily have broken up; over Suez, over Kashmir, and our inability to discuss these matters at formal meetings; over Rhodesia most of all. But it has not broken up. . . .

At the moment, it seems that the Commonwealth is being taken less seriously every month in the world, and even among its own members. Yet the very difficulties of holding it together underline the importance of doing so; because the Commonwealth in its varied, multi-racial membership does reflect the world in which we live. It's a pluralistic, multi-racial political association representing every tribe, every creed, every color, every continent.

I would like to think that such associations as that of the Commonwealth are stages in development to something more formal and united. But certainly if we tried to make the Commonwealth a more formal association now, with demands on its members, with a constitution binding on them; convert it into some kind of confederation, however loose, it would simply break up.

But if we can develop, on this new multi-racial basis, a new kind of family feeling, the kind which once made it almost automatic that members all should at least try to act together, and usually did, then we will have moved toward a modification of national sovereignty in the interest of greater international unity.

3

The problem today is subordinating the sovereign freedom of all states to the necessity of peace, security, and progress. There could be no more essential task.

If we don't do something urgently to solve the basic problems of the world, political problems, security problems, problems of the rich and poor, and developed and underdeveloped, if we don't at the very least do something to make it possible for all of us to live with these problems, there will be an explosion. And I mean a nuclear explosion.

CHAPTER 21

World Government in the Cybernetic Age

by Reuben Schafer

Reuben Schafer has been a major sponsor of the World Federalist Movement. He is internationally known as a leading manager and multi-million underwriter for the Occidental Life Insurance Company of California. Here is a successful businessman who has become aware and is giving a great deal of time, money and energy toward the establishment of a global community. His article was written specially for "This Cybernetic Age" by invitation from the editor.

1

The Bomb or World Government

DURING THE PAST TEN YEARS there's been more talk about world government than in the preceeding fifty. Why? Because the world is ready for it—for two reasons.

The first is interdependence. In a complex world, "shrunk" by jet aircraft and communication satellites, nations have become more dependent on one another than ever before.

One example is in the field of economics. A major move such as devaluation, in a country with wide and important trading connections, seriously affects economic conditions in many countries throughout the world. Corrective or, better, preventive action for such events can best be taken by a governmental agency operating on a world scale. We now need rules and laws that will apply to the whole world. Local government administers rules and laws in the local community. World government would do the same in the world community.

The second but more important reason why we are ready for world government is our fear of the consequences of nuclear and chemical-biological war. Pick up your daily newspaper. Read the front page—or the international news section. Odds are there are one or more "warm" wars coming to a boil, or "hot" ones threatening to spill over, embroil the big powers and lead to the possibility of World War Three.

Such a conflict would make wars of the past look like parlor games by comparison. A 5,000 megaton (one megaton equals one million tons) nuclear attack on the United States would leave an estimated 145 million men, women and children dead, (according to the Hudson Institute), and many millions more maimed or diseased. It's conceivable that, as the power and number of these weapons increase, virtually the entire population could be obliterated. Communications would be totally disrupted, plant and animal life severely damaged. The survivors might end up living like beasts.

The adversary would suffer similar devastation because the United States with its underground missiles and roving nuclear armed submarines would be able to strike back in sufficient strength to at least destroy the enemy's major centers of population. No one really could be said to have won such a war. Even the "winner" would have lost. The wholesale use of nuclear bombs and biological-chemical weapons on a world scale, could lay waste our entire planet, and civilization would cease to exist.

Obviously war has become too dangerous to use as an instrument of foreign policy, as a means of settling international disputes. But nations will continue to have disputes. Since war is no longer an acceptable way of settling them, an alternative must be devised.

That alternative is world government.

2

From Government to World Government

Government is almost as old as man. It began shortly after he started living in primitive tribes. Elders regulated the conduct of the tribe. Life was simple, and such regulation constituted the simplest form of government.

As life became more complex, simple government was modified and expanded. Laws were drafted to regulate behavior of and between individuals, courts were established to interpret the laws, soldiers or police were recruited to enforce them and taxes were levied to support these activities. By and large, this system operated successfully to keep peace between individuals in the community. Over the centuries larger regional and national governments were formed to regulate larger and more complex units of society and maintain peace within their borders.

Today, government between nations is necessary in the same way that government between individuals is necessary. Man does not tolerate lawlessness among individuals because of the harmful effects on the local community. He can't afford to tolerate lawlessness among nations any longer because of the harmful effects on the world community. (According to the Encyclopedia Brittanica, military and civilian deaths as a result of World War Two were in excess of 50 million. Many millions of men, women and children were permanently crippled, and property damage amounted to hundreds of billions of dollars.)

Throughout the world, government has proven to be the best agency for maintaining peace at local, intermediate and national levels. It seems reasonable that government would also be the most promising method for maintaining peace at the world level. This idea of government at the world level, or world government, is hundreds of years old. (Emeric Cruce, a French monk, wrote a plan for it in 1623.)

Would world government eliminate war altogether? No. There will always be war, just as there will always be crime. But in the same way that your government "controls" crime and prevents it from operating with no restrictions whatsoever, a world government, while not being able to prevent all wars, would be able to intercede and stop them from becoming major conflagrations.

How can world government become a reality? There are various ways.

One country could conquer the entire world (as Hitler might very well have done) and impose its system throughout. However this is hardly desirable, nor is it a stable arrangement because defeated countries might rebel periodically, and overthrow the conqueror, leaving the world without government once again.

Another way would be the joining together of neighbouring countries in various regions (all the countries in Europe, all the countries in Asia, etc.) and the subsequent union of these regions into one political entity.

Yet another could be through the federation of nations with the same systems of government (all democracies, all communist countries) followed by the union of their respective federations.

The most logical approach, however, is to strengthen the United Nations. The League of Nations, formed after the First World War, could be considered man's first practical but abortive attempt at world government; the United Nations, man's second. The League failed because it was too weak. The U.N. is failing too, primarily for the same reason. It hasn't been able to bring about disarmament and it doesn't have the power or authority to enforce its decisions. As a result, the big powers, because of their tremendous armed might, do as they please while thumbing their noses at it, and the U.N. looks on helplessly. Examples? The Russian invasion of Czechoslovakia; the U.S. invasion of the Dominican Republic.

Nevertheless a weak United Nations is better than no United Nations. Despite its weaknesses, it still represents an improvement over the League of Nations. For example, a temporary "world police force" was used by a world body (the U.N.) for the first time in history—to stop the shooting in the Suez crisis in 1956.

Two American lawyers, Grenville Clark and Louis B. Sohn, have devised one plan, (there are others), for building on the existing U.N. framework, eliminating its weaknesses, strengthening it and transforming it into a world government. Initially this government would have powers related only to the maintenance of international order. It would not be able to interfere in national affairs except when a domestic situation threatened world peace. Additional powers could be given to it at a later date, by mutual consent.

3

Here are the essential features of the plan. Full details are available in the text *World Peace Through World Law*.

1. *Voluntary Co-operation*

   It must have the voluntary co-operation of the nations of the world, especially the big powers. One of the things they would have to give up would be their right to wage war.

2. *Revision and Amendment of the Present U.N. Charter*

   The present charter would be revised and strengthened. It would have to be approved by at least five sixths of the world's nations (including the twelve largest) with a population equal to at least five sixths of the total world population. Naturally this would include mainland China.

3. *The General Assembly and Voting Rights*

   The General Assembly would have the power to make laws, but the "one nation—one vote" rule in the present assembly would be changed to give the four largest nations thirty votes each, the next eight largest fifteen votes each and so on, with the three smallest nations having one vote each. This would eliminate the complaint that smaller nations now have a disproportionately large vote in relation to their populations.

4. *The Executive Council*

The present Security Council and the veto would be scrapped. An Executive Council with seventeen members elected by the General Assembly would replace it. It would be the executive arm of the world government and would have such powers as the supervision of disarmament.

5. *Disarmament*

World Government would be impossible without disarmament. Therefore all nations would disarm at the rate of ten per cent a year so that in ten years there would be no national military forces or armaments whatsoever. An Inspection Commission would make sure that disarmament was actually taking place.

6. *The World Police Force*

Disarmament by itself would be useless. It must be accompanied by the formation of a police force to enforce world laws. Law must be enforced or it ceases to be law. Police protect a community from individuals who break the law. In the same way, a World Police Force is necessary to protect the world community from nations who break the law by secretly arming or by invading their neighbours. The world Police Force would be recruited mainly from the smaller nations. The standby component, consisting of full time professionals, would be divided into groups, stationed throughout the world to enable them to act swiftly if needed, much the same way as police stations are scattered throughout our larger cities. A reserve component of partially trained individuals could be called upon if necessary. The initial weapons for the Police Force would be obtained from the disarming nations.

7. *Courts, a Tribunal and a Counciliation Board*

An international Court of Justice, with compulsory juris-
diction over all the nations in the world and composed
of fifteen judges elected by the General Assembly would
be set up. (The present International Court of Justice
can't do its job effectively because two-thirds of the
world's nations don't recognize its authority.)
Individuals who committed offences which endangered
world peace would appear in Regional Courts established around the world.
Non-legal disputes between nations would be settled by
a World Equity Tribunal and a World Conciliation Board
could be used for voluntary arbitration.

8. *A World Development Authority*

A World Development Authority would help the world's
under-developed areas. It would provide free grants and
interest free loans to help their economic and social
development.

9. *A Revenue System*

Each nation would be assessed an annual tax in the same
proportion its gross national product bears to the gross
world product (subject to certain credits).

10. *Specialized Agencies*

All of the U.N.'s Specialized Agencies such as the Universal Postal Union would be continued because they've
proven their value in the past.

Now think of your own governments, local and national,
with their law-making bodies, courts to interpret the laws, police forces to enforce them, specialized agencies such as de-
partments of health, and taxation systems for financial support. Think of these same concepts on a world scale and you
have the Clark and Sohn plan for world government.

226 / THIS CYBERNETIC AGE

Will it work? I think so—if given a chance. It worked successfully on a miniature scale in the "world" of Greece more than 2200 years ago. The Achaean League, with a Council to judge disputes and an army to enforce its decisions, kept peace for 130 years (until conquered by the Romans), between twelve Greek city-states, each of which functioned much the same as sovereign nations of today.

4

World Government or the Bomb

In a governed world, men would no longer fear that any day, they, their families, their friends and their relatives might be killed or maimed in a war and their property and possessions destroyed. In addition, with the cessation of nuclear testing, death and serious physical and mental damage suffered by newborn children as a result of radioactive waste would eventually end.

Another benefit would arise from the elimination of military budgets. In 1967 the world spent 182 billion dollars on armaments. The yearly cost of operating Clark and Sohn's world government is an estimated 50 billion dollars. This would leave approximately 130 billion dollars for neglected yet essential projects in the fields of research, health, education, etc.

It doesn't take too much imagination to think of other benefits arising for man in such a world.

But which will come first—world government or nuclear war? It's a race against the bomb.

Here are some of the factors obstructing world government's arrival.

Military men are strongly entrenched in nearly every country throughout the world. Their entire training makes it perfectly natural for them to think of war as the ultimate way of settling differences between nations. They exert tremendous influence on their governments and have a tendency to oppose the disarmament procedure which is essential to the formation of a world government.

In some countries manufacturers of armaments have reaped and are still reaping enormous profits as a result of wars and armament build-ups during times of peace. World government is a direct threat to their means of livelihood. With their powerful connections in government they too present a serious obstacle to the disarmament process.

The vast majority of people are obliged to use nearly all of their energies to earn a day-to-day living and to solve the problems in their immediate environment. They have little or no strength left to expend on world affairs.

Finally, a new way of international thinking is needed in the nuclear age. Men in government, diplomats and even average citizens have a natural tendency to act and re-act as they did before, when faced with international disputes. After all, ever since childhood they've been taught to think in nationalistic and militaristic terms. *This old way of thinking is perhaps the most formidable stumbling block in the path of world government.*

There have also been some encouraging developments. The last twenty-five years have been years of growing interests in, and active support for, world government. The prime force has been the World Federalist Movement. It grew from a few spontaneously-formed groups just before and after the Second World War to its present representation in thirty-five countries with about 75,000 dues-paying members. World Federalists are hindered in their efforts by a lack of funds and a shortage of trained personnel. Yet they exert an influence on governments, out of all proportion to their numbers.

Increasing interest and support are being shown by Members of various Parliaments. There are now Parliamentary Groups for World Government in fourteen countries with more than 1100 members. It's possible that as these groups increase in number and strength (for example ninety-eight percent of the Danish M.P.'s belong), world government might not be so far off.

A third positive feature is the existence of the U.N.'s thirteen Specialized Agencies such as the International Telecommunications Union, the World Health Organization and the Food and Agricultural Organization. They are doing internationally what national government organizations are doing nationally. *In the functioning of these agencies we actually have some world government existing here and now.* As a matter of fact, there are people who believe that world government will develop from such agencies and the many other international organizations that now serve man's needs.

Despite this gradual progress toward world government, *unless there's a radical change,* the odds are 10 to 1, 20 to 1, 100 to 1—take your pick—that global nuclear war will happen first.

The risk of nuclear war increases as the number of nations possessing nuclear weapons grows. It doesn't seem believable that such a stupid war could happen. And yet in the same way that nearly all youngsters simply must burn themselves before accepting the fact that fire is dangerous, so it seems that the world has to learn its lesson the hard way—by suffering virtual total destruction.

H. G. Wells, in his book *The World Set Free,* tells of a global nuclear war with the survivors of that war establishing a world government. History may very well take that course— if there are any survivors.

Gloomy? Yes.

Realistic? Yes.

Pessimistic?

No.

As long as there are men who try, there is hope.

CHAPTER 22

Resources for the Developing World

An Interview with Robert S. McNamara

by Henry Brandon

Robert McNamara is President of the World Bank. He was formerly Secretary of Defense in the United States Government and a top executive for the Ford Motor Company. This article is adapted from an interview which was published in Saturday Review. Henry Brandon is the famous correspondent for the London Times.

1

THE TECHNOCRAT AND HUMANIST in Mr. McNamara have been vying with each other for a long time, and gradually the two found it increasingly more difficult to live harmoniously inside the same cranium. Now the humanist and developer have the satisfaction of being in the driver's seat.

Q: Do you think the Western world has the resources with which to develop the enormous developing world?

Mr. McNamara: There is absolutely no question about it in my mind. Whether the application of the resources of the developed world will lead to as rapid a rate of development as the people of the developing world hope for is another issue, and I'd like to separate these two points. One has to bear in mind that it may not be resources alone that stand in the way of achieving a satisfactory rate of economic advance in the developing world; it may well be that adaptation of political institutions, social reforms, and other actions within the developing nations themselves form a limiting factor. But as far as resources are concerned, the rich nations could easily contribute far more than they have to the poor nations.

We in the United States can do far more to cure our own national problems, which are very serious indeed; and just as we can do far more to correct those conditions, so can we do far more to contribute to the economic development of the developing nations. It's simply a question of getting a proper order of priorities. At the present time we place too high a priority on producing 9,500,000 automobiles—a substantial number of which simply increases our traffic problems. We place a higher priority on the production of these 9,500,000 automobiles than we do on taking measures to make our cities more attractive places to live in for all their citizens, than we do on correcting the very serious weaknesses in our educational system, or than we do on eliminating smog and controlling water pollution.

If that be our desire, then let's make it as a conscious choice, but let's not say that we can't afford these other things. We simply prefer to use our resources in a different way. Exactly the same can be said of aid from a rich nation to the poor nations. If we would prefer (again taking automobiles as an example, and I use them as only one of a hundred examples one could take) to spend our resources on building automobiles we don't need, rather than on helping the Indonesian people to progress from the margin of subsistence to a level of caloric intake that will at least give them a chance of optimum intellectual development, or doing the same thing for India, then, that's a conscious decision, but let's not say we can't afford to transfer our resources to Indonesia and the Indians. We prefer to have cars we don't need than to give human beings an opportunity to reach an optimum level of physical and intellectual development.

Another measure of the same point is that the rich nations have expanded their annual income within the last eight years by an amount that exceeds the total annual income of all the developing nations. That statistic shows the tremendous gap that exists and the degree to which we are capable of helping to close it if we choose to do so. We may not choose to do so.

Q: But how can you, in the free enterprise society, impose such priorities?

Mr. McNamara: I don't think one can. I think one can simply expose the problem to the people and then, in a democracy, accept the judgment of the people. So far, I don't think the problem has been exposed to them properly. People are worried by higher taxes—and of course that's what's involved here. But people mistakenly believe that an increase in taxes moves us toward bankruptcy. It doesn't have anything whatsoever to do with bankruptcy. Taxation is a transfer device which governments use when they want to make a shift in priorities. We ought to have an intelligent discussion of what people in this country want to do with our national wealth. Do we want to spend it on adding to our luxury goods —many of which we don't need—or on education for the poor, or elimination of pollution in our waters, or on aid to the developing nations of the world? In the long run, these kinds of expenditures will add far more to our personal happiness and self-fulfillment than will expenditures on luxury goods. But this is an issue for the people to face. All I ask is that they face it directly.

Q: How can any President really demand that without losing his popularity overnight?

Mr. McNamara: Oh, he can't demand it, but what he can do is say to the people, "It's your choice."

Q: Do you think it would be possible to impose, say, a tax on all industrial nations?

Mr. McNamara: No. In the first place, I wouldn't be in favor of trying to impose any such tax. I think in the long run it might be desirable to have the rich nations' contributions to development measured in terms of a percentage of national income.

Q: Isn't there a growing disillusionment with foreign aid in almost all industrial nations?

Mr. McNamara: There is a certain disillusionment with development today, especially in the richer countries, but it's a disillusionment based on unreasonable expectations.

In any case, it's precisely at a time of temporary disillusionment in other quarters that we in the Bank must make a firm commitment to continuing and expanding the development effort. I'm absolutely clear on this; the feelings of disillusionment among the developed countries—and the frustration among the developing countries—must and will be halted. The rich countries feel that their balance-of-payments difficulties make it necessary for them to cut down on the assistance they give to the developing world—forgetting that balance-of-payments problems relate almost exclusively to transfers within the developed world, and that the money spent on development returns very quickly to the advanced economies in the form of payment for goods and services purchased by developing nations. The poor countries, on the other hand, feel that they have been left behind in the surge of economic growth which has occurred during the last decade— and to some extent they are right. But they forget the real advances which have been achieved, and the time it takes to improve on them. I think today's discontents—especially those of the developed world—are misconceived and temporary, and it's our job to counter them.

Q: Are you sure this is a temporary phase? I think this is the long-term trend. The young of today are far more isolationist than the young of ten or twenty years ago.

Mr. McNamara: I think even an isolationist is in favor of economic aid to the disadvantaged. Surely that's true of today's youth. They're certainly more idealistic than the young of ten or fifteen years ago. Where they're isolationist is in extending military commitments abroad; development investment, especially if it's multilateral, doesn't involve any military or foreign policy commitments. I haven't noticed any feeling on the part of the young that we shouldn't extend economic aid to the poor nations of the world. It's their parents who say that. But even there, I think that after the Vietnam war is over, there will be less excuse for some of the parents to take that position.

Q: I have a feeling that governments these days have come to think that even though they are giving less foreign aid now, nothing really catastrophic has happened.

Mr. McNamara: The effects of not giving aid may not be

immediately apparent, but sooner or later I think they will show up through the growth of progressively more serious instabilities in the developing world, with a ripple effect spreading to the developed nations.

Q: What sort of instability are you thinking of?

Mr. McNamara: I'm thinking of a revolution of rising expectations. The political institutions of the developing countries are bound to become less stable if their growth, particularly their economic growth, is less than the expectations of their people and if it's small in relation to the growth of the rich nations of the world.

Q: Do you see any possibility of building bridges between East and West through loans?

Mr. McNamara: We're quite willing to receive approaches by any Eastern European or other Communist bloc members not now members of the Bank. One socialist country, Yugoslavia, is now a member of the Bank. In total, the loans the Bank has made to Yugoslavia exceed $330 million. This represents a very large contribution by the Bank—very large in relation to its contribution to the growth of Yugoslavia's economy. I mention this only to indicate that the Bank is a nonpolitical institution. We're not concerned with whether an enterprise is government-owned or private-owned; what we are concerned with is efficiency of management and efficiency in the use of capital. As for Yugoslavia's membership in the Bank, it's been, I think, a very happy relationship for both parties.

Q: You once wrote that man is a rational animal but with an infinite capacity for folly, and that he draws blueprints for utopia but never quite gets it built. You seem to be a rare combination of the rationalist and the idealist. The idealist, I think, had a difficult time at the Pentagon. How is the realist faring at the World Bank?

Mr. McNamara: I think our program is a realistic one, in the sense that it's one we can accomplish; it's also one which is consistent with the objectives of an idealist.

BOOKS FOR FURTHER STUDY

Adams, Walter (Ed.). *The Brain Drain,* Macmillan, N.Y., 1968.

Barringer, Herbert R., Blanksten, George I., & Mack, Raymond W. *Social Change in Developing Areas,* Schenkman, Cambridge, Mass., 1965.

Boulding, Kenneth E. *Conflict and Defense,* Harper and Row, N.Y., 1963.

Calder, Ritchie. *Common Sense About a Starving World,* Macmillan, N.Y., 1962.

Cepede, M., Houtart, F., & Grond, L. *Population and Food,* Sheed and Ward, N.Y., 1964.

Clark, Grenville & Sohn, Louis B. *World Peace Through World Law,* Harvard University Press, Cambridge, Mass., 1958.

Davison, W. Phillips. *International Political Communication,* Frederick Praeger, 1965.

Freedman, Ronald (Ed.). *Population—The Vital Revolution,* Aldine, Chicago, 1964.

The 45th Anniversary Edition, Foreign Affairs, Vol. 46, No. 1, Foreign Affairs, N.Y.

Galt, Tom. *Peace and War—Man-Made,* Beacon, Boston, 1962.

Geiger, Theodore. *The Conflicted Relationship,* McGraw-Hill, N.Y., 1967.

Gross, Bertram (Ed.). *Action Under Planning,* McGraw-Hill, N.Y., 1967.

Hanson, John W. & Grembeck, Cole S. *Education and the Development of Nations,* Holt, Rinehart and Winston, N.Y., 1966.

Hauser, Philip M. *Population and World Politics,* Free Press of Glencoe, N.Y., 1964.

Heer, David M. *Society and Population,* Prentice-Hall, Englewood Cliffs, N.J., 1968.

Hitch, C. J. & McKean, R. N. *The Economics of Defense in the Nuclear Age,* Harvard University Press, Cambridge, Mass., 1960.

Horowitz, Irving L. *Three Worlds of Development,* Oxford University Press, N.Y., 1966.

Kelman, Herbert C. (Ed.). *International Behavior,* Holt, Rinehart & Winston, N.Y., 1965.

Klineberg, Otto. *The Human Dimension in International Relations,* Holt, Rinehart & Winston, N.Y., 1965.

Lerner, D. & Schramm, W. *Communication and Change in the Developing Countries,* East West Center Press, Honolulu, Hawaii, 1966.

Little, I. M. D. & Clifford, J. M. *International Aid,* Aldine, Chicago, 1965.

Lipsett, Seymour M. *Revolution and Counterrevolution,* Basic Books, N.Y., 1968.

McLuhan, Marshall & Quentin Fiore. *War and Peace in the Global Village,* Bantam Books, N.Y., 1968.

McWhinney, Bill, & Godfrey Dave (Eds.). *Man Deserves Man,* Ryerson Press, Toronto, 1968.

Mudd, Stuart (Ed.). *The Population Crises and the Use of World Resources,* Indiana University Press, Bloomington, 1964.

Mudd, Stuart. *Conflict, Resolution and World Education,* Indiana University Press, 1966.

Myint, Hla. *The Economics of the Developing Countries,* Praeger, N.Y., 1965.

Nevett, A. *Population Explosion or Control?* Chapman, London, 1964.

Newcombe, Hanna. *Peace Research Reviews Alternative Approaches to World Government,* Canadian Peace Research Institute, Oakville, Ontario, 1967.

Ohlin, Goran. *Population Control and Economic Development,* Development Centre of the Organization for Economic Cooperation and Development, Paris, 1967.

Organization for Economic Cooperation and Development. *Development Assistance Efforts and Policies,* 1967.

Organization for Economic Cooperation and Development. *The Flow of Financial Resources to Less-Developed Countries,* 1961-65.

Pincus, John. *Trade, Aid and Development,* McGraw-Hill, N.Y., 1967.

Price, Daniel O. *The 99th Hour,* University of North Carolina Press, 1967.

Power, Thomas S. General, USAF Ret., *Design for Survival,* Coward, N.Y., 1964.

Rapoport, Anatol. *Fights Games and Defences,* University of Michigan Press, Ann Arbor, Mich., 1966.

Sauvy, Alfred. *Fertility and Survival,* Criterion Books, N.Y., 1961.

Schurman, F. L. *The Commonwealth of Man,* Alfred A. Knopf, N.Y., 1952.

Silvert, K. H. (Ed.). *Expectant Peoples,* Vintage, N.Y., 1967.

Singer, H. W. *International Development Growth and Change,* McGraw-Hill, N.Y., 1964.

Snow, C. P. *The Two Cultures and a Sound Look,* Cambridge University Press, Cambridge, Mass., 1964.

Tinbergen, Jan. *Shaping the World Economy,* Twentieth Century, Chicago, Ill., 1962.

Thayer, George. *The War Business,* Simon and Schuster, N.Y., 1964.

UNESCO. *The Birthright of Man,* Paris, 1969.

Wrong, Dennis H. *Population and Society,* Random House, N.Y., 1956.

Ward, Barbara. *Rich Nations and the Poor Nations,* Norton, 1962.

Wright, Quincy & Evans, William M. & Morton, Deulsch (Eds.). *Preventing World War III,* Simon & Schuster, N.Y., 1962.

Wynner, Edith & Lloyd, Georgia. *Searchlight on Peace Plans,* Dutton, N.Y., 1944.

PART
FIVE

There have already been many exciting books and articles written predicting the nature of the twenty-first century and the intervening period between today and the year 2000. In my opinion, the most encouraging submission of all is the tentative projection of a four-stage plan submitted by a leading Russian scientist by the name of Andrei D. Sakharov (Chapter 23). Sakharov's plan and arguments are so sound as to be acceptable to all political forces which are concerned with the welfare of human beings. The plan would seem to represent the thinking of the younger generation in Russia, yet, at the same time, must be, to some extent, acceptable to the ruling class because Sakharov remains a respected member of the establishment itself. His views and his plans cannot be dismissed lightly. In fact, if enough leaders in leading countries support his concepts, this could represent the big breakthrough in a coming age of unity. If it is ever translated into English, his book on Progress, Co-existence and Intellectual Freedom should become more influential than either the Communist Manifesto or the Declaration of Independence.

I imagine that commentators such as Milton Friedman and Kenneth Galbraith (Chapter 24) would unite their intellectual capabilities in helping to make the Sakharov dream come true. Galbraith makes it clear that there is great change occurring within all economic systems because of the impact of technology and the emergence of what he calls "the industrial state". In a sense, because of the new technology, Russia has become one vast industrial state and is being forced to decentralize in almost the same manner as General Motors decentralized in the days of Alfred Sloan. Galbraith also comments on the growing importance of the educational and scientific state which is not inhibited politically by the ties of organization. He also says, "There is little doubt as to the ability of the industrial system to serve man's needs."

The need of most people around the world today is to be able to participate in the potential affluence which can be created by an all-out unrestricted cybernetic approach to the usage of science and technology by industry. In the meantime, the elimination of want becomes a matter of survival for industry itself. Martin Stone (Chapter 25) is an imaginative, successful young executive whom some might label as conservative. He argues that, "Every man who is willing to work has a right to a decent job at a decent rate of pay and every person who is unable to work has a right to a minimum level of annual income." He strongly advocates extended training facilities involving partnership of participation between government and the business community. He sees extended training outside the formal system as being most meaningful but, until this major breakthrough develops, will settle for more government anti-poverty programs which have generally been "wasteful and badly administered." He calls for a guaranteed income.

Dr. Robert Theobald (Chapter 26) is, of course, the great pioneer of the idea of a guaranteed annual income and we are proud to include his famous essay. He recently commented that "the powerless people in our society are those who are trapped by their institutions. Men cannot understand the programs of change because mass media deals with events, not changes. Our greatest need is for conceptual change."

Obviously, when we can produce more goods and services in less time while dramatically increasing the gross national product and lowering the per unit cost as Japan has done, there should be more leisure and more opportunity for self-fulfillment. Professor John Farina (Chapter 27) examines the matter of leisure and makes some concrete prognostications.

Professor Harold Wilensky (Chapter 28) discusses the impact of change on work and leisure and observes that "modern populations on the average remain busy—with some groups becoming busier while other groups are condemned to forced leisure." He agrees that there should be a floor of income below which no family should be allowed to fall but he also says, "We need to bend our abundance to great purposes, pay people for work that needs doing—create jobs part-time and full that will harness the energies of millions."

With the increase in leisure, art and culture assume greater significance. Professor Harley Parker (Chapter 29) presents a scholarly overview in the McLuhan tradition. People do not see the environment in which they live; they only see the content and this is always the preceeding environment which in the past was not seen.

Dean McCormack Smyth (Chapter 30) places emphasis on "the community for human development" and says that "the notion that we can learn enough in the first two decades of our lives to last us for all our remaining lives is as preposterous as the thought that a jet liner can remain aloft after all its fuel has been exhausted." He suggests that those "who know" should "sum up and integrate" for human purposes what they know.

This section concludes with an article by an industrial engineer. Barrington Nevitt (Chapter 31) says, "We are born in the age of speed-up. There is urgent need to explore and discover the present by improving our probes." Using cybernetic terms, he says, " 'Feed-forward' for anticipating the effects of changes must supplement 'feed-back' which can only lead to stability, or to breakdown, but never to novelty. 'Truth' is not something we match, not a label; it is something we make, in the process of changing the world, which changes us."

CHAPTER 23

The Sakharov Manifesto

by Marshall D. Shulman

This essay, in the opinion of the editor, is the most important selection in the book. It includes some very important statements by Andrei Sakharov himself from his book "Coexistence and Intellectual Freedom" and a commentary by Marshall Shulman which was published in the Saturday Review. Dr. Shulman is director of Soviet Studies at Columbia University.

1

DR. SAKHAROV IS a physicist, now forty-seven years old, who distinguished himself at an early age by theoretical contributions to the Soviet thermonuclear bomb and the development of controlled thermonuclear fusion, for which he was elected to full membership in the Soviet Academy of Sciences. He has received the Order of Lenin and the Stalin Prize; his credentials are solid. A few years ago Dr. Sakharov began to emerge in public from his world of highly classified military research as a thoughtful social critic, with articles on the Soviet educational system.

Sakharov advances two basic theses: that the division of mankind threatens it with destruction, and that intellectual freedom is essential to human society. He writes of the threat of thermonuclear war. His discussion of the futility of anti-missile systems is sophisticated and shows knowledge of the Western literature. What lifts the heart in these passages is his lofty sense of proportion in measuring the destructiveness of war against the forces which increase the divisions of mankind. (". . . any preaching of the incompatibility of world ideologies and nations is madness and a crime.").

2

In addition to the threat of war, Sakharov writes feelingly of the danger to civilization from hunger and overpopulation, man's pollution of the sea and the air, and other despoliation of nature. He argues that these problems can only be dealt with effectively by overcoming divisions between the United States and the Soviet Union and by eliminating the pressure of transitory local interests. He also indicts, among the threats to civilization, "stupefaction from the narcotic of 'mass culture', and bureaucratized dogmatism, a spreading of mass myths that put entire peoples and continents under the power of cruel and treacherous demagogues"—an even-handed attack in both directions.

Writing before the Soviet occupation of Czechoslovakia, Sakharov expressed the intense interest of many Soviet intellectuals in the Czech experiment with liberalized Communism, and the recognition of its relevance for the USSR. "Today the key to a progressive restructuring of the system of government in the interests of mankind lies in intellectual freedom. This has been understood, in particular, by the Czechoslovaks and there can be no doubt that we should support their bold initiative, which is so valuable for the future of socialism and all mankind."

3

After the analysis of dangers comes a section called "The Basis for Hope," part prescription and part prediction. Casting aside the dogmatic critique of capitalism, Sakharov acknowledges that it has shown itself capable of continuing economic progress, and that a revolution in capitalist countries would not benefit the workers. "Both capitalism and socialism are capable of long-term development, borrowing positive elements from each other, and actually coming closer to each other in a number of essential aspects." Sakharov speculates that the two systems will move toward convergence, based upon a spread of government and cooperative ownership in the capitalist system and upon democratic trends in Soviet socialism. The result will be a cooperative coexistence, which he sees as the only alternative to mutual annihilation.

This leads Sakharov into a tentative projection of a four-stage plan covering the period to the year 2000. In the first stage, the ideological victory of the "realists" in the Soviet Union will lead to support for the policy of peaceful coexistence, strengthening of democracy (including elements of a multiparty system) in the Soviet Union, and the expansion of economic reforms. This will be accompanied by a sharpening of the ideological struggle in the socialist countries against the Stalinist and Maoist forces.

In the second stage, the "leftist reformist wing of the bourgeoisie" will lead the way in the United States to a victory over racism and militarism, to changes in the structure of ownership, and toward a policy of collaboration and peaceful coexistence with socialism abroad. This phase is scheduled to begin in 1972 (presumably after the next Presidential elections?)

In the third stage, the Soviet Union and the United States will address themselves to the poverty problem, and devote 20 per cent of their national income to economic assistance to the underdeveloped nations. Scientific techniques will be applied to this task, and this will be made more feasible by concurrent progress toward disarmament.

Finally, in the fourth stage, progress will be possible toward the creation of world government and the widespread utilization of scientific advances in space, nuclear power, biology, etc. to benefit mankind. Here Sakharov returns to his central theme of warning against the danger of a thoughtless bureaucratic use of the scientific and technological revolution; it will require, he says, "the greatest possible scientific foresight and care and concern for human values of a moral, ethical and personal character."

4

The imperatives of industrialization may produce some superficial similarities in Moscow and New York (urban congestion, smog, standardization, mobility, etc.) but it seems likely that the cultural and political differences will cause each country to adapt to industrialization and modern technology in its own way, just as each child goes through adolescence in his own way, with some characteristics in common. There is no reason why the two societies cannot continue to emphasize different qualities and to experiment with different institutional forms according to their respective cultural preferences, providing that the ascendant forces within each country share the essential human values described by Sakharov.

The important thing is that Sakharov, like so many of his excellent scientific colleagues in the Soviet Union, is a cultivated man of broad humane spirit; he addresses himself to the right questions with an elevated perspective and a vigorous intelligence.

May he know that his essay has been received and read and thought about, and that it has awakened hope for the time when the great humanistic tradition of Russia will speak to the world, aloud and unafraid.

From "Progress, Coexistence and Intellectual Freedom"
by
Andrei D. Sakharov

International affairs must be completely permeated with scientific methodology and a democratic spirit, with a fearless weighing of all facts, views, and theories, with a maximum publicity of ultimate and intermediate goals, and with a consistency of principles.

Specialists are paying attention to a growing threat of hunger in the poorer half of the world. . . . What is involved is a prognosticated deterioration of the average food balance in which localized food crises merge into a sea of hunger, intolerable suffering and desperation, the grief and fury of millions of people. This is a tragic threat to all mankind.

It is apparently futile only to insist that the more backward countries restrict their birthrates. What is needed most of all is economic and technical assistance to these countries. This assistance must be of such scale and generosity that it is absolutely impossible before the estrangement in the world and the egotistical, narrow-minded approach to relations between nations and races is eliminated. It is impossible as long as the United States and the Soviet Union, the world's two great superpowers, look upon each other as rivals and opponents.

A fifteen-year tax equal to 20 per cent of national incomes must be imposed on developed nations. The imposition of such a tax would automatically lead to a significant reduction in expenditures for weapons. Such common assistance would have an important effect—that of stabilizing and improving the situation in the most underdeveloped countries, restricting the influence of extremists of all types.

Mankind can develop smoothly only if it looks upon itself in a demographic sense as a unit, a single family without divisions into nations other than in matters of history and traditions.

The problem of geohygiene (earth hygiene) is highly complex and closely tied to economic and social problems. This problem can therefore not be solved on a national and especially not on a local basis. . . . Otherwise, the Soviet Union will poison the United States with its wastes and vice versa. At present, this is a hyperbole. But with a 10 per cent annual increase of wastes, the increase over 100 years will be multiplied 20,000 times.

The continuing economic progress being achieved under capitalism should be a fact of great theoretical significance for any nondogmatic Marxist. It is precisely this fact that lies at the basis of peaceful coexistence and it suggests, in principle, that if capitalism ever runs into an economic blind alley it will not necessarily have to leap into a desperate military adventure. Both capitalism and socialism are capable of long-term development, borrowing positive elements from each other, and actually coming closer to each other in a number of essential aspects.

Only the competition with socialism and the pressure of the working class made possible the social progress of the twentieth century and, all the more, will insure the now inevitable process of reapprochement of the two systems. It took socialism to raise the meaning of labor to the heights of a moral feat. Before the advent of socialism, national egotism gave rise to colonial oppression, nationalism, and racism. By now it has become clear that victory is on the side of the humanistic, international approach.

The capitalist world could not help giving birth to the socialist, but now the socialist world should not seek to destroy by force the ground from which it grew. Under the present conditions this would be tantamount to suicide of mankind. Socialism should ennoble that ground by its example and other indirect forms of pressure and then merge with it.

CHAPTER 24

The Future of the Industrial State

by John Kenneth Galbraith

Dr. John Kenneth Galbraith is a Professor of Economics at Harvard University who has become world-known through his books "The Great Crash" (1929)", "Economic Development", "The Affluent Society", and "The New Industrial State" from which this adaptation has been made by special permission, Houghton Mifflin Company, Boston. He was born in Canada, and has been a Reith lecturer in England, an Ambassador to India and a presidential advisor.

1

A CURIOSITY of modern economic life is the role of change. It is imagined to be very great. Yet not much is supposed to change. The economic system is praised on all occasions of public ceremony as a largely perfect structure. This is so elsewhere also. It is not easy to perfect what has been perfected. There is massive change but, except as the output of goods increases, all remains as before.

As to the change there is no doubt.

Seventy years ago the corporation was still confined to those industries—railroading, steamboating, steel-making, petroleum recovery and refining, some mining—where, it seemed production had to be on a large scale. Now it also sells groceries, mills grain, publishes newspapers and provides public entertainment, all activities that were once the province of the individual proprietor or the insignificant firm.

Seventy years ago the corporation was the instrument of its owners and a projection of their personalities. The men who now head the great corporations are unknown. The men who now run the large corporations own no appreciable share of the enterprise.

Equally it is a commonplace that the relation of the state to the economy has changed. The services of Federal, state and local governments now account for between a fifth and a quarter of all economic activity. In 1929, it was about eight per cent. This far exceeds the government share in such an avowedly socialist state as India, considerably exceeds that in the anciently social democratic kingdoms of Sweden and Norway, and is not wholly incommensurate with the share in Poland, a Communist country which, however, is heavily agricultural and which has left its agriculture in private ownership. A very large part (between one-third and one-half) of public activity is concerned with national defense and the exploration of space. This is not regarded even by conservatives as socialism. Elsewhere the nomenclature is less certain.

Additionally, in the wake of what is now called the Keynesian Revolution, the state undertakes to regulate the total income available for the purchase of goods and services in the economy.

Three further changes are less intimately a part of the established litany of accomplishment. First, there has been a further massive growth in the apparatus of persuasion and exhortation that is associated with the sale of goods. In its cost and in the talent it commands, this activity is coming increasingly to rival the effort devoted to the production of goods.

Second, there has been the beginning of the decline of the trade union. Union membership in the United States reached a peak in 1956. Since then employment has continued to grow; union membership in the main has gone down.

Finally, there has been a large expansion in enrollment for higher education together with a somewhat more modest increase in the means for providing it. This has been attributed to a new and penetrating concern for popular enlightenment. As with the fall in union membership, it has deeper roots. Had the economic system need only for millions of unlettered proletarians, these, very plausibly, are what would be provided.

2

Technology means the systematic application of scientific or other organized knowledge to practical tasks. Its most important consequence, at least for purposes of economics, is in forcing the division and subdivision of any such task into its component parts. Thus, and only thus, can organized knowledge be brought to bear on performance.

Nearly all of the consequences of technology, and much of the shape of modern industry, derive from this need to divide and subdivide tasks and from the further need to bring knowledge to bear on these fractions and from the final need to combine the finished elements of the task into the finished product as a whole.

First. An increasing span of time separates the beginning from the completion of any task.

Second. There is an increase in the capital that is committed to production aside from that occasioned by increased output. The increased time, and therewith the increased investment in goods in process, costs money.

Third. With increasing technology the commitment of time and money tends to be made ever more inflexibly to the performance of a particular task.

Fourth. Technology requires specialized manpower.

Fifth. The inevitable counterpart of specialization is organization. This is what brings the work of specialists to a coherent result.

Sixth. From the time and capital that must be committed, the inflexibility of this commitment, the needs of large organization and the problems of market performance under conditions of advanced technology, comes the necessity for planning.

Technology, under all circumstances, leads to planning; in its higher manifestations it may put the problems of planning beyond the reach of the industrial firm. Technological compulsions, and not ideology or political wile, will require the firm to seek the help and protection of the state. This is a consequence of advanced technology of no small interest.

3

As the trade unions retreat, more or less permanently, into the shadows, a rapidly growing body of educators and research scientists emerges. This group connects at the edges with scientists and engineers within the technostructure and with civil servants, journalists, writers and artists outside. Most directly nurtured by the industrial system are the educators and scientists in the schools, colleges, universities and research institutions. They stand in relation to the industrial system much as did the banking and financial community to the earlier stages of industrial development.

The educational and scientific estate, like the financial community before it, acquires prestige from the productive agent that it supplies. Potentially, at least, this is also a source of power. Likewise, and even more than the financial community, it acquires a position within the apparatus of government.

But there remain general sources of conflict between the educational and scientific estate and the technostructure. One is the management of individual behavior.

Thus the paradox. The economy for its success requires organized public bamboozlement. At the same time it nurtures a growing class which feels itself superior to such bamboozlement and deplores it as intellectually corrupt.

This conflict, in one form or another, is inevitable with planning. That requires that the needs of the producing mechanism take precedence over the freely expressed will of the individual. This will always invite the disaffection of the individual. In the Soviet-type economies the resentment is expressed against the state and the heavy and visible apparatus by which it exercises control over the individual. Under non-Soviet planning it is expressed against the techniques and instruments—advertising and the mass communications which carry it—by which the individual is managed. Curiously in neither society does the attack center on the planning which is the deeper cause.

Finally, there is potential competition and conflict between the educational and scientific estate and the technostructure growing out of their respective relations to the state. The member of the technostructure is strongly inhibited in his political role. He cannot divest himself of the organization which gives him being. And he cannot carry it with him into political life. On the other hand, he wields great public influence as, in effect, an extended arm of the bureaucracy.

The educational and scientific estate is not inhibited politically by the ties of organization. It is also growing rapidly in numbers. This could, in turn, threaten established associations between the bureaucracy and the technostructure, for they, in a fashion not different from the management of demand for consumer products, require a substantial measure of popular illusion.

4

The two questions most asked about an economic system are whether it serves man's physical needs and whether it is consistent with his liberty. There is little doubt as to the ability of the industrial system to serve man's needs. As we have seen, it is able to manage them only because it serves them abundantly. It requires a mechanism for making men want what it provides. But this mechanism would not work—wants would not be subject to manipulation—had not these wants been dulled by sufficiency.

The prospects for liberty involve far more interesting questions. It has always been imagined, especially by conservatives, that to associate all, or a large part, of economic activity with the state is to endanger freedom. The individual and his preferences, in one way or another, will be sacrificed to the needs and conveniences of the apparatus created ostensibly to serve him. As the industrial system evolves into a penumbra of the state, the question of its relation to liberty thus arises in urgent form. In recent years, in the Soviet-type economies, there has been an ill-concealed conflict between the state and the intellectuals. In essence, this has been a conflict between those for whom the needs of the government, including above all its needs as economic planner and producer of goods, are pre-eminent and those who assert the high but inconvenient claims of uninhibited intellectual and artistic expression. Is this a warning?

The instinct which warns of dangers in this association of economic and public power is sound. But conservatives have looked in the wrong direction for the danger. They have feared that the state might reach out and destroy the vigorous, money-making entrepreneur. They have not noticed that, all the while, the successors to the entrepreneur were uniting themselves ever more closely with the state and rejoicing in the result. They were also, and with enthusiasm, accepting abridgement of their freedom. Part of this is implicit in the subordination of individual personality to the needs of organization. Some of it is in the exact pattern of the classical business expectation. No modern head of the Ford Motor Company will ever react with the same pristine vigor to the presumed foolishness of Washington as did its founder. Manner may be involved. But it would also be conceded that "too much is at stake."

The problem, however, is not the freedom of the businessman. Business orators have spoken much about freedom in the past. But it can be laid down as a rule that those who speak most of liberty are least inclined to use it. The high executive who speaks fulsomely of personal freedom carefully submits his speeches on the subject for review and elimination of controversial words, phrases and ideas, as befits a good organization man. The general who tells his troops, and the world, that they are in the forefront of the fight for freedom is a man who has always submitted happily to army discipline. The high official, who adverts feelingly to the values of the free world, extravagantly admires the orthodoxy of his own views.

The danger to liberty lies in the subordination of belief to the needs of the industrial system. In this the state and the industrial system will be partners.

5

If we continue to believe that the goals of the industrial system—the expansion of output, the companion increase in consumption, technological advance, the public images that sustain it—are coordinate with life, then all of our lives will be in the service of these goals. What is consistent with these ends we shall have or be allowed; all else will be off limits. All other goals will be made to seem precious, unimportant or antisocial. We will be bound to the ends of the industrial system. But it will not be freedom.

If, on the other hand, the industrial system is only a part, and relatively a diminishing part, of life, there is much less occasion for concern. Aesthetic goals will have pride of place; those who serve them will not be subject to the goals of the industrial system; the industrial system itself will be subordinate to the claims of these dimensions of life. Intellectual preparation will be for its own sake and not for the better service to the industrial system. Men will not be entrapped by the belief that apart from the goals of the industrial system—apart from the production of goods and income by progressively more advanced technical methods—there is nothing important in life.

The foregoing being so, we may, over time, come to see the industrial system in fitting light as an essentially technical arrangement for providing convenient goods and services in adequate volume. Those who rise through its bureaucracy will so see themselves. And the public consequences will be in keeping, for if economic goals are the only goals of the society it is natural that the industrial system should dominate the state and the state should serve its ends. If other goals are strongly asserted, the industrial system will fall into its place as a detached and autonomous arm of the state, but responsive to the larger purposes of the society.

We have seen wherein the chance for salvation lies. The industrial system, in contrast with its economic antecedents, is intellectually demanding. It brings into existence, to serve its intellectual and scientific needs, the community that, hopefully, will reject its monopoly of social purpose.

6

Although the large corporation, like the union, is far from new, it has never been really assimilated into the main body of economics.

Extensive government procurement in areas of high technology; extensive government intervention on wages and prices; widespread affluence, with its evident effect on the economic problem that it partly solves, have still to work their passage into the main body of economic theory.

The fringes of economic discussion have long been afflicted by aborted revolutions or ones that turned out to be inconsequential.

THE FUTURE OF THE INDUSTRIAL STATE / 261

But economics also resists consequential and durable change because it seems more scientific to do so. To accept underlying change is to be dubiously respectful of the scientific aspirations of economics. To deny that it has relevance is to assume a much better scientific posture.

These attitudes also accord well with vested interest. Knowledge for the intellectual is what skill is for the artisan and capital for the businessman. In all, the instinct is to fear obsolescence. But the intellectual is in a far better position to resist obsolescence than the craftsman or businessman. The machine that replaces the craftsman is wholly tangible. His only line of resistance is overt—a strike or a sledgehammer to smash the thing. Both encounter social disfavor. The out-of-date machine of the businessman is equally objective. His modes of recourse—to regulate or suppress innovation—are equally reprehensible. He can be a Luddite without violence and indeed without knowing it.

The work of modern science and technology is highly visible. It will be assumed by most that it must have its effects on economic organization and social behavior. The great corporation is not easily concealed. Not many will imagine that the social impact of General Motors—on employees, markets, customers and the state—is the same as that of the dairy farm. The state is clearly a vastly greater force in economic affairs than it was fifty years ago. That science, technology and organization have placed new demands on educational institutions or that they have changed the balance of power as between capital and organization will not seem improbable.

Indeed many will agree that the burden of proof is on those who aver that these changes have left conclusions concerning economic life unchanged. And that, precisely, is where I wish to have that burden placed.

CHAPTER 25

Elimination of Want-- A Matter of Survival

by Martin Stone

Martin Stone is a member of the Young Presidents' Organization which is comprised of presidents of major corporations who are under forty years of age. His company is Monogram Industries, Inc., and this article is taken from his keynote address to the Conference on Education and Technology, American Management Association, New York Hilton, 1968. Again here is a successful businessman who is relating to the issues of the time and doing something about it.

1

"SOLELY BY VIRTUE of the fact of permanent residence a man who is willing to work has a right to a decent job at a decent rate of pay and every person who is unable to work has a right to a minimum level of annual income which will enable that person to live in respect and decency and without the necessity of having to be subjected to the humiliation of begging a welfare system for the opportunity to live."

"The major portion of the solution to our problem of unemployment is training. I would divide the training problem into two stages: the first stage being the development of entry level or prevocational skills and the second stage being the development of specific job skills. To pass through stage one, a man must be able to communicate satisfactorily and he must have a receptive attitude towards the disciplines and expectations of job performance."

"The second stage of the job training problem is that which entails the development of specific job skills. Here is where private industry must play the decisive role. Actually, over the past years, there has been a strongly increased awareness of the problem by the business community. More and more firms are setting up programs for job trainees from the ranks of the unemployed and the so-called 'hard-core unemployables'. These are being set up both under existing Federal programs and independently of Federal support."

"The programs I have advocated involve a partnership of

264 / this cybernetic age

participation between the government and the business community. . . ."

2

We businessmen are the ones with the muscle and the competence to solve these problems. Along with most of you, I share a belief in the incompetence and wastefulness of a good many government programs, but unless we are willing to take over the leadership of the fight against poverty and indecency, the governments are going to continue wasteful and badly administered anti-poverty programs. In that event, I, for one, am going to support its badly directed efforts because I prefer to fight for these goals even through inadequate means rather than to give up and continue to let people live in poverty. And if you think those people are going to simply continue to peacefully accept the degradation which their present serfdom entails, you are seriously mistaken.

Our country is perched precariously on the edge of open rebellion. We have already witnessed the first skirmishes of this revolution and the situation is bound to get much worse before it gets better. Furthermore, it isn't going to get better until we eliminate the underlying causes of these riots. The only other answer is to stifle the protests of the poor through ever stronger repressive measures which will eventually turn the country into a garrison state in which we have the necessary limitations of freedom, concentration camps and huge police establishments necessary to "maintain law and order."

Which of these solutions will you choose? I think you are kidding yourself if you think there are any other alternatives. If we haven't got the stomach for the measures necessary to insure the repressive containment of vast numbers of people then we must provide damn quick solutions to the underlying problems of poverty and multiple classes of citizenship.

3

The Scope of the Problem

This prelude now brings me to the question of remedies for these ills. First and foremost, I am convinced that the most important problem is one of jobs. In the U.S.A. the realistic problem of necessary job supply is estimated at one and one-half million jobs. The Canadian average is about the same. It has also been estimated that there are unfilled job requirements for more than this number of people. Our unemployment problem therefore boils down to a problem of geographics and training: geographics to get the jobless to places where jobs exist or to locate industry in areas of high unemployment, and training to equip the jobless to handle the technical skill requirements of unfilled job openings.

4

The Role of Training

The major portion of the solution to our problem of unemployment is training.

There are a number of ways in which the prevocational training can be effectively handled. The present methods under the anti-poverty program are not overly successful. The primary instruments of this program are the Job Corps and the local Skill Centers operated under The Manpower Development and Training Act. By and large, the institutional type Job Corps camps do not seem to be producing adequate results. Even at this late date, the costs of the Job Corps are approximately $8,000 per person per year and the end result of the training has generally been discouraging.

In all fairness, however, it should be pointed out that the

cost and success of a program often depends on the type of trainee accepted by it. The more "hard core" the trainee, the higher the cost because the drop out rate is higher and more counseling, training, and supervision is needed.

5

Job Skill Training

The second stage of the job training problem is that which entails the development of specific job skills. Here is where private industry must play the decisive role. More and more firms are setting up programs for job trainees from the ranks of the unemployed and the so-called "hard core unemployables."

General Dynamics in Fort Worth, Texas has a program to train 18 to 25 year olds as aircraft assemblers, lathe operators, metal fitters, electrical installers, etc. The training period is 10 to 14 weeks and trainees are paid $32.00 per week plus $5.00 per week per dependent. Thus far, approximately 80 percent of the trainees have been permanently employed and are now earning an average rate of $2.43 per hour. In addition to the cost of allowances, the program costs about $450.00 per trainee which is being reimbursed by the Federal government under the Manpower Development Training Act.

The Lockheed Missiles and Space Center in Sunnyvale, California, has a 10 week program: Four weeks of classroom instruction and six weeks of on the job training. During the training period, trainees are paid regular wages. Prior to acceptance in the program trainees must have at least three weeks of prevocational training in a skill center. The training cost has averaged $1,300 per trainee. Ninety percent of the trainees complete the program. The skills trained for are electrical assembler, key-punch operator, sheet metal helper, machine shop helper, etc. Lockheed pays for all but 6 percent of the costs.

The Cleveland Pneumatic Tool Company trained 328 disadvantaged youths for jobs as grinding machine, milling machine and lathe operators.

The Philco-Ford Corporation administers a program in Philadelphia called "Project Team." Trainees are given six to eight weeks of prevocational training and are then placed with companies which provide skill training on the job.

Many other industrial corporations have set up on-the-job training programs. These companies are too numerous to mention. Some have programs considerably larger than those I have mentioned.

The major program for on the job training by private industry is the "JOBS" program set up under the auspices of the National Alliance of Businessmen and headed by Henry Ford, Chairman of the Board of the Ford Motor Co. Under the program, participating companies in 50 cities make available openings specifically for the hard-core unemployed. The program's goal is 500,000 by June, 1971. The Department of Labor grants up to $3,500 per trainee to the employer to cover the extra costs of training and counseling and otherwise assisting such underqualified trainees. Thus far, it appears that the original target for full time jobs will be met and the program's directors are now confident that they will meet or exceed the long term targets.

6

To build a successful training program requires the same kind of executive and middle management skills as are needed in achieving that most basic of corporate objectives: the earning of a satisfactory profit. And profit growth does not come easy. It takes skill and effort.

The kinds of problems we have encountered start with the finding of prospective trainees and run all the way from the employment application itself through the potential for advancement that exists throughout your entire organization.

It is not easy to reach people who have previously found it almost impossible to get a job with a convincing message that someone seriously intends to give them a job and train them.

A great many existing employment requirements exclude people who have been arrested for, or convicted of, criminal offenses. Employers who have dropped the criminal arrest, and to some extent the criminal conviction, bars to employment have found no difference in the eventual results between employees with or without criminal records.

Another limiting factor in employment procedures is the psychological testing procedure a number of companies follow. Recent results have shown that most of these tests are programmed around a person who comes from a typical white, middle class environment and are particularly difficult for people from strikingly different environmental backgrounds.

Another problem relates to the filling out of the employment application. To avoid embarrassment and confusion, it is better to have the job interviewer fill out the application for the prospective employee.

In many cities, lack of adequate sources of public transportation to the job sites is a difficult problem.

Lack of fluency with the English language is sometimes a serious problem. The best answer to this problem is to have some bilingual leadmen or supervisors.

7

Another major problem for trainees is the attitude of fellow workers and supervisors around them in the shop. There is often a problem of resistance to the trainees by co-workers. We have simply taken the position that fairly rapidly, the trainees will become as productive as other workers, and in the meantime this is a social obligation that simply must be shouldered by all segments of our society.

The tendency on the part of supervisory personnel to use the trainees for menial work which does not contribute towards the training process must constantly be watched. You will find yourself involved with getting the trainees into hospitals and out of jail. You will have to deal with the problem of getting gas and electricity turned back on, fighting off finance companies, getting cars towed off freeways and many other annoyances you normally wouldn't put up with. But bear in mind you will likely be the only real link these people have with "the establishment" and you may represent their only real way of coping with it until they have built up some kind of a "stake."

There are a great many other problems which come up in programs of this sort, not the least of which are the twin problems of tardiness and absenteeism.

Last but not least trainees must see the opportunity to advance within the organization and to achieve increasingly better levels of pay.

8

The Use of Tax Credits to Private Industry

I mentioned earlier that the real unemployment problem consisted of training approximately one and one-half million people to handle presently unfilled job openings.

To provide meaningful starting jobs at $2.00 per hour for 1,500,000 people would cost approximately $4,400 per person per year or approximately $6,600,000,000 per year. The problem with our present anti-poverty efforts is that they have created a vast Federal overhead structure to administer the programs so that a small proportion of the funds allocated actually reach the intended beneficiaries or are brought to bear on the real problems of poverty.

270 / THIS CYBERNETIC AGE

I propose that the bulk of the job training portion of the anti-poverty effort be put into the hands of private industry. If the Federal government, as an incentive to business, granted a credit of approximately 7½ percent against Federal income taxes for amounts paid to certified "trainees" for the first twelve months of employment, it would create a pool of approximately $7½-billion which businesses could, at their election, either pay in taxes to the Federal government or to training the presently unemployed.

As a final overriding factor in the question of providing jobs for anyone able to work, the Government should recognize its obligation as an employer of last resort to provide work for those unable to obtain work in the private sector of the economy. This point will take considerable further development but I include it here as part of the over-all problem.

9

The Use of the Negative Income Tax

The second part of the problem relates primarily to those people who are unable to work. It is in this area that our present multi-faceted welfare programs are highly inadequate and completely degrading. Our society is wealthy enough to see that these people need not live in poverty, humiliation and despair.

It has been estimated that in the United States we now spend approximately $8-billion annually on welfare programs which reach approximately one-third of our people who live in poverty. It has also been estimated that the additional social costs, including police, detention systems, courts and riot damage far exceed the direct cost of welfare payments. Certainly, it does not stretch the imagination to conclude that present welfare and poverty related social costs exceed $20-billion per year.

A blue ribbon panel of businessmen in New York State, headed by Joseph C. Wilson, concluded that it would take a total of $19 billion per year to raise every American above the poverty level (defined as $3,300 per year for a family of four). They concluded that this sum was less than present welfare and poverty-related social costs and should be spent.

If we assume that we want to eliminate poverty in this country, how do we spend the money without dramatically increasing the costs through inevitably expensive Federal administrative programs. The best answer I have seen is the "Negative Income Tax" originally proposed in 1950 by Milton Friedman, the economist from the University of Chicago, who recently served as an economic consultant to Barry Goldwater during the 1964 Presidential election. This is simply a means of implementing the idea of a Guaranteed Annual Income with minimum administrative cost.

It has also been recommended by the highly prestigious Committee For Economic Development.

Under the negative income tax plan, each person would file a tax return and those above the minimum level of guaranteed annual income would pay their appropriate tax, those below it would receive a payment from the government equal to the amount necessary to bring them up to the minimum annual income. This program would have to be tied in with the job training program described earlier and would be in lieu of all welfare payments other than those for special health care problems.

An ancillary benefit from this entire approach is the healthy stimulus it would provide to the economy. Imagine how important it would be to our economy to find within our midst an untapped market of some 25 million people who would have the economic capacity to become consumers of goods and services deemed minimally necessary in our society.

There have been estimates by highly competent economists that such a program would add absolutely nothing to over-all taxes when the true additional tax costs and economic costs of poverty are added up. These include not only the police and court costs cited earlier but also property losses in riots, loss of business in riot areas and a multitude of other economic costs.

10

A Partnership Between Government and Business

The programs I have advocated involve a partnership of participation between the government and the business community. Although they contemplate economic incentives to industry for the training of the unemployed, the business community will, along with all other taxpayers, bear the additional (perhaps temporary) burden of the higher tax rates necessary to support the training expense contributions and the payments under the Guaranteed Annual Income plan to those unable to work.

The minorities have realized the failure of the so-called "liberals" who have stolen their decency, self-respect and manhood by clinging to old-fashioned ideas of patronizing charity. A man wants decency, self-respect and to earn his way. He wants an equal shot at earning his share of the benefits of an affluent society. We businessmen are a major component of "the establishment." We have the most to protect in this system and society. Let us be the progressives of the future. It is high time that we developed a clear cut and forthrightly announced "business social conscience." A social conscience which is in tune with the needs of the times and which can be applied first and foremost to the achievement of a major social revolution which will, for the first time in our history, give all true equality of participation in every aspect of our economy and our society.

CHAPTER 26

Guaranteed Incomes for All

by Robert Theobald

Dr. Robert Theobald is an India-born British socio-economist who, since 1957, has been studying the effects of abundance on the American socio-economy. Previously he was associated with the Organization for European Economic Cooperation. He is internationally known for his consulting, lecturing, speaking, and writing. His books include "Free Men and Free Markets", "The Challenge of Abundance", and "The Rich and the Poor". This paper is adopted from his essay: "The Guaranteed Income Proposal" as set out in "Free Men and Free Markets" and published in "The Guaranteed Income—Next Step in Economic Evolution" (Doubleday). Like Diebold's essay on automation, this has become a classic on guaranteed income.

1

WHAT PRACTICAL STEPS need to be taken in order to reap
the benefits of the scientific and technological revolution rather
than its destructive growths? It is the attempt to keep the
economy growing fast enough to provide jobs for all that
harnesses man to the juggernaut of scientific and technological
change and that keeps us living within "a whirling-dervish
economy dependent on compulsive consumption." This essay
proposes the establishment of new principles specifically
designed to break the link between jobs and incomes. Implementation of these principles must necessarily be carried out
by the government as the sole body concerned with every member of society and with the adequate functioning of the total
socio-economic system. W. H. Ferry has enlarged on the
necessity for "due-income" principles: "Abundance may
compel social justice as conscience never has. The liberated
margin (those unable to find work) will have to get 'what is
its due.' This means developing a basis of distribution of income which is not tied to work as a measure. For decisions
about 'dueness' will have to be made without economic criteria; at least without the criterion of what members of the
liberated margin are worth in the employment market, for
there is no such market for them."

In order to ensure that government concern with the total
socio-economic system would not outweigh its responsibility to
every member of society, a due-income from government

should be given as an absolute constitutional right; for unless this is guaranteed, the government would have the possibility of developing the most extreme form of tyranny imaginable. During the process of implementation of the due-income principles, the number of people obtaining the totality of their living expenses from the government would increase rapidly; if the right to these incomes could be withdrawn under any circumstances, government would have the power to deprive the individual not only of the pursuit of happiness but also of liberty and even, in effect, of life itself. This absolute right to a due-income would be essentially a new principle in jurisprudence. Most present constitutional rights can be curtailed when the overall good of society is held to require this; however, the right of an individual to a due-income could not, in itself, endanger the state.

It is clear that any attempt to break the strangle hold of the job-income link will have to be made with the interests of both the individual and society kept firmly in mind. There is now a growing awareness that in recent years the interest of the individual has been subordinated to the drives of the economy, and that this subordination is withdrawing the values of freedom and human dignity from the lives of a significant proportion of the American population. In an article in The New Yorker, Dwight MacDonald outlines the case for a recognition of the necessity to provide for the individual:

. . . a second line of government policy is required; namely, direct intervention to help the poor.

We have had this since the New Deal, but it has always been grudging and miserly, and we have never accepted the principle that every citizen should be provided, at state expense, with a reasonable minimum standard of living regardless of any other considerations.

It should not depend on earnings, as does Social Security, which continues the inequalities and inequities and so tends to keep the poor forever poor. Nor should it exclude millions of our poorest citizens because they lack the political pressure to force their way into the Welfare State.

The governmental obligation to provide, out of taxes, such a minimum living standard for all who need it should be taken as much for granted as free public schools have always been in our history.

The need is clear: the principle of an economic floor under each individual must be established. This principle would apply equally to every member of society and carry with it no connotation of personal inadequacy or implication that an undeserved income was being received from an over-generous government. On the contrary, the implication would clearly be one of responsibility by the total society for ensuring that no member of the society lived in a manner incompatible with the standards acceptable to his fellow men merely because he lacked purchasing power. In this respect his position as a member of society would be secure; such a principle should therefore be called Basic Economic Security.

Basic Economic Security can be best regarded as an extension of the present Social Security system to a world in which conventional job availability will steadily decline.

We will need to adopt the concept of an absolute constitutional right to an income. This would guarantee to every citizen the right to an income from the federal government sufficient to enable him to live with dignity. No government agency, judicial body, or other organization whatsoever should have the power to suspend or limit any payments assured by these guarantees.

2

We can first examine how entitlements to BES might be established. One of the fundamental principles of the present tax system is the "exemption" of part of an individual's income from taxation. At its inception, this exemption ensured that taxes would not be paid on that portion of income required to provide a reasonable standard of living. However, the government lost sight of this original aim when increasing the tax load to pay for World War II, and the value of the exemption has been further reduced since the end of World War II by the effects of inflation. The original aim of the federal tax exemption should be restored and exemptions should be raised immediately to a level which would guarantee an untaxed income adequate for minimum subsistence. Those whose incomes from earnings or from capital did not reach this level would then be entitled to receive federal government payments sufficient to raise their incomes to this level and insure their Basic Economic Security.

At what levels should these BES entitlements be set initially? Two factors must be taken into account in making this decision: first, the necessity of providing an income adequate for minimum subsistence for everybody; and second, the necessity to prevent the overburdening of the administrative operation at the beginning of the scheme. The full economic implications of any particular level of BES entitlements would probably have to be worked through on computers, but it might be expected that a level of $1,000 a year for every adult and $600 for every child would in fact be feasible levels to use as a starting point for calculations.

So long as entitlements are only adequate to allow minimum subsistence, it seems appropriate that the exemption pattern should be very simple and probably this split between adults and children would be sufficient. When incomes were raised to a level adequate to allow human dignity, the question of introducing a declining level of exemptions for families with more than two or three children would have to be seriously considered. Indeed, there would have to be detailed examination, at this time, of the degree of complexity that would be desirable in the pattern of exemptions; for the monetary cost of supporting a six-year-old child is very different from that of a fourteen-year-old, while the cost of living varies widely from place to place. On the other hand, the amount of government verification necessary would increase if the pattern of exemptions were made more complex.

In spite of the evidence on disparity of incomes, a considerable number of readers may still deny the need for any proposal which would provide such low income guarantees. For example, it should shock these people to learn that in 1960, 16.4 percent of all unattached individuals, or about 1,800,000 Americans, received less than $1,000 per year; almost all these people would benefit from BES entitlements. Although it is not possible to determine with equal certainty how many families would benefit, almost all the 7.3 percent of families receiving incomes below $2,000 would benefit, as would many of the 15.8 percent of families receiving between $2,000 and $3,999.

3

It may be asked why a higher level of exemptions should not be set even at the outset of the scheme. The difficulty is not in terms of the financial burden; this would not of course be of any great magnitude in terms of productive capacity and the effect on the budget. However, an immediate higher level for the exemption would probably not be wise, for it is essential that the operation of the scheme be efficient, and this goal might not be achieved if the initial number of beneficiaries were too high. An overload and consequent breakdown would be disastrous for confidence in the feasibility of the plan. However, a rapid rise in entitlements should be achieved, for the $2,000 suggested for a retired couple is about $1,000 below the Bureau of Labor Statistics estimate of a "modest but adequate" budget in cities, and the $3,200 allowed for a man, his wife, and two children is little more than half the sum required for a similar "modest but adequate" budget.

One of the difficulties in determining an appropriate level for initial BES entitlements stems from the fact that certain additional free services urgently need to be introduced. Sufficient evidence now exists to show that one of the major causes of proverty among the old is excessive medical bills, and that it is precisely those who have been poor all their lives who are most likely to suffer from chronic ill health. A full-scale medical-care bill is required to ensure that nobody's savings are wiped out because of an unavoidable illness for which they are not responsible and which they cannot avoid. Health is a community responsibility. Similarly, education must be treated as a community responsibility. This has, of course, been recognized and free education has been provided as the essential basis for upward mobility in the population, as the method of giving everybody an opportunity to make use of his talent. However, the policies necessary to fulfill this valid and accepted principle have not been re-examined in the light of the new conditions of the middle of the twentieth century, when a university education is often essential if people are fully to realize their potential.

Basic Economic Security would be very simple to operate compared to the present mosaic of measures—Social Security, unemployment compensation, welfare, "stamp plans," subsidies to housing—which have been introduced at various times in the past to meet the same goal. Payments under BES would progressively take the place of these schemes. Recalculations of BES entitlement, based on the individual's total income record for the year, would be made annually; the entitlement payments would be made weekly. Although this simplicity of operation is attractive, it nevertheless appears necessary to add one complication, which is probably required both to secure equity in the early states of the scheme and also to encourage acceptance. Although soon after the introduction of the plan, many recipients of BES would come to depend on BES payments for their total income, others would continue to receive private income from their market-supported work or would have some interest payments on their savings. (We will use "private income" to cover both income received from a conventional market-supported job and income received from interest on savings throughout this discussion.) In calculating BES payments, the amount of this private income should not simply be deducted from the BES entitlement so that those with private income and those without receive the same total income. Instead, those with private income should be entitled to additional payments in the form of a premium, thus raising the level of their total entitlement. The size of the premium could only be determined after extensive study.

CHAPTER 27

Toward Leisure and Self-Fulfillment

by John Farina

Dr. John Farina is a Professor of Social Work at the University of Toronto and has spoken and written extensively on automation and leisure. He was one of the principal collaborators in the creation of "This Cybernetic Age" and his paper was developed from various lectures which he has given.

1

WHEN WE TALK of free time an obvious, frequently-ignored question arises—of what is free time free? The term usually suggests freedom from work and implies a simple dichotomy between work time and free time.

Most societies tend to dichotomize time, and the tendency is to function on the basis of the work time, non-work time dichotomy. Despite common usage, however, non-work time is not the same as free time. If we restrict the meaning of work time to that time required for maintenance of or for securing material gain for self and dependents, or time spent for material reward, it is generally synonymous with employment. The operational definition of work offered by Kleemeier is consistent with this notion: ". . . those activities for which one receives pay for which pay was a major, and generally the most important, reason for engaging in the activity" are considered work.

The focus here, however, is on non-work time. Free time, recreation and leisure can be conceptualized in terms of several dimensions. Each can be discussed in reference to time which is an essential definer of recreation and free time, but is not a primary definer of leisure. Activity is viewed as essential to the ideas of recreation and leisure but not as central to the notion of free time. Recreation herein is presented as a type of free-time activity while leisure is discussed in terms of freely chosen activity not limited to a specific time period.

Non-work time may be classified on a continuum ranging from that time during which a type of activity is necessary, to that time during which a type of activity is obligatory, to that time when there is a free choice of activity. At the necessary end of the continuum are those activities such as sleeping, eating and body elimination which are biologically essential to life. While all these activities may be deferred for varying periods of time, it is necessary to occupy minimal amounts of time repeatedly in their performance for maintenance of life.

Much non-work time that is assumed to be free time in fact is not free from necessary activity. Nor does freedom from necessary activities consistently grant freedom from obligatory activities. Required activities consonant with the expectation of one's primary role impose obligations on non-work time. Kaplan suggests a minimum of social role obligations as a precondition to leisure. The corollary, it seems, is that the existence of specific, recognized role obligations precludes leisure and identifies the time during which such obligations are recognized as non-free. De Grazia suggests that much of our presumed free time is indeed obligatory non-work time. This is adequately illustrated by such characteristic suburban activities as putting up and taking down storm and screen windows, mowing the lawn, driving children to music or dance lessons, shopping trips and sundry obligatory "voluntary" activities. These may or may not be satisfying modes of behavior. No judgment is being made on the value of these activities. The fact is, this range of activity seems to occupy a great deal of non-work time.

Obligatory non-work time varies in quantity both between and within cultures. For example, Canadian culture probably makes greater quantitative demands in this class of time than do most European cultures. In middle class culture, father is expected, with varying degrees of intensity, to assist in child rearing, help in household maintenance, and give assistance on shopping expeditions. Mother is expected to take responsibility for disciplining children, baking for various community groups, participating in the P.T.A. and being informed on the literature of popular experts in child rearing. Thus the popular notion of free time is significantly limited as conceived herein. It does not embrace all non-work time but is restricted to that time which is not limited in choice of activity by virtue of biological necessities or socially imposed obligations. It is this balance of time, the free-choice range of the continuum that is the focus of this paper. This range will be termed "free time", which is identified as time free from biological need and obligations imposed by primary social role expectations.

2

In addressing ourselves to free time and its real or assumed increase, we tend to be bound by values, judgments and patterns of thought more relevant to the period of the Industrial Revolution than to an age of automation and cybernetics. Reductions in hours of work are thought of in terms of the work week or the work day. Holding a job is viewed as more important than work. Too much free time is frequently viewed as dangerous as contrasted to work which is said to build character, security and sense of purpose.

Perhaps a brief look at these attitudes will help us to orient our thinking towards the future and a society with an abundance of free time rather than to the past and a society where work was considered honorable no matter how debilitating and degrading.

There are unions in the United States that have bargained for and achieved a 25-hour work week. This amount of work time is usually encompassed in a five hour per day, five-day work week. Assuming a fifty-week work year 25 hours per week is 1250 hours of work per year. Surely a more imaginative—and incidentally more businesslike—approach to the distribution of 1250 hours of work can be conceived than the five-day five-hour week. Why not work a seven-hour, six-day week every second month? This would give a 1250-hour work year with every second month free with salary assuming the same rate of pay. Or why not work a forty-five-hour week for twenty-eight weeks and have twenty-four weeks free? If a fifty-hour week doesn't sound too grim—and I'm sure many work at least that—then the 1250 hours for the year could be accomplished by working every second week.

Even within the 24-hour span of a given day, our thinking about hours of work tends to ignore the invention of electric lights. Why if a man is working a five, six or even eight-hour day, should the best daylight hours be the preferred work time? Surely on a five-hour work day something more imaginative than a nine a.m. to three p.m. schedule can be devised. Indeed, the whole idea of the desirability of the fixed shift needs critical examination. On a 5-hour day surely variable shifts would bring great benefit to the individual, to business and industry and to our communities. Aside from the myriad social benefits that would accrue from a more realistic approach to hours of work, the economic benefits are incalculable. By operating 24 hours per day production could be tripled or quadrupled without any extension of plant. If such continuous production schedules became general then the rush hour would become a thing of the past, recreation facilities would not be idle for much of the time and overcrowded at peak periods, the life style of adults would not necessarily be tied to the time demands of an educational system designed for children, every day would be a "free" day for a substantial proportion of the population.

3

In an affluent society—a society of unprecedented abundance—a society wherein productivity is more closely related to productive machinery than to human labor—a society where many jobs are literally disappearing—a society wherein no class can be identified solely by virtue of the fact that it alone has leisure, in such a society, to assume that work in and of itself is good is patently ridiculous!

The man who says he needs work to maintain his health, his feeling of self respect, of self worth, really means that he needs a job rather than work.

Firemen have a job on the deisel locomotives. Therefore they have: income, a sense of belonging and participating in society, average mental and physical health, security and self respect.

Take away the job and he may lose these benefits—YET HE DOES NOT WORK!!!

In contrast consider a widow with five children. She works:

> Washing for five children
> Meals three times a day
> Housecleaning
> Shopping
> Ironing
> Sewing and mending
> Escorting children to doctor, dentist,
> teacher, dancing classes, etc.
> Juggles a budget that keeps her well below
> the poverty line—but
> SHE DOES NOT HAVE A JOB!!!

Indeed the government does not allow her to have a job. You see she is a welfare case.

The question arising from these illustrations is—In our society who is more highly regarded, who has the higher status—the man with a job who doesn't work or the woman on welfare who works but has no job?

To this point this presentation has dealt primarily with free time as a consequence of automation coupled with a value system of an age of work. There is, however, another critical factor which might also have great consequences for our future—developments in the life sciences. Killer diseases are being steadily conquered, infant mortality is becoming rare, life spans are increasing, and hence the population explosion, urban congestion and birth control programs. From a recreation point of view the pill of course is a tremendous development. With it has come demands to remove legislative control over morality.

4

While these points all have important implications for the future, are more explicit prognostications possible? Having due regard for the constant perversity of man and his social systems and the possibility of yet more astonishing scientific achievements—the following predictions are tentatively put forward:

1. If a firm notion of the potentiality of the future is held with conviction by significant leaders in our communities then such convictions can be important factors in present day planning for the future. If a leader can help to orient a group towards legitimate goals, if he can gain their confidence regarding the achievement of those goals and then is prepared to take action towards those goals—then he is a leader in fact

in addition to the status he may hold by virtue of his appointment. Many people in our communities (leaders in religion, education, business, recreation, service clubs, churches, social agencies, government, etc.) are strategically placed to assume this leadership role. The logic of their assumption of such a role in a society of free-time is unassailable. It must be emphasized however, that the individual will only be sanctioned in the role of leader if he merits community support. The support does not go with the position, it is granted on the basis of individual merit as a leader.

2. The growing awareness of the irrelevance of the diurnal variable will gradually lead to a re-scheduling of man's activities on a 24-hour basis. That is, night and day will cease to have the same relevance in relation to the scheduling of activities. This will probably be true of both work and free-time activities.

There is no doubt that we are moving in this direction. Night football and baseball are now commonplace. Night shift work patterns are typical of industrial communities. Shopping at night is actually an innovation of the past ten years. With more workers on night shifts we might soon see a resurgence of day time professional sports, of the theatre and motion picture matinee, of morning or twilight symphony concerts, indeed the cocktail hour might become any hour of the day or night.

3. Increased control over the environment will eliminate the seasonal nature of many activities. We will ski if we so choose in July and swimming and beach parties will not be limited to summer months. Domed cities with climate control will modify travel patterns. Following the sun will not be as strong a motivation for tourism as it is today. Rather, intercultural involvement will become a primary motive for travel.

Just as today a visit to the astrodome in Houston is a recreation activity, so in the future an excursion or a vacation outside the astrodome may become a typical free-time activity. The national park, provincial park, conservation area and so-called wilderness areas will become even more critical recreation areas in relation to the needs to be served.

4. Communication will be remarkably improved. With the assistance of a transistor-like instrument tuned into a central control we will be able to communicate across language barriers. In the home it will be possible to tune in our 'T.V.—like' communicator so we can hold a dialogue with an image of Socrates, or engage Einstein in a discussion with Newton. The contribution of such gadgetry to inter-cultural exchange will be immeasurable.

Meaningful communication with a Tanzanian, a Turk or even a Texan will be an everyday possibility. Through a home communication set the whole range of world culture, past and present will be immediately available via a simple programming procedure. Education in its present institutionalized form will become extinct. Rather education in the Aristotelian sense will become the dominant pattern—i.e., the object of education is to prepare a man to occupy his leisure.

5. In association with new communication patterns, the rate of travel will so increase that McLuhan's concept of the Global Village will become operational for all races of men.

Aircraft, ground craft and water craft of tremendous speed and versatility will provide an intricate network of services throughout the world. Within the cities the elimination of the rush hour will be an essential prerequisite to improving the speed and efficiency of transportation. Trucks and freight trains will be replaced by surface and underground cargo carrying pipe lines and tubes. Public transportation will be a tax supported service, much as sewers and roads are today. Their efficiency will contribute to the demise of the automobile as anything but a form of recreation. To this extent it will be analogous to the canoe, the horse, and sail boat in today's scheme of living.

6. A secondary consequence of radical changes in communication will be an accelerated increase in miscegenation— Mitchner's Golden Man will be an increasingly familiar figure in our society. Ultimately we will return to one race— the race of man. There are clear indications of this trend today, in the Hawaiian Islands, the West Indies, Singapore, Latin America, and to a lesser extent in Canada. Again, effective communication, extended travel, and changing values, should result in great acceleration of this trend.

7. Community leaders will be working very hard during the evolution from a work society to a free society.

The ideal citizen in the society of the future will be economically secure, and will not need a job in order to maintain his sense of self respect. Rather he will be free in a context much broader and more meaningful than simple political freedom. He will be free to seek self fulfillment, self realization, through activities which may or may not be economically productive. Motivation will be determined by such seeking. Stimulation will not necessarily be from external sources. The individual in terms of recreation will be a self-starter—every citizen will be available for leadership roles and hence a potential volunteer. Community leaders and social workers may maintain more subtle roles as of gyroscopes in maintaining the goal of freely participating citizens in a free society.

8. More people will occupy their free-time in community service, intellectual pursuits and participatory activities. Conspicuous consumption during free time will be associated with poverty—the only true poverty—poverty of mind. In a society of plenty, displays of material possessions will be regarded at the best as vulgar, at the worst as pathetic. Only one lacking the inner resources to achieve meaningful self-fulfillment will need to stoop to ostentatious display.

CHAPTER 28

Impact of Change of Work and Leisure

by Harold L. Wilensky

Dr. Harold L. Wilensky is Professor of Sociology, University of California at Berkeley. This article consists of excerpts from a paper presented at the seventeenth annual conference of McGill University's Industrial Relations Centre. The conference theme was Human Values and Technology. Reprinted by special permission from the September 1967 issue of the Monthly Labor Review. Published by the United States Department of Labor. For elaboration, see H. L. Wilensky, "The Uneven Distribution of Leisure", *Social Problems,* 9 (Summer, 1961, pp. 32-56), and *Work, Leisure and Freedom* (New York, The Free Press, Macmillan, forthcoming.)

1

THE WIDER DIFFUSION of freedom, more chance for self-expression in personal relationships, pluralism in organizational life and culture, more educational opportunity, perhaps even more civil order—in the long view these are clear accompaniments of abundance. But these positive achievements have their cost, and it is by no means certain that we can count on continued growth in freedom and equality as an automatic byproduct of continued economic growth. For abundance brings its burdens as well as its blessings.

The first burden is the burden of indifference to relative poverty at home and abroad. This indifference is determined in part by (1) the tendency toward uneven distribution of work common to all modern economies; and (2) the tendency of defense budgets to become bloated and thereby generate a demand for overtime work and job mobility. Both these tendencies "increase the natural indifference of hard-working, adaptable majorities to the fate of those who can neither work nor adapt."

The most striking thing about work in modern society is that it is unevenly distributed.

When people hear that I'm studying leisure styles they often say, "Oh, yes. Isn't it awful; what will we do with all this leisure time? " And then they are apt to mention the electricians in New York City who struck for and won a 25-hour week. Or they'll mention "suburban neuroses"—the ills of women with time on their hands.

Well, scratch the surface a bit and you'll find that those electricians are actually on the job 45 or 50 hours a week (logging overtime); and those women, like women everywhere, are putting in as long a "work" week as their ancestors of preindustrial times, logging time in childrearing, housekeeping, and the like.

Talk of the leisure-oriented society and the decline of the Protestant Ethic has obscured the basic fact of the matter: Modern populations on the average remain busy—with some groups becoming busier while other groups are condemned to forced leisure.

The average man's gain in leisure has been exaggerated by elective comparison of gross daily or weekly averages in working hours with those of the "take off" period of rapid economic growth in England, France, and America—a time of blood-curdling schedules and conditions. Estimates of annual and lifetime leisure and comparisons with earlier times suggest a different picture. The skilled urban worker has now achieved the position of his 13th century counterpart, whose long workday, seasonally varied, was offset by many holidays, rest periods, and long vacations; annual hours of work now, as then, remain in the range of 1,900 to 2,500.

2

Income Versus Leisure.

The upper strata have lost out. Even though their work-lives are shorter and vacations longer than those of lower strata, these men work many hours, week after week—sometimes reaching a truly startling lifetime total. Top leaders in political and economic life, in the military establishment, education, welfare, aesthetics, and entertainment show a marked preference for income over leisure.

How about women—who, after all, have the most apparent choice in the matter? Economic growth everywhere brings more women into the nonagricultural labor force. This, of course, excludes the "work" of home and family. It seems plain that emancipation, while it has released women for the job market, has not to any equal extent released them from housewifery. Studies of the weekly round of women report a range of averages of 50 to 80 hours a week in housework, child care, and paid labor. If a woman takes a job today, she has to figure on adding her work-week to a 40- or 50-hour homemaking minimum, unless she can afford and obtain a maid.

3

Leisure Stricken or Leisure Oriented.

On balance, the female workweek may be as long as it was a century ago, while pace-setting elites, the main carriers of cultural traditions and values, have likely increased their time at work. The uneven distribution of work among those working and the incidence of involuntary retirement and unemployment suggest that men who have gained most leisure need and want more work. The "leisure stricken" are not replacing the poverty stricken; the two are becoming one.

In short, I disagree with those social critics who hold that modern society is leisure-oriented; that leisure must now take up the slack caused by the disruption of the job market in the new era of cybernation or by the new alienation of modern work; that we will have to break the once-tight relationship between income and employment or rewards and type of work; that the typical man once had a stable career, but now, with greatly accelerated technological change, he does not or will not.

If the arguments of the students of the "triple revolution" merely imply that, for economic and humanitarian reasons, there should be a floor of income below which no family should be allowed to fall, I enthusiastically agree. If they imply that we are becoming a leisure-oriented society, quickly moving toward the day when the average citizen has no useful work to do, and we therefore must find substitutes for work, I doubt it. We need to bend our abundance to great purposes, pay people for work that needs doing—create jobs, part-time and full, that will harness the energies and channel the idealism and enthusiasm of millions of men, women, and young people. Even for the long run of 20 years, it still makes sense to talk about education, vocational training, and public policy as they relate to jobs, job markets, and careers.

CHAPTER 29

Art and Culture in the Cybernetic Age

by Harley Parker

Professor Harley Parker has long been associated with Marshall McLuhan at the Center of Culture and Technology at the University of Toronto and is co-author with Dr. McLuhan of "Through the Vanishing Point", and designer of *Counterblast* also by Dr. McLuhan. He has also been Associate Professor, Albert Schweitzer Chair of Humanities at Fordham University.

1

THIS ARTICLE deliberately avoids any critical analysis of the works of contemporary artists, for, as I shall point out, the function of the critic may be largely irrelevant today. Probing the environment and illuminating its capacity to restructure sensory response may give the reader an opportunity to conceive of the world of art as more than an exercise in esthetics. Ezra Pound has stated that, "the artists are the antennae of the race". It is in this sense that creative activity is a powerful factor in social change. However, let us not construe this to mean that art is propaganda inasmuch as they are always culturally structured and therefore disseminate and plead for cultural attitudes.

On March 17, 1968, there appeared in the New York Times as interview with John Cage, the composer. He is quoted as saying:

"Do you know, for instance, any criticism now which you can use? I find myself more and more questioning the professional function of the critic. I don't find what they have to say is interesting. What they do doesn't seem to change what I do. What artists do changes what I do." This present article affirms that art appreciation today, like art itself, is concerned with process and not with package. Further, the arts now, and indeed the whole of life, demand involvement. The total immersion which is so much a part of today is antithetic to dispassionate survey-the sine qua non of all criticism.

For five hundred years the preoccupation of the western world has been with the percept of visual order, of spaces that are uniform, continuous, and therefore rational. This resulted in an alienation from the "irrational" subconscious life. Today, with the waning of the power of the visual bias in our age of electric immediacy and participation, Western man is, in the arts, increasingly motivated toward involvement with all-encompassing cosmic forces.

The primitive artist when he makes a mask does not think of it as a work of art. He regards it as an image controlling the cosmic forces. It is a magical object which does not represent anything. It is. Susan Sontag was recently quoted in the New York Times, "the basic unit for contemporary art is not the idea but the analysis and extension of sensations". This is, in one sense, a reversal of the intent of the primitive image maker. Instead of directing his efforts to the control of outer cosmic forces Susan Sontag implies that the contemporary artist turns inward to control the microcosmic forces within the psyche. Nevertheless, in the terms of E. H. Gombrich, it is a stress on making, not on matching, and is therefore allied to the primitive mode. However, it is the immediacy inherent in our electronic extensions which creates the quality of introspective involvement reflected in contemporary arts.

2

Today, when our sentient antennae, extended by electronic technology, are capable of probing all the crags and crannies, both psychological and geographical, of our world; when computers make the storage of data by humans practically obsolete; when automation eliminates the need for Western man to spend his time on the unimaginative, routine tasks of this world, the only area left unviolated by our technology is that of creativity. And it is only in the creative act that the power of the preconscious is a meaningful force. Our recent insights into the power of the preconscious, in both the creation and perception of art, indicate that the subliminal is indeed a strong force in psychic reorganization. For, contrary to the conscious perception of visually based Western man, the subliminal utilizes all the senses in balanced interaction. It is this injection of the preconscious into our awareness which has, in part, given rise to the so-called irrational works of art. To the usual literate man (not the artist) such irrationality is anathema, for it seems to attack the very structure of civilized living. And indeed it does, if we equate civilization with literacy. An obvious manifestation of the rise of the irrational is the current attitude of the teenagers. Dialogue with adults seems to be impossible, for the younger generation has a different sensory orientation from the adult. The mature mind, structured as it has been, by the linear organization inherent in typographic literacy finds it impossible to deal with the child or the artist who "dig" the patterns of simultaneous communication. Inasmuch as the child today has little sense of perspective and is therefore not goal oriented, the adult regards him as illogical. Logical positions have for two thousand years been equated with progression of thought on a single line with connections between each point. Any deviation from this is regarded as illogical even though it is quite obvious that life as we live it today increasingly bears little relationship to this arbitrary imposition of a mode of thought legislated by the medium of writing.

It is the contention here that visual realism runs parallel to the development of phonetic literacy. Except for an isolated instance in the reign of Akhenaton in Egypt when there was a stress on phoneticism probably derived from the first alphabet containing phonetic characters (Linear B from Cnossus), realistic art never became officially or even corporately accepted until the cultural vitalization of Greece. This was coincident with the Greek interest in and development of the

alphabet derived from the Phonecians. Realism developed
further in the psychological portraits of the Romans, tended
to wane in the Middle Ages, and came into full power when
typographic printing became pervasive.

The action in a painting concerned with the illusion of
three-dimensional images on a two-dimensional plane takes
place in a cul de sac, in an artifically contrived moment of
time which is seen from a single point of view. Such a percept
is only possible when the sense of sight is highly preferred
over the other senses. For it is only the visual that can connect
spaces or can permit time to be conceived as a line capable
of being infinitely fragmented. Many historians have pointed
out that, to the medieval man, time was multi-layered. Many
times and spaces existed concurrently.

3

With the speed-up of information flow via electronics,
what we call logical, i.e. visual, organization becomes obsolete. Kenneth Boulding, the economist, has pointed out
that the educational system is trying to cope with "operation
overload". There is too much data coming into the system.
A proposed answer to this which bears relevance to the arts
is pattern recognition. This is a mosaic approach which, however, is too often thought of simply as multiple points of
view. While this is certainly a salient aspect of the mosaic, we
must think of it as simultaneous insights into a total pattern.
For there is a great difference between many points of view
perceived in a linear or Cartesian time sequence and the
simultaneity of perception inherent in the mosaic.

The use of a pattern approach automatically removes us
from verisimilitude as we understand it through the eye. In
"Through the Vanishing Point" [1], which I wrote with Mar-

[1] "Through the Vanishing Point", McLuhan and Parker. Harper and Row,
New York, 1968.

shall McLuhan, great stress is laid upon the difference between iconic and illustrative art. In tribal cultures which stress
corporate indivisibility, the iconic, with emphasis on the
tactile-kinetic, will be the mode of art. In such societies there
is no possibility of separation from the visual bias which
allows for detachment with its concomitant of private specialism. The individual genius in his ivory tower, objectively
surveying the scene is no longer possible. He now wears the
corporate mask of his audience as he dances to the tribal
drums. All this has been the result of a reorchestration of
sensibility. We have moved from the intensely visual stance
of Western civilization to a tactile bias. Tactility encompasses
all the senses; it is the mother of the senses. (In the development of the human foetus the initial manifestation of
sensory life is wholly tactile. From this ganglion, sensitive
to touch alone, eventually come all the other specialized sensory receptors.)

> Seeing is believing
> but to touch is the word of God.

The iconic mosaic created by electric instantaneity is a
move away from visual verisimilitude. If we recognize the
partial hiatus of the Middle Ages, it is a move away from a
consistent development stretching over two thousand years.
This augurs well for our age, for any culture which feeds
only on its direct antecedents is dying. Periods of great artistic activity occur when one culture is abraded against
another. The Renaissance jumped over its direct antecedent
the Medieval, to Greece and Rome. We today leapfrog over
the Renaissance to the Middle Ages, over the Greeks and
Romans to the primitives. This is not to say, however, that
the arts of our developing post-literate culture bear direct re-
semblance to those of the primitives or the artists of the Middle Ages. The similarity lies in the return to involvement of

the total sensory life with a definite bias toward the tactile-kinetic.

Parallel to the waning of visual verisimilitude in the arts is the fact that the ten greatest scientific discoveries of the last forty years cannot be seen. They have occurred in areas of electronics, atomic physics or medicine which are below the level of perception even with the aid of an electron microscope. Of course, the swing away from the bias of the visual places most of the middle-aged and older generations in a state of total bewilderment unaleviated by the obfuscations of many critics. These last too often attempt to place contemporary works within the old visual format, or else they postulate a new world without recognizing that changing sensory modalities are at the root of the new dynamic.

4

Today's world can only be successfully interpreted with the use of the total sensorium in balanced interaction and with the logic of a total sensory response. But one asks: what is logic inherent in total sensory involvement? Alex Leighton, the sociologist, commented that, "to the blind all things are sudden". In other words, the blind man walking through the world, cut off from our still visually biased culture, finds his sensory responses structured in a manner which is very familiar to the contemporary artist. Interestingly the artists' alienation from the visual is demonstrated by their increasing interest in the interval, which is so much a part of the art of the Orient. In "The Book of Tea" [2] Kakuzo Okakura uses the metaphor of the vacuum:

"Only in vacuum lay the true essential."

2 "The Book of Tea", Kakuzo Okakura. Tokyo, Kenkyusha.

The reality of a room, for instance, was to be found in the vacant space enclosed by the roof and walls, not in the roof and walls themselves. The usefulness of a water pitcher dwelt in the emptiness where water might be put, not in the form of the pitcher or the material of which it was made. Vacuum is all potent because all containing. In vacuum alone motion becomes possible. One who could make of himself a vacuum into which others might freely enter would become master of all situations. John Cage, the musician, sensitively aware of the power of the interval, has written a book called "Silence".[3] The pregnant interval can be thought of as the closure to the tangible tactile experience. In the past, the bias of the visual tended to eliminate the power of the interval. For, to the sighted man nothing is sudden—everything is connected. The stress on the eye which was so much a part of man's life from the fifteenth to the middle of the nineteenth century expressed itself in perspective, the ability to look back upon the past and to speculate about the future. The logic of the senses in balanced interplay, as these are brought into action by electronic media, is involvement and involvement is now.

The eye with its scalpel-like incisiveness, its ability to dissect and fragment, is in direct opposition to the other senses which tend to be diffuse and in low definition. The stress on the eye leads to the possibility of uninvolved perception. For example, in a high definition photograph or painting (a great deal of correspondence to visual reality) it is not necessary for imaginative or mnemonic closure to take place. There is sufficient information for the depicted objects to be labelled and pigeonholed and, in effect, dismissed. Input through senses other than the eye is comparatively low in definition so that closure is demanded. If one wishes to understand the sensory structure inherent in an artifact, look for

3 "Silence", John Cage. Wesleyan University Press, Middletown, Connecticut, 1961.

what is left out, for that will be filled in by memory or the imagination. The recipient mind will be involved in that specific area.

To elaborate on this, Wilhelm Ostwald, the Nobel prize winning physicist and color theoretician of the late nineteenth and early twentieth century, has stated that in color all experience is one hundred percent. We cannot have less than a total sensory response. It can be noted that we are constantly feeding in to any experience varieties of mnemonic data which serve to provide a subjective completion so that experience can be total. In other words, the sensory life is in a constant state of reorchestration. Ostwald said it was as if one had a test tube full of color; if one wished to add another color it could only be done at the expense of the original ingredients. In the same way, any stepping up of one sense can only be done at the expense of another. So, in painting, for example, if the tactile quality is stressed it will always be at the expense of the purely visual image. The traditional icon is an excellent example of exactly this process. The heavy stress on outline coupled to extensive patterning is the hallmark of the tactile bias. This is in direct opposition to the concepts of perspective, foreshortening and chiaroscuro, and in fact to the whole visual orientation. While it is true that one observes paintings through the eye, the real sensory implication of any painting is dependent upon the bias of the painter. The traditional icons are largely tactile and kinetic, and the visual image is so designed as to call upon the observer to place himself in the sensory stance of the creator.

5

The very speed of our communication systems structure the human mind in such a way as to make it particularly sympathetic to the iconic or mosaic approach. At high speeds, patterns become more obvious, and as I have pointed out earlier, pattern recognition is probably the only formula for survival in our world of overpowering overload. On the other hand, in the film, "Dream of the Wild Horses" [4] it becomes apparent that slowing down also moves the image toward iconography. This is apparent in any slow-motion picture. "Dream of the Wild Horses" was chosen because it appears to be the most forceful demonstration of this principle. The slowness of movement eases the images of the great brutes into a world of fantasy and myth. In short, it would seem that any depiction which interferes with the culturally structured normal apprehension of time over images into the iconic—the mythic. In the same way any change from the perceptual norm in the depiction of spaces has the same tendency. The hallucinogenic drugs have this power to distort both time and space, to make the user see the environment in iconic rather than purely illustrative terms. It may be this very factor which makes these drugs so attractive to the young who have little taste for the purely illustrative but feel most profoundly the relevance of iconic perception.

Along with the speed of communication, we have acceleration of change and this makes meaningful perception of our environments most crucial. People do not see the environment in which they live; they only see the content—and this is merely the last environment which in the past was not seen. Lyndon Johnson sadly announced that the Ship of State had entered troubled waters. A Republican replied that of course the waters looked troubled: the President was in the stern looking at the wake. This, however, is the state in which all Western men find themselves. As Marshall McLuhan has pointed out, all, or almost all, men see through a rear-view mirror. This is to say that man is constantly estrapolating the

[4] "Dream of the Wild Horses" (film), Denys Colomb de Caunant.

past into the present under the illusion that he is looking at the future. The immediate environment in terms of its structural impact is totally unperceived.

Although the quality of being unaware of the environment has been common to all men in all societies, it has been exaggerated by literacy. This is the legacy of typographic technology, for it imposes an arbitrary linear, visual form upon the society which actually lives multidimensionally. While phonetic literacy results in an attitude of detachment from events, this is not synonymous with perception. With a balanced sensory intake we closely approach the state of tribal man—total involvement. Perception lies in the act of living fully. Herein lies the meaning of meaning. We may be approaching a time when the marriage of involvement to the legacy of detachment will allow us to enter our brave new world with a finger on the control button.

6

There can be little question that the new corporate stance as manifested by the tribal "hippie", in fact by a large number of our teenagers, more or less eliminates those factors of intense individualism which have been observed for the last five hundred years. The youngster of today is totally involved. This is not to say that there is no possibility of private existence but rather that the individual cannot envision any meaningful existence separate from his tribe. To give an example, the African schizophrenic moves to action while his European counterpart moves to the privacy of hallucination. The African native, even in his madness, cannot conceive of any separation from his tribe. He lives a corporate existence.

As I have pointed out earlier, one of the salient factors in the restructuring of human sensibility is automation. Buckminster Fuller, in a recent talk, pointed out that birth itself is a remarkable example of automation: "we merely push a few buttons". While people are generally unaware of the self as automated, the contemporary creative individual has become aware of his awareness. This is a commentary on his ability to plug into the most responsive and sentient computer of them all.

Finally the question arises: are we moving toward a renaissance of the mythic or toward a continuing development of the hallucinatory factors inherent in individualism? (After all, in Greek, the word "idiot" means a private person.) Individualism is synonymous with specialism, fragmentation, and privacy or alienation from the society. These are the building blocks of the hallucinatory state.

While perched on the brink of what the literate man often regards as anarchy, the human spirit is actually moving toward the great mythic contours which will ultimately delineate a new and integral man, profound in his corporate arts.

CHAPTER 30

The Community for Human Development

by D. McCormack Smyth

D. McCormack Smyth has been Dean of Atkinson College, York University, Toronto since the University first opened. He is also Vice-Chairman of the Board of Regents for Community Colleges in the Province of Ontario. This article has been adapted from his keynote address to a special meeting organized by the Ontario Association for Continuing Education to consider the need for a Metropolitan Toronto plan for human development. His reflections might be applicable to any metropolitan area.

1

THERE IS WIDESPREAD concern in our time that despite the billions of dollars we are investing in formal education and other state supported social services, these services are not contributing to the extent they should to the improvement of the quality of our individual lives, nor to the quality of the common life we share. Instead of experiencing human advancement to the degree predicted by the supporters of the doctrine of the inevitability of progress, we are now realizing that the premonitions of long run disaster, outlined by men like Alexis de Toqueville, George Simmel and others, were more accurate than we would have wished.

In human life, there should be a close relationship between our formal education, our character, our conduct and the resultant conditions of our individual and collective life. Unfortunately, however, too often when we discuss the present impact and desirable directions for the reform of systems of learning we are concerned neither with the character, conduct and conditions of individual life, nor with our community life. Rather we are concerned too exclusively with the improvement of techniques or the development of some particular talent or desirable skill.

There is, of course, urgent need for co-ordinated action in fields other than human development. I need make only a single reference to indicate the extent and critical nature of the problem in one area. It has been estimated that one automobile consumes well over 1,000 times as much oxygen as does an individual. To carry off the exhaust gases and dilute them to harmless concentrations, requires from five to ten million times as much air as does the driver. The end result is obvious, if the spread in the use of internal combustion engines continues at its present rate, and forests continue to be destroyed. A time may soon come when there is simply not enough natural uncontaminated air to support life.

If we are to solve some of these enormous problems, each of us must become aware of the extent to which we as individuals are contributing to these frightening conditions. We must learn how we, as individuals, can use our resources of mind, spirit, and thoughtful action to reduce, rather than to increase, these major social problems. Then we must begin to utilize our individual and collective resources to reduce and hopefully eliminate these problems and simultaneously to create new types of human communities.

2

Thus I suggest that our first objective should be to identify what kind of a community we would like twenty years from now. Then we must decide on those positive steps which must be taken so that we will achieve our objectives. Naturally there would be a host of problems to be resolved. However, I suggest that we clearly have the resources to solve the problems. What we require is the will to solve them. Our objective surely must be to ensure that the community develops as a community of humane human beings for human beings, ruled according to principles for human development. In short, our physical planning must be rooted in the central abilities, shortcomings and needs of human beings and their social groups. Physical plans must reflect the felt needs and be designed to aid in the development of human beings. We must ask of every planning proposal, "How will this affect the human development of individual citizens physically, emotionally, spiritually and financially? " In place of a fumbling 'ad-hocracy'—government based on an unrelated series of ad hoc plans and decisions—and an increasingly critical democracy torn by competing interests, we need a system of government based on the implementation of proven principles for human growth and development. Here is not the place and now is not the time to discuss how such a form of government should develop and the systems whereby it would be operative. It will be sufficient to say that it would not be government by the mob—government by opinion which reflects the mindless activism of our age. It would be government based on enlightened human knowledge of the strength and weaknesses of individuals and groups, expressed through new social institutions and groupings and a view of education and other means of human development as processes designed to facilitate the growth of human awareness, consciousness, humane self-direction and cooperative action.

In addition to education designed to assist individuals in a world of competition, we need education for cooperation. We need education not only that we may acquire, but that we may share, and not only that we may act, but that we may also contemplate. Above all, we need to remind ourselves constantly that the primary purposes of education should be to enable us to act properly, to live fully to help others live and constantly to seek right knowledge—knowledge of our own ignorance and how to remedy it.

The notion that we can learn enough in the first two decades of our life to last us for all the remaining years is today as preposterous as the thought that a jetliner can remain aloft after all its fuel has been exhausted. Learning that lasts and is of value is the result of continuing conscious effort on the part of the learner to leave the world better off than he found it.

Our central need is to identify our strategic problems, to develop the will to use our accumulated knowledge to solve these problems—and then to solve them.

One of the main impediments to solving social problems—to creative change—is that we are locked into institutional patterns and social systems which make it difficult to use our knowledge and abilities in strategic situations, and at the particular times it should be used, so that human growth and development may be optimized. It has been suggested that those "who know" never get together "to sum up and to integrate" for human purposes what they know. And those who act, often don't know what is really in the interests of individuals and society on a continuing basis.

3

Thus the second item on our agenda should be to develop an inventory of our knowledge and agree on how our knowledge about our community in its totality can be brought to bear on problems, so that our government and our planning may facilitate the development of a human community. If we are to develop such a plan we must recognize the inadequacy of ad-hoc approaches to human growth and development in our pluralistic society.

Take time to ask yourselves whenever you are involved in contributing to educational costs, "What is the economic and social rationale behind the way in which these public funds are invested".

There is an equally and perhaps even more important question—namely "What is the effect on human growth and development of individuals and groups of individuals of the way in which we conduct our formal programmes of education". Briefly, I believe the following criticisms can be made of educational systems generally:

(a) Present patterns of education lack integration and are excessively terminal in relation to individual and social needs in our time of radical change.

(b) Formal systems of education are too exclusively concerned with the accumulation of factual knowledge, whereas they should give more attention to providing assistance to help people learn how to learn continually, how to use the experiences of life as learning situations, how to develop and use one's own resources, and how to act humanely.

(c) Formal education systems must increasingly be oriented to the individual and his need for continuing development rather than oriented to knowledge, its classification and abstraction. Individuals are the ends and knowledge is the means of human development. Too often the opposite view is taken.

(d) The formal educational system today is particularly inadequate in that far too many adults in places of central responsibility—to say nothing of young people who, on leaving school or college and moving into the affairs of the world—do not know

—that their knowledge and approaches to learning are inadequate;

—that they are devoid of the abilities required for continuing voluntary self-education;

—that they are without the motivation required to continually improve their own awareness and consciousness.

4

My conclusion is that the primary candidates for education in the present and in the future are and will increasingly be adults. Our present haphazard non-integrated, largely financial and efficiency-dominated programmes for adult learning which involve enormous expenditures and considerable duplication must be gradually replaced by a whole new approach to human growth and development through education. A whole new human and group oriented approach for conscious life-long learning and service must be developed, implemented and modified according to changing needs.

CHAPTER 31

Matching the Old and Making the New

by Barrington Nevitt

Barrington Nevitt is a consultant on Innovations and Management Training for the Ontario Development Corporation and is a close associate of Marshall McLuhan through the Institute of Culture and Technology. He is a fellow of the Institute of Electrical Engineers in Great Britain, the American Association for the Advancement of Science and many other professional associations. He has served as consultant to RCA International in New York and Ericsson Telephone Company, Stockholm, Sweden and Public Utilities projects in Caracus and Rio de Janeiro, Brazil.

1

WE ARE BORN in the "age of speed-up". As we move from open to closed societies, from jobs to roles, change itself is taking over from stability as our chief concern. While mini-groups are sprouting, maxi-combinations are also growing. Everywhere, "software" processes of learning, and for communicating with computers and people, are demanding more and more of our energies, while production of "hardware" things requires less and less. New knowledge-making is replacing old experience-matching no longer able to keep pace with change. There is urgent need to explore and to discover the present by improving our probes. But in order to cope with still more rapid changes of the future, we must also learn quicker means of acticipating their undesired effects, faster ways of gaining new knowledge of their present causes, so that we may control them now—before it is too late. "Feed-forward" for anticipating the effects of change must supplement "feedback", which can only lead to stability, or to breakdown, but never to novelty.

We are transforming our industrial man-made environment so that not only change, but information itself, is now becoming environmental in our world of communication media operating everywhere, all-at-once, all of the time. The knowledge industries—research, education, and government —have become our main occupations. We are now entering the age when cybernation can match any hardware product, or software information, that computers can store and we might need; these are jobs that cybernation can do better than man. This advancing technology gives us fresh opportunities to play uniquely human roles in seeking the new knowledge that only man can make. It also creates new problems that only man can deal with.

The advent of space-craft has sharpened our awareness of the physical, psychic, and social processes involved in transforming ourselves through our total environment, through extensions of our own technologies, to increase our potential powers. As Marshall McLuhan demonstrates,[1] until our "age of speed-up", previous slowly changing environments always total, also remained invisible. There were no direct means of perceiving and understanding one's own time except in terms of the preceeding visible age. People looked to the past for guidance. Human choice was limited—matching the old through experience rather than making the new by discovery.

We are beginning to understand how communication with people differs qualitatively from communication with computers. Both use telecommunication techniques which depend upon converting inputs into electrical signals, for transmission through measurable noise to distant terminals, that will match inputs to outputs with predictable error. Cybernation also involves similar information coding by other than electrical means. Nevertheless, we begin by defining our communication or control problems, in terms of our medium, in the unambiguous categories and relationships of current technology. Whether our computers or telecommunications involve digits or analogues, their functions are reduced to an information content that is expressible in the one-to-one correspondence of "bits", the ultimate information atoms— single YES or *NOT* YES choices. Given enough time and

[1] *Understanding Media,* Marshall McLuhan, McGraw Hill, New York, 1964.

resources, systems engineers can then provide the program and the "Black Boxes" that will solve these problems for us.

Indeed, there are some who claim, as Herbert Anschutz does, in a recent symposium on *Purposive Systems* [2] that any restrictions existing for machines also exist for human brains. In the same symposium, however, Yehoshua Bar-Hillel also maintains that we must remain satisfied with rigidly defined, relatively simple, "languagettes"—mini-languages—as means of communicating between ourselves and computers. We also know from Edward T. Hall's *Silent Language* [3] that human silences as well as human utterances, are full of meaning dependent on their linguistic co-text (its resonant implications and redundancies) as well as their context (social customs—one man's compliment is another's insult). Human communication is a constantly changing "system". We cannot reduce it to purely linguistic terms, nor to any other rigid scheme of classification. Only machines and computer languages communicate by attempting to match known inputs to programmed outputs. Their representation is replica. This is their basic strength. It also limits their ultimate potential.

People communicate with each other not merely by matching but by remaking all-together and all-at-once, all the physical, psychic, and social components entering into their entire process of communication, including the effects of their total environments, both natural and man-made. Human sensory responses are never the same as human sensory inputs. Their representation is neither reflection nor replica. The human mind makes its own message in its own way, depending upon its entire previous history, as well as its present environment. This is no linear, step-by-step, one-at-a-time, chain of connecting causes and effects. It is a process where everything goes on simultaneously. It creates resonances, patterns

[2] *Pusposive Systems,* Spartan Books, New York, 1968.
[3] *Silent Language,* Edward T. Hall, Premier Books, New York, 1965.

of awareness, that we can learn to recognize by starting with the responses, by making an inventory of the observed effects, physical, psychic, and social. Such process patterns point to their own causes, independently of our personal preferences and preconceptions. In this approach, the recognizing of process patterns replaces the conceptualizing of causal connections. We become aware and can get rid of our cultural preconceptions by interfacing with, by rubbing against, other cultures.

My article, *Communication with People through Media*[4] illustrates by "McLuhan Diagrams" the psychic and social effects of speech, and of alphabet writing, as new technologies in preliterature human societies. Eric Havelock's *Preface to Plato*[5] shows more dramatically the consequences —both the services and the dis-services—engendered by writing, as it displaced memorizing in the educational establishment of ancient Greece. We do not have to be literate in order to feel the effects of book dominance, anymore than we need to watch TV in order to feel its consequences. They resonate at every level of human activity. They transform our total environment. They remake us.

Sensory inputs through our technological extensions—the communication media—induce the percepts that make our ideas, categories, concepts, and multi-sensory images of the external world. From these concepts we develop our mental armory of approaches, ideologies, and Utopias. In *The New Utopians*,[6] Robert Boguslaw discusses computerdom's latest versions. We seek to match their similarities with every new percept of the external world, and we tend to ignore the inconvenient differences. Nevertheless, we learn our mother-

[4] *Communication with People through Media,* The Northern Electric Company Labs., Ottawa, Ontario, 1968.

[5] *Preface to Plato,* Eric Havelock, Harvard Univ. Press, Cambridge, Mass., 1963.

[6] *The New Utopians,* Robert Boguslaw, Prentice-Hall, Englewood Cliffs, N.J., 1955.

tongues as children by total immersion—no schools, no specialists, no failures—in the manner of pre-literate oral-aural societies. In literature societies, however, we continue to refine these languages through "disciplines"—humanities and sciences—structured alike by the printed word; now further sharpened by "general systems" and mathematical models, that we seek ultimately to reduce to the "bit" language—the YES or *NOT* YES choices—of decision-making and information theories. These are the hidden assumptions, the preconceptions, the analytical foundations, the ultimate "bits" that underlie our industrial civilization. They also bias us, unless we learn to protect ourselves from the consequences by understanding their causes.

Corresponding to "homeostatis", the tendency toward stability, Duane Schultz [7] has shown that the human brain also exhibits a tendency toward "sonsoristasis", whereby its sensory activity tends to remain constant under given physiological conditions. For an increase in sensory impact of one kind, (say, the visual), we can thus predict a corresponding reduction in the sensory responses of other kinds, (say, the audile or tactile). "Sensory closure" is the process of making up in the sensory responses for what is lacking in the sensory inputs. It also changes our conscious awareness —the patterns of total sensory interplay—by changing the relationships of our sensory activities to each other. It implies—"hearing with the eye and seeing with the ear". And E. H. Gombrich [8] discusses how:

> "*Synesthesia,* the splashing over of impressions from one sense modality to another, is a fact to which all languages testify—from sight to sound and from sound to sight we speak of 'loud' colours and 'bright' sounds, and everyone knows what we mean. Nor are the ear and the

[7] *Sensory Restriction,* Duane Schultz, Academic Press, New York, 1965.
[8] *Art and Illusion,* E. H. Gombrich, Pantheon Books, New York, 1960.

322 / THIS CYBERNETIC AGE

eye the only senses that are thus converging on a common centre. There is touch in such terms as 'velvety voice' and 'cold' light, taste with 'sweet harmonies' of colours or sounds. . . ."

Gombrich thus confirms through the history of art that the meaning of words is what they do—what they make; it is not merely what they say—what they match, their labels.

Poets know how to use words as probes for exploration to create poetic vision, not merely as packages defined and categorized for dictionaries, scientific jargons, or computers. As James Joyce in *Finnegans Wake* [6] expressed it, to "love thy label as thyself" is the bias of industrial man. Machines and computers, so far, can only take data—the given "labels"—convert, program, connect, or match them to other data stored in computer memories. They explore the consequences of given premises by YES-OR-NO logic, in the one-to-one correspondences of analogues, or of digital "bits". They are complex cliches—things in daily use—with immense potential for expanding our mental powers. Human brains, however, take the same data and make them into "facts" by mental processing. They combine the new and the old to make fresh discoveries, to create novelty. They can violate the barriers of fixed categories and change the rules of programming consciously, to establish new process patterns of physical, psychic, and social resonances with their total environment. Human brains can anticipate the effects of future processes by understanding their present causes, through recognizing and projecting their dynamic patterns of development. This is human freedom. Any attempt to explain or to reduce human brains to categories of language or to mere automata composed of engineers' "Black Boxes", will inevitably break down. Human brains are systems of physical

9 *Finnegans Wake,* James Joyce, Viking Press, New York, 1968.

and psychic resonance processes—like chemical valency bonds—in constantly changing patterns of interplay with their entire environment.

Our breakthrough will not be merely to simulate, to imitate, to match intelligence and consciousness, but actually to make them. We can choose our materials to suit our needs and techniques. To do this, however, we must first learn how the actual world of closed* systems—heterarchies of resonating processes "on the make"—differs from the mental world of open* systems—hierarchies of connected ideas "on the match". We must learn how to make "White Boxes" that perceive the world directly without the media that destroy the processes. We must learn to cope with both matching the old by abstracting concepts, and making the new by direct perception—so must "White Boxes".

In *Through the Vanishing Point* [10], Marshall McLuhan and Harley Parker show how the history of painting and poetry, among pre-literate tribes and in literate industrial societies, provide the process patterns we need for breakthroughs. Pre-literate men lived in tribal mini-worlds of oral-aural communication, where everything happens all-at-once all-the-time, from all directions. This is the "acoustic space" structure that characterizes all closed systems—no centers and no margins, no points-of-view, but only resonating processes that *make* their own patterns, their own space, and their own times simultaneously. A biological system also

* In this discussion, an "open system" is one to which new components may be added (or from which items may be deleted) without affecting the nature of the system. By contrast, the "closed system" reacts *in toto* to each and every addition or deletion, as well as to even the slightest internal re-structuring. There is "a place for everything" in the open system, where the component's identity is the determining criterion. This is of little value in the closed system, wherein the delicate balance of interrelationships is paramount.

[10] *Through the Vanishing Point: Space in Poetry and in Painting*, by H.M. McLuhan and Harley Parker, Harper and Row, New York, 1968.

exemplifies "acoustic space" since every addition or subtraction changes its entire structure, transforms its *resonances,* while reshaping whatever is added.

In print-oriented industrial society, men live in highly visual hierarchies, where things are judged by appearances— everything in its proper place, and at its proper time, each man with his own "ideas" and private point of view. This is the "visual space" structure characterizing all open systems —each center with its margins, its definite limits, its clear-cut connections, to be *matched* with any others, one at a time. A mechanical system also illustrates "visual space", since any addition of mechanical elements to it merely changes its *connections* without transforming it qualitatively.

In today's post-literate, multi-media, electronic environment, as we revert to "acoustic space", we are witnessing the psychic and social consequences, the manifold clashes with previously dominant "visual space" structures, which are here for all to feel. But we are also approaching the situation where it will be possible to deal with the total environment as a "work of art". We can now organize our information for both matching and making—in the "visual space" pattern for retrieval, and in the "acoustic space" pattern for discovery.

We can also recognize that both the multiplication of things and the speed-up of processes may transform "visual" to "acoustic" patterns: particles become fields, things become processes, and matching becomes making. Indeed if we push any process far enough we get reversal—the "chiasmus" pattern: gas becomes solid, virtue becomes vice, sense becomes nonsense, and order becomes ordure. Quantitative change thus induces qualitative transformation. If the process continues, it can lead to re-reversals to retransformations—the "phoenix" pattern. We observe it in today's processes of centralization, decentralization, and recentralization of human organization, in the growth of both "minis" and "maxis".

In the process of innovation, as new products and technologies replace the old, they reveal the *cliché-to-archetype pattern* of development. While still in the "novelty" stage, every innovation acts as an abrasive counter-environment to the prevailing environment. This abrasion makes both environments visible until the new archetype becomes pervasive and a new cliché in *its* turn. This process both transforms and displaces the older, pre-innovation environment; it creates a new environment which also becomes invisible as such until it too is transformed by yet another innovation. The new cliché junks the old by displacement while simultaneously converting it into the makings of fresh archetypes. This junk is added to the cultural "midden-heap" and becomes a fresh artistic resource: the old cliché is regenerated in fresh archetypal forms as "found art", as pastime, and as a component of new art objects. These new archetypes generate nostalgia for other, similarly-structured cultural antiques, which then find their way into various forms of "modern art", or into museums and private collections. Innovation thus dredges up the long-forgotten past while continuing to generate unperceived new needs. For necessity is the child of invention. Marshall McLuhan and Wilfrid Watson discuss a rich variety of examples in *From Cliche to Archetype*.[11]

Such patterning occurs far more rapidly with "software" information than with "hardware" products. As McLuhan suggests, "consciousness" itself may well be the speedup effect of a "cliche-to-archetype" process. It would be a process whereby the brain, while constantly forming archetypal "modules"— mini-groupings of information, would convert them by instantaneous use into cliches, immediately junked, and replaced by new ones. Theilhard de Chardin's "noosphere" of "cosmic consciousness" is also conceivable in these terms.

When any new and faster process envelopes some old but slower one, we can witness the "rim-spin" pattern. The faster

11 *From Cliche to Archetype,* Marshall McLuhan and Wilfred Watson, Viking Press, New York, scheduled for publication 1969.

process erodes the slower one, by going around it, and eventually replacing it in the "cliche-to-archetype" pattern. We know that telephone conversation goes around the slower exchange of written correspondence. This faster medium of communications makes obsolete the old organization chart, based on written orders and lines of command; it replaces pyramids with task forces, and "positions of power" with "roles of competence". If we examine current ideologies, or long-term plans, to see how they deal with the multiple "rim-spins" involved in physical, psychic, and social processes while our total environment changes, we can foresee where their development patterns would lead. We can predict potential breakdowns, and convert them to actual breakthroughs, by replacing old experience based on established concepts, with new knowledge gained through pattern recognition.

In the physical sciences, we still continue to "explain", and to extrapolate our measurements, either in "visual space" structure or blindly by mathematical "formalism". We match "properties" to "elementary particles" and discuss concepts for an "expanding" or a "contracting" galactic universe. But we are still unable to "explain" the nature either of "gravity", that holds our star systems together, or to "empty" space, that propogates light and other radiant energy between them. We remain ensnared in the earlier metaphors of "normal" science. Our urgent need is to probe the possibilities of "imploding" universes, perhaps much vaster, in patterns of "acoustic" resonance. These make their own "spaces" and "times", not as separate "factors" but as process relationships.

Likewise in the "social disciplines", we are prevented by the concepts of prevailing ideologies, always based on past experience with "visual" bias, from coming to grips, by direct perception, with actual happenings. We look for "plots" and "counterplots", for "checks" and "balances", for "responses" to "stimuli", to presumed "causes" of observed "symptoms", while totally ignoring the hidden environment that makes just those effects and no others possible. In the "age of speedup" we are living in an "acoustic space" created by all the communication media operating ceaslessly, everywhere. This global man-made environment envelopes and transforms all other human activities, physical, psychic, and social. Who could contrive or conspire to produce the resonance of daily events revealed by the news headlines? Neither general systems, nor ideological concepts, but only pattern recognition by direct perception, is adequate for navigating a changing environment of change itself.

During the nineteenth century, "reality" was something to measure by some standard, or norm, to match against. Machines, with their magnitudes of forces, frictions, masses, powers, and with their rigid connections, gave rise to the dominant metaphors. They were the guides to thinking, whether about "missing links" or about "manipulating" people, or about human "progress". It was the age of the mechanical sciences. During the twentieth century, we are still influenced by mechanical metaphors, still making "blueprints" for goals and targets that change faster than our plans do. But we are adopting biological processes as our models for exploring total fields—both ecologies, and societies. Nevertheless, they remain inadequate for the "age of speedup". We need more rapid, more direct, approaches.

At Toronto University's Centre for Culture and Technology, with Marshall McLuhan, we are constantly "organizing our ignorance" to reveal structures and patterns of change, which occur while exploring current problems, and that repeat in entirely different situations. The structures we seek are not mere quantitative measures—numerical projections. They are dynamic process patterns in constant interplay. They are patterns that we can all learn to push forward with increasing confidence to foresee and to anticipate change, not through manipulation, but through consensus. Too facile analogy can lead us astray, but waiting for "ocular proof" is to court

Othello's fate. "Truth" is not something we match, not a mere category or label; it is something we make, in the process of changing the world, which changes us.

BOOKS FOR FURTHER STUDY

Anderson, Nels. *Work and Leisure,* Free Press, N.Y., 1962.
Arendt, Hannah. *The Human Condition,* University of Chicago Press, Chicago, 1958.
Asbell, Bernard. *The New Improved American,* Dell, N.Y., 1966.
Black, C. E. *The Dynamics of Modern Man,* Harper and Row, N.Y., 1966.
Boulding, Kenneth E. *Beyond Economics,* University of Michigan Press, Ann Arbor, Mich., 1968.
Bowen, H. & Mangum, G. *Automation and Economic Progress,* Prentice-Hall, Englewood Cliffs, N.J., 1967.
Brickman, William W. (Ed.). *Automation, Education and Human Values,* School and Society Books, N.Y., 1966.
Brightbill, Charles K. *The Challenge of Leisure,* Spectrum Books, Prentice-Hall, Englewood Cliffs, N.J., 1962.
de Grazia, Sebastian. *Of Time, Work, Leisure,* Anchor Books, Doubleday, N.Y., 1964.
Doob, Leonard W. *Becoming More Civilized,* Yale University Press, New Haven, 1960.
Drucker, Peter. *The Concept of the Corporation,* Mentor, N.Y., 1964.
Dumazedier, Joffre. *Toward a Society of Leisure,* Free Press, N.Y., 1967.
Dunne, George H. (Ed.). *Poverty in Plenty,* P. J. Kenedy, N.Y., 1965.
Evans, Luther H. & Arnstein, George T., *Automation and the Challenge to Education,* National Education Association of United States, 1962.

Friedmann, George S. *The Anatomy of Work, Labor, Leisure and the Implications of Automation,* Free Press, N.Y., 1964.

Galbraith, John Kenneth. *The New Industrial State,* Houghton Mifflin, Boston, Mass., 1967.

Galbraith, John Kenneth. *The Affluent Society,* Houghton Mifflin, Boston, 1958.

Gombrich, E. H. *Art and Illusion,* Pantheon Books, N.Y., 1960.

Hall, Edward T. *Silent Language,* Premier Books, N.Y., 1965.

Harbison, Frederick, and Myers, Charles A. *Education, Manpower and Economic Growth,* McGraw-Hill, N.Y., 1964.

Heckscher, August. *The Individual and the Mass,* The Twentieth Century Fund, N.Y., 1965.

Helstein, Ralph, Piel, Gerard & Theobald, Robert. *Jobs, Machines and People,* Center for the Study of Democratic Institutions, Santa Barbara, Calif., 1964.

Larrabee, Eric & Meyerjohn, Rolf (Eds.). *Mass Leisure,* Free Press, Glencoe, Ill., 1958.

Lobsenz, Norman. *Is Anybody Happy?* Doubleday, N.Y., 1962.

Mason, Edward S. (Ed.). *The Corporation in Modern Society,* Harvard University Press, 1959 (Cambridge, Mass.).

Markham, Charles. *Jobs, Men and Machines,* Frederick A. Praeger, N.Y., 1964.

McLuhan, Marshall & Watson, Wilfred. *From Cliche to Archetype,* Viking, N.Y., 1969.

Nevitt, Barrington. *Communication with People through Media,* The Northern Electric Co. Labs., Ottawa, 1968.

Reagan, Michael D. *Politics, Economics and the General Welfare,* Scott Foresman, Chicago, 1965.

Reichardt, Jasin. *The Computer and the Arts,* Frederick A. Praeger, N.Y., 1969.

Reid, Timothy. *Contemporary Canada: Readings in Economics,* Holt, Rinehart and Winston, Toronto, 1969.

330 / THIS CYBERNETIC AGE

Rosenberg, Jerry Martin. *Automation Manpower and Education,* Random House, N.Y., 1966.

Salter, W. E. *Productivity and Technical Change,* Cambridge University Press, N.Y., 1960.

Schultz, Duane. *Sensory Restriction,* Academic Press, N.Y., 1965.

Smelser, Neil J. *The Sociology of Economic Life,* Prentice-Hall, Englewood Cliffs, N.J., 1963.

Smigel, Edwin O. *Work and Leisure,* College and University Press, New Haven, Conn., 1963.

Steere, Douglas V. *Work and Contemplation,* Harper & Brothers, N.Y., 1957.

Theobald, Robert. *Free Men and Free Markets,* Clarkson N. Potter, N.Y., 1963.

Theobald, Robert. *The Industrial Economy,* Houghton Mifflin, N.Y., 1952.

Theobald, Robert. (Ed.). *The Guaranteed Income,* Doubleday, N.Y., 1966.

Theobald, Robert (Ed.). *Committed Spending: A Route to Economic Security,* Doubleday, N.Y., 1968.

Wilcock, R. C. & Franke, W. H. *Unwanted Workers,* Free Press, N.Y., 1963.

Will, Robert E. & Valter, Harold G. *Poverty in Affluence,* Harcourt Brace and World, N.Y., 1965.

Venn, Grant. *Man, Education, and Work,* American Council on Education, Washington, D.C., 1964.

PART
SIX

This book was inspired by a comment that, throughout recorded history, people have always opposed what they do not understand. Today, with the vast information output of each moment, it is almost impossible for the average man, who has been forced to become a specialist in order to thrive or even survive, to keep up with the new data relating to even his own specialty. So we witness the phenomenon of more and more people concentrating "more and more on less and less"! In a broad sense, the multitudes are apathetic and unconcerned. Most people are wrapped up in themselves and their tribes.

In light of these circumstances, it is not at all surprising that there is so much misunderstanding, so many communication gaps, and, consequently, so much protest, violence and opposition.

Therefore, opposition to change is logically great. As we previously observed, each move forward has been revolutionary with enormous and bitter opposition, yet today even the most reactionary person writes letters, reads books, uses the radio and television and uses the telephone. These things were all opposed by people who did not understand.

Dr. Van Court Hare (Chapter 32) is a social scientist and a leading authority on systems analysis. Systems analysis has become important because it is the first step in "the systems approach" which, ideally, arranges the components of the specialists into a framework which is integrated toward the achievement of a single goal.

One authority in this field groups all human beings under

three labels: (a) analysts (b) synthesists (c) anasythesists (d) nincompoops. Class (c) is rare.

Historically, institutions have been slow to change, if at all, and so, in a period of very rapid change, tend to become the enemies of the human beings on whom they rely for support.

Historian Elting Morison (Chapter 33) was one of the group of men who met regularly with Norbert Weiner in the early days of cybernetics. He is one of those rare people who, like Alice in the Looking Glass, has the ability to look backwards and forwards at the same time. He proposes an experimental society with man as the great criterion.

This leads to a major treatise on the hidden theme of this book, "humanization through cybernation". Dr. Eric Fromm (Chapter 34) discusses the humanization of a technological society and suggests some procedures for humanistic planning.

When this book was being compiled, Zakir Husain (Chapter 35) was the president of India which has a population larger than both Africa and South America. Husain was a Moslem though most Indians are predominantly Hindu. Husain was an anasythesist and a humanitarian who set an example for all the world. He recognized that education is continuous and for life.

The same statement might be made about Chapter 36 which will probably come as a shock to many of the inhabitants of the North American Continent; excepting young revolutionaries who are sometimes called communists because, like Korolev, they are really pleading for humanitarianism. In view of Korolev's position, this article might almost be described as an official statement of the purposes of adult education in the Soviet Union today. It might well be adopted as part of a policy statement by the United States of America and the United Nations. So, in spite of the militarists, people are coming together.

But the cause of humanity has its enemies and some of the enemies are very close. Norman Cousins (Chapter 37) wrote

PART SIX / 335

this check-list of enemies several years ago. It is still highly valid.

"Afterwords" is the wind-up. It is intended to synthesize some of the thinking of our distinguished contributors and to leave you with a great deal to think about and to act upon. In the language of cybernetics, the entire book has intended to be "feed-forward" which might put the general reader in closer touch with the bigger issues and problems of the age. The "feed-back" should come in the form of constructive action in relationship to your personal insights and objectives.

CHAPTER 32

Social Science and Technological Change

by Van Court Hare

Dr. Van Court Hare, Jr. is a Professor at Columbia University and a leading authority on systems analysis. Systems analysis is a selection of elements, relationships, and procedures to achieve a specific purpose i.e. road map to a city. This chapter is adapted from a chapter in his book "Systems Analysis: A Diagnostic Approach" (Harcourt Brace & World, Inc.).

1

SOCIAL SCIENTISTS have long been concerned with the problems of technological change and how they influence the society and the culture in which we live. The reverse problem, of course, is also important because the historical setting, and the tools and ideas presently known, affect the selection of projects considered worthwhile.

In viewing this grand process of technological advancement and social change we generally find a conflict between those who propose change and those who prefer the present state of affairs.

The instrumental process, which is concerned with "the facts," stresses replication, verifiability, and usefulness in social life. "The authority of the instrumental process is rational, deriving from its demonstrable usefulness to the life process. The final appeal is to the evidence."

The institutional process, on the other hand, builds certainty, not doubt, for the individual. It seeks stability, sure-footedness, a rock of ages. Change, particularly rapid change, is shunned.

The introduction of change, particularly change that seems to the individual beyond his control and which therefore threatens, or reduces perceived security, elicits reactions that are not necessarily logical. If the systems analyst proposes change, which is the essence of the instrumental process, he meets the proponents of status quo, for the essence of the institutional process is to stand pat.

Indeed, some institutional processes are so rigid, that the innovator contests them at his peril. In his Letter from Earth, Samuel Clemens wrote,

> We do not know how or when it became custom for women to wear long hair, we only know in this country it is the custom, and that settles it. . . . Women may shave their heads elsewhere, but here they must refrain or take the uncomfortable consequences. . . . The penalty may be unfair, unrighteous, illogical, and cruelty; no matter, it will be inflicted, just the same.

And, some habits are so strongly ingrained that they are impervious to change. Many individuals work at night to avoid change. As one elderly worker, who had worked the night shift for forty years expressed it to the author:

> When I went to work there were no cars on the street, only horses. Wagons and horses. Now there are cars, and too many people. Too many. Why do I work at night? Things never change much at night. In the morning there are cars and people. But, things never change much at night. Who needs those cars and people?

2

It is interesting that the instrumental and institutional processes have been compared to the term ego and superego used in individual psychoanalysis.

In those terms, the ego represents the executive department of the human personality—the instrumental activities that recognize facts, marshall resources, devise plans of action, and get things done.

The superego is the judicial department, which performs a screening function, directs awareness, vetoes unacceptable proposals, and sets values and effectiveness measures used in goal formation. The superego is institutional in character, and derives its "conscience" from the culture, its customs, habits, and mores.

Most studies show that the conscience so formed is highly relative to the culture or society in which the individual lives.

For many important issues, constraints upon the superego are set by a small group—those near home as it were. Thus, the constraints are greater where families live together for several generations than where they do not, greater in small towns than in large, greater at home than abroad, greater when there are strong religious beliefs or formal institutional ties than when there are none, greater when only one set of values is perceived than when there are many that seem relative to time or place. We are all familiar with acts and common phrases that illustrate these facts.

> Things happen in motels that do not happen in homes, and towels are swiped in distant hotels by persons who would not steal a pin in their hometowns. Some persons, indeed, travel for just this purpose—to lose an unwanted reinforcement of conscience. For them wanderlust is not a lust for wandering but a wandering for lust.

Similarly, methods exist for strengthening the superego or judicial function in the personality (and therefore the institutional function in the culture), and also for reducing its effect. Street lights reduce burglaries, and double-entry bookkeeping reduces embezzlement. Conversely, in surroundings where multiple values are evident and where institutional restrictions are consciously relaxed, the range of acceptable value and goal choices are consciously relaxed, the range of acceptable value and goal choices increases, leading to a greater variety of possible actions or considerations and to a greater potential for change. Thus, as institutional restrictions become less (and instrumental efforts are, relatively speaking, more respected), new proposals become more easily accepted by those who must approve and use them and vice versa.

3

Note also that the capacity of the investigator or the individual to effect system change, or to alter his perception of the facts to suit his needs, is due to his capacity for the creation and manipulation of symbols. Language and abstraction form the concepts, ideas, and instructions that permit learning and the transfer of experience (and the very act of systems definition and analysis).

This capacity, which permits the analyst to generalize, also permits him to change the name of the game to suit his needs.

Although it would appear to be a fact that a rose by any other name could smell as sweet, for individuals who view a scene this invariance of description may not hold. A plain ham-and-cheese sandwich may taste better if it is described as a "wedge of cheddar wedded to a generous portion of prime Virginia ham surrounded by California tomatoes and Florida lettuce and a discrete portion of pure egg mayonnaise." Even though a simple yes or no might suffice, a problem solution may seem more impressive and convincing if couched in mathematical symbols and presented with a slight but correct accent by a man with a Ph.D from Cambridge.

But, because our symbols, our abstractions, and our ability to conjure up favorable or unfavorable impressions with a word or gesture are products of our culture, and because the participant-listener's symbols and abstractions are formed by his culture, a knowledge of how symbols are formed and held is the key to our understanding of culture.

Finally, we should note that institutional problems are

magnified as the instrumental process advances with time. Although institutions do change under the impact of technology and instrumental advances, they change slowly and reluctantly, ". . . and make peace, finally, with the conditions which altered them."

But institutional change is slower than instrumental change. By the time the institutional process, or the culture, has made peace with instrumental change, ". . . technology has moved on, and the laggard is still trailing." Indeed, the discrepancy between instrumental growth and institutional change becomes worse with time. The combinatorial possibilities of instrumental growth are geometric: more tools, more techniques, more facts, and more concepts lead to a cornucopia of new possibilities. The instrumental process is regenerative, but the institutional process does not partake of this bounty and holds steadfast, unless intimidated, coerced, and pummeled into movement.

The resulting effect is a cultural lag—an ever increasing gulf between what is possible and what is acceptable.

Changes that alter no dearly held belief, custom, or mode of habitual operation are often introduced with relative ease in highly technical areas. Tools may be redesigned, new production methods may be introduced, new weapons may be brought out; tactics, competitive goals, and impersonal means may all be changed with relative ease. However, primary group relations, territorial and religious stability, systems of prestige, customs, mores, and habits resist activation.

In short, the introduction of change is eased if the symbols of change present no apparent alteration or modification of the culture's widely held symbols. Indeed, change is greatly facilitated if the culture's present symbols and instructions reinforce the proposed alterations in operation.

CHAPTER 33

What Are We Going to Do?

by Elting E. Morison

Elting E. Morison is Sloan Fellows Professor of Management, M.I.T., and Chairman of the Social Studies Curriculum Program of Educational Services, Inc. He was closely associated with an interdisciplinarian exploratory group at M.I.T. which included Norbert Weiner. He looks at the cybernated global community through the eyes of a historian. This chapter is adapted from "Men, Machines and Modern Times" (M.I.T. Press) which offers a positive alternative to an Orwellian 1984.

1

MACHINES WHEREVER USED over the last hundred and fifty years may not have let in much sweetness and light, but they have steadily made the physical facts of life much more tolerable. This position, which has much solid evidence to support it, is usually held by those who tend to believe that human experience is not so much a matter of unheard melodies as of blood, bread, and money.

The sum of all these varying attitudes has been a persistent allegation that what men did with their engines and power-houses had very little to do with what Matthew Arnold, called the best that had been thought and said—and felt—by human beings. There has always been a small school of thought with a somewhat different view of things, a number of men who have tried to establish some sort of connection between sweetness, light, coal, iron, and railroads. In quite different ways Henry George, Graham Wallas, and even Max Weber may be said to have taken on the job. The most thorough-going and by far the most influential of this school was Karl Marx. Holes have been found in his economic theory, and some eccentricity appears in his definition of sweetness and light. Furthermore, his scheme in practice has tended to produce weird results.

But neither the intellectual limitations of the Marxian system, nor the fact that the system was conceived less in affection than in indignation, nor yet the fact that it doesn't seem to work very well should diminish the significance of the effort of intent. Marx was out after a plan that would fit the persistent human energies and desires into the developing mechanical and economic energies of his time. His failure may have been that in discerning some of the most important elements in the human condition, he thought he had discerned them all, but in failing, he established some very illuminating connections between man and machinery.

They were all—George, Marx, Arnold, and the rest—in one way and another making somewhat the same point. None made it more bluntly than Thomas Huxley. He came to Baltimore toward the end of the last century to say that he remained unimpressed by all the power, natural resources, knowledge, and machinery that had so greatly extended man's competence over his physical environment. "The great issue," he went on, "about which hangs a true sublimity and the terror of overhanging fate is, what are you going to do with all these things?"

2

To state the case in its simplest form, the current problem is how to organize and manage the system of ideas, energies, and machinery so it will conform to all the human dimensions. Experience suggests first that there are three things not to do.

In the older, simpler days the solution, often, was simply to burn down or break up the new mechanisms when they introduced distortions in settled customs. This is what C. P. Snow has called the Luddite approach. This primitive response produced, historically, only temporary and local accommodations, as in the ancient case of the Pythagoreans who attempted to preserve the purity of their mathematical expressions by putting to death the man who discovered incommensurables. Whether it appears in the form of an angry workman dismembering a loom or as a fireman in a cab without a fire-bed—which is a kind of symbolic destruction— it does not get to the heart of the problem. Indeed, it merely complicates it.

Nor will it do to try to arrest the movement in the system that produces new ideas and machines by adopting a modern equivalent of the direct and literal-minded attack of the Luddites—that is, by burning down or cutting up the budgets of universities or commercial laboratories from which the novel thoughts and applications so often come. In a world in which the trained intelligence plays a continuously larger part, conditions to sustain the lively mind must be preserved.

Nor will it serve the purpose to develop some grand synthesis to bring the whole system of ideas, energies, and machines under suitable control. For one thing, such grand syntheses—whether Platonic or Marxian—never work out very well in practice. There are, apparently, too many variables in any situation where human beings enter in to be successfully comprehended in any fixed grand design. And in this particular situation, which is dominated by accelerating change, any grand design would soon become quite obsolete.

3

One way to begin thinking about this problem is to creep up on it out of the simpler past. The introduction of the pasteurizer in the last century may supply a suggestive point of departure. Pasteur developed his idea in the 1850's while working on the diseases that had attacked the vines in the French wine country. The first general application of the idea appears to have taken place about a decade later in Denmark. The Danes made a considerable part of their living by exporting cheese.

In Germany somewhat later, it all began with beer, when the brewers found that they too could ensure a greater standardization of product by using the process. Toward the end of the century—German chemists and medical men began to accumulate evidence that raw milk often carried bacteria harmful to people as well as to beer, wine, and cheese. Pasteurization of the milk sold by commercial dairies then became a requirement imposed by the German Emperor.

In America the case was different. Pasteurization was introduced in quite a few city dairies in the late eighties and early nineties clandestinely. They did so secretly because the citizens had a natural resistance to drinking milk with, as they often said, dead bodies in it.

This resistance was overcome in the first instance in an interesting way. A wealthy New York German Jew on a trip back to the old country in the nineties heard about the new process and its possible useful effects. With the aid of a biologist at Columbia he made two blocks of the Lower East Side the site of a considerable experiment. In one block the residents were persuaded to get their milk from his free kitchen, while in the other they bought as before unpasteurized loose milk from the itinerant dealers. Over a period of several months a careful count of the appearance of scarlet fever and diphtheria in the two blocks was maintained. The final reckoning produced a rather dazzling demonstration of the effectiveness of pasteurizing in reducing the incidence of disease. It was not long after that the process was required of commercial dairies by New York City ordinance, and quite rapidly after that other cities in the country passed similar ordinances.

Contemporary machinery is far more elaborate and powerful and pervasive in the social fabric than it was in the days of the pasteurizer. The cultural constraints of today seem, on the whole, far less binding on any society than half a century ago. Yet if one went about it in the right way, it seems still quite possible that a new kind of culture could be built up that would contain the new technology within appropriate limits.

The creation of such a new culture would seem to be a first order of business. At a time when we are developing the capacity to do almost anything that occurs to us, from going to the moon to transplanting one man's brain to another man's head, new means to select and judge among all the things that are possible must also be developed. If we are to manage the powerful system we have created in our own interests, we must also create a new sort of culture that will give clear definition to what, in the new scheme of things, our interests really are. Here is a suggestion!

4

At a time when we are all involved in technological change and are therefore all interested and affected members of the community, the suggestion here is to introduce a massive expansion of this process throughout all parts of the society, to create the mood and means that will enable the members of the society to explore new instruments and new procedures by designed experiments while pondering alternatives and reserving judgment until the returns are in. In all the areas of difficulty and doubt—the organization of cities, the control of traffic, the intelligent, indeed the loving care of the sick, the process of education, the structure of existing institutions, the means of transport, and the like—in all these areas the development of a series of small experiments, with the means available for observing the evidence produced and analyzing the results, would produce a set of alternative solutions and the data necessary both for fuller understanding of the nature of new situations and for intelligent selection among alternatives.

The creation and preservation of this experimental mood

may in itself be of the first importance. It suggests that members of the society can have a direct part in the decisions affecting the shape of the society; by offering the possibility of reasoned change, it may measurably reduce the natural human resistance to changes not fully understood. The opportunity of free choice within a broad band of alternatives is in fact the essence of the democratic process. But at present it appears that as the weight and mass of the technical system increase, the opportunity for the whole society to renew itself by natural processes of conscious selection is sadly diminished. On the one hand there is the tendency to concentrate the power of decision in those few who seek to manage the system, and on the other hand there is the tendency in the system itself to proceed toward whatever is economically and technically possible without regard to other considerations of interest and value. The point of the experimental society is to redress those tendencies by consciously supplying a series of reasonable alternatives, varied solutions, for the whole society to think over as it makes up its mind about what it would like to do and, equally important, to be.

So the proposal is to start all experiments with man as the great criterion. Put him in any number one wishes of mechanical systems—for transport, communication, making things, and so forth—to discover where he breaks down and where he thrives.

The object of all these exercises is to take the measure of what man is in the new environment he has created for himself and to give him the evidence necessary to modify, limit, and organize the developing environment so that he may extend his own range within it.

CHAPTER 34

The Humanization of Technological Society

by Eric Fromm

Dr. Eric Fromm is world-known for his writings and lectures on psychoanalysis, philosophy, political science and religion. Born in Germany, he has taught at several universities including Michigan State, Yale and New York where he is still an adjunct professor. His many books include "Escape from Freedom", "May Man Prevail?" "The Heart of Man", "The Art of Loving", "Beyond the Chains of Illusion", "Man for Himself," and "The Revolution of Hope Toward a Humanized Technology" from which this chapter has been adapted with permission of the author and Harper & Row.

1

IF WE ARE now to consider the possibility of humanizing the industrial society as it has developed in the second Industrial Revolution, we must begin by considering those institutions and methods which for economic as well as psychological reasons cannot be done away with without the total disruption of our society. These elements are: (1) The large-scale centralized enterprise as it has developed in the last decades in government, business, universities, hospitals, etc. This process of centralization is still continuing, and soon almost all major purposeful activities will be carried on by large systems. (2) Large-scale planning within each system, which results from the centralization. (3) Cybernation, that is cybernetics and automation, as the major theoretical and practical principle of control, with the computer as the most important element in automation.

But not only these three elements are here to stay. There is another element which appears in all social systems: the system Man. As I pointed out eariler, this does not mean that human nature is not malleable; it means that it allows only a limited number of potential structures, and confronts us with certain ascertainable alternatives. The most important alternative as far as the technological society is concerned is the following: if man is passive, bored, unfeeling, and one-sidedly cerebral, he develops pathological symptoms like anxiety, depression, depersonalization, indifference to life, and violence.

Indeed, as Robert H. Davis wrote in a penetrating paper, ". . . the long-range implications of a cybernated world for mental health are disturbing." It is important to stress this point, since most planners deal with the human factor as one which could adapt itself to any condition without causing any disturbances.

The possibilities which confront us are few and ascertainable. One possibility is that we continue in the direction we have taken. This would lead to such disturbances of the total system that either thermonuclear war or severe human pathology would be the outcome. The second possibility is the attempt to change that direction by force or violent revolution. This would lead to the breakdown of the whole system and violence and brutal dictatorship as a result. The third possibility is the humanization of the system, in such a way that it serves the purpose of man's well-being and growth, or in other words, his life process. In this case, the central elements of the second Industrial Revolution will be kept intact. The question is, Can this be done and what steps need to be taken to achieve it?

2

Whatever the merits of the source of the validity of humanist norms, the general aim of a humanized industrial society can be thus defined: the change of the social, economic, and cultural life of our society in such a way that it stimulates and furthers the growth and aliveness of man rather than cripples it; that it activates the individual rather than making him passive and receptive; that our technological capacities serve man's growth. If this is to be, we must regain control over the economic and social system; man's will, guided by his reason, and by his wish for optimal aliveness, must make the decisions.

Given these general aims, what is the procedure of humanistic planning? Computers should become a functional part in a life-oriented social system and not a cancer which begins to play havoc and eventually kills the system. Machines or computers must become means for ends which are determined by man's reason and will. The values which determine the selection of facts and which influence the programing of the computer must be gained on the basis of the knowledge of human nature, its various possible manifestations, its optimal forms of development, and the real needs conducive to this development. That is to say, man, not technique, must become the ultimate source of values; optimal human development and not maximal production the criterion for all planning.

Aside from this, planning in the field of economics must be extended to the whole system; furthermore, the system Man must be integrated into the whole social system. Man, as the planner, must be aware of the role of man as part of the whole system. Just as man is the only case of life being aware of itself, man as a system builder and analyzer must make himself the object of the system he analyzes. This means that the knowledge of man, his nature, and the real possibilities of its manifestations must become one of the basic data for any social planning.

3

It follows, from all that has been said about man, that one basic requirement for his well-being is to be active, in the sense of the productive exercise of all his faculties; that one of the most pathogenic features in our society is the trend to make man passive, by depriving him of the chance of active participation in the affairs of his society, in the enterprise in which he works, and, in fact, although more hidden, in his personal affairs. This "passivation" of man is partly due to the "alienated bureaucratic" method used in all centralized enterprises.

Here, as so often, people are confronted by a confusing false dichotomy. They believe that the choice is between an anarchic system without any organization and control and, on the other hand, the kind of bureaucracy which is typical both for contemporary industrialism and even more so for the Soviet system. But this alternative is by no means the only one, and we have other options. The option I have in mind is that between the "humanistic bureaucratic" or "humanistic management" method and the "alienated bureaucratic" method by which we conduct our affairs.

This alienated bureaucratic procedure can be characterized in several ways. First of all, it is a one-way system; orders, suggestions, planning emanate from the top and are directed to the bottom of the pyramid. There is no room for the individual's initiative. Persons are "cases," whether welfare cases or medical cases, or, whatever the frame of reference is, cases which can all be put down on a computer card without those individual features which designate the difference between a "person" and a "case."

Our bureaucratic method is irresponsible, in the sense that it does not "respond" to the needs, views, requirements of an individual. This irresponsibility is closely related to the case-character of the person who becomes an "object" of the bureaucracy. One cannot respond to a case but one can respond to a person. This irresponsibility of the bureaucrat has another aspect which has been a feature of bureaucracy for a long time. The bureaucrat, feeling himself part of the bureaucratic machine, most of all wishes not to take responsibility, that is to say, to make decisions for which he could be criticized.

Our bureaucratic method gives the individual the feeling that there is nothing which he can initiate and organize without the help of the bureaucratic machine. As a result, it paralyzes initiative and creates a deep sense of impotence.

4

The basic principle of the humanistic management method is that, in spite of the bigness of the enterprises, centralized planning, and cybernation, the individual participant asserts himself toward the managers, circumstances, and machines, and ceases to be a powerless particle which has no active part in the process. Only by such affirmation of his will can the energies of the individual be liberated and his mental balance be restored.

The same principle of humanistic management can also be expressed in this way: While in alienated bureaucracy all power flows from above downward, in humanistic management there is a two-way street. The "subjects" of decision making have a right to challenge the decision makers. Such a challenge would first of all require a rule that if a sufficient number of "subjects" demanded that the corresponding bureaucracy (on whatever level) answer questions, explain its procedures, the decision makers would respond to the demand.

5

Active participation in the affairs of the country as a whole and of states and communities, as well as of large enterprises, would require the formation of face-to-face groups, within which the process of information exchange, debate, and decision making would be conducted. Before discussing the structure of such groups in all kinds of centralized enterprises and political decision making, respectively, let us have a look at the characteristics such face-to-face groups should have.

The first is that the number of participating people must

be restricted in such a way that the discussion remains direct and does not allow the rhetoric or the manipulating influence of demagogues to become effective. If people meet regularly and know each other, they begin to feel whom they can trust and whom they cannot, who is constructive and who is not, and in the process of their own participation, their own sense of responsibility and self-confidence grows.

Second, objective and relevant information which is the basis for everyone's having an approximately clear and accurate picture of the basic issues must be given to each group.

6

The aim of the activation of man in the technological society requires another step as important and as difficult as replacement of the alienated bureaucratic structure by methods of humanist management.

It is time we began to examine the whole problem of subjective needs and whether their existence is a sufficiently valid reason for their fulfillment; to question and examine the generally accepted principle of satisfying all needs—while never asking about their origins or effects.

In trying to find adequate solutions, we meet with two powerful obstacles. First, the interests of industry, whose imagination is fired by too many alienated men who cannot think of products which would help to make a human being more active rather than more passive. Besides this, industry knows that by advertising it can create needs and cravings which can be calculated in advance, so that there is little risk in losing profit if one continues the safe method of creating needs and selling the products which satisfy them.

The other difficulty lies in a certain concept of freedom which gains ever-increasing importance. The most important freedom in the nineteenth century was the freedom to use and invest property in any form which promised profit. Since managers of enterprises were at the same time the owners, their own acquisitive motivations made them emphasize this freedom of the use and investment of capital. In the middle of the twentieth century, most people do not own much property—even though there are a relatively large number of people who own large fortunes. The average person is employed and he is satisfied with relatively small savings, either in cash, stocks, bonds, or life insurance. For him, the freedom of investment of capital is a relatively minor issue; and even for most people who are able to buy stocks, this is a form of gambling in which they are counseled by investment advisers or simply trust the mutual investment funds. But the real feeling of freedom today lies in another sphere, in that of consumption. In this sphere, everybody except those who live a substandard existence experiences the freedom of the consumer.

I believe that the transformation of our society into one which serves life must change the consumption and thereby change, indirectly, the production pattern of present industrial society. Such a change would obviously come not as a result of bureaucratic orders but of studies, information, discussion, and decision making on the part of the population, educated to become aware of the problem of the difference between life-furthering and life-hindering kinds of needs.

The first step in this direction would be studies which would distinguish between these two kinds of needs. A group of psychologists, sociologists, economists, and representatives of the consuming public could undertake a study of those needs which are "humane," in the sense that they serve man's growth and joy, and those synthetic needs suggested by industry and its propaganda in order to find an outlet for profitable investment. As in so many other problems, the question is not so much the difficulty in determining the difference between these two types of needs and certain intermediate types but rather the raising of an extremely important question which can be brought up only if the social scientists begin to be concerned with man, instead of the alleged smooth functioning of our society or their function as its apologists.

7

The point I want to make is to uphold the principle that a person has an inalienable right to live—a right to which no conditions are attached and which implies the right to education and to medical care; he has a right to be treated at least as well as the owner of a dog or a cat treats his pet, which does not have to "prove" anything in order to be fed. Provided this principle were accepted, if a man, woman, or adolescent could be sure that whatever he did his material existence would not be in jeopardy, the realm of human freedom would be immensely enhanced. Acceptance of this principle would also enable a person to change his occupation or profession by using one or more years in preparing himself for a new and, to him, more adequate activity. This problem is by no means solved by unemployment or welfare dole. As many have recognized, the bureaucratic methods employed here are humiliating to such a degree that many people are afraid of being forced into the dole-receiving sector of the population, and this fear is sufficient to deprive them of the freedom not to accept certain working conditions.

The guaranteed annual income could serve, as some economists have observed, as an important regulating feature in our economy. "What we need," C. E. Ayres writes, "is some device that can be permanently instituted as a regular feature of the industrial economy by which demand can be made to keep pace with a constantly proliferating supply. The guarantee of a basic income to all members of the community irrespective of the earnings of employment, would provide the flow of effective demand that the economy more and more desperately requires."

The principle of the guaranteed annual income has to cope with the objection that man is lazy and would not want to work if the principle of work-or-starve were to be abolished. In fact, this assumption is wrong. As overwhelming evidence shows, man has an inherent tendency to be active, and laziness is a pathological symptom. Under a system of "forced labor" where little attention is paid to the attractiveness of work, man seeks to escape from it if even for a short time. If the whole social system is changed in such a way that coercion and threat are removed from the work obligation, only a minority of sick people would prefer to do nothing. It is quite possible that a certain minority of people would prefer what would be the equivalent of the monastic life, devoting themselves completely to their inner development, to contemplation, or study. If the Middle Ages could afford to tolerate monastic life, certainly our affluent technological society is much more able to afford it. But again, as soon as we introduced bureaucratic methods necessitating that somebody had to prove that he really made "good use" of his time, the whole principle would be spoiled.

We have argued that the system Man does not function properly if only his material needs are satisfied, thus guaranteeing his physiological survival, but not those needs and faculties which are specifically human—love, tenderness, reason, joy, etc.

Indeed, inasmuch as he is also an animal, man needs first to satisfy his material wants; but his history is a record of the search for and expression of his trans-survival needs, such as in painting and sculpture, in myth and drama, in music and dance. Religion was almost the only system which incorporated these aspects of human existence.

With the growth of the "new science," religion in its traditional forms became less and less effective, and there appeared the danger that the values which in Europe were anchored in the theistic frame of reference would be lost.

Abbe Pire has expressed it in a very simple and forceful way: "What matters today is not the difference between those who believe and those who do not believe, but the differences between those who care and those who don't."

This new attitude toward life can be expressed more specifically in the following principles: Man's development requires his capacity to transcend the narrow prison of his ego, his greed, his selfishness, his separation from his fellow man, and, hence, his basic loneliness. This transcendence is the condition for being open and related to the world, vulnerable, and yet with an experience of identity and integrity; of man's capacity to enjoy all that is alive, to pour out his faculties into the world around him, to be "interested"; in brief, to be rather than to have and to use are consequences of the step to overcome greed and egomania.

I submit that if people would truly accept the Ten Commandments or the Buddhist Eightfold Path as the effective principles to guide their lives, a dramatic change in our whole culture would take place. There is no need at this point to argue about details of the values which need to be practiced, for what matters is to gather those who accept the principle of practice rather than of submission to an ideology.

Another common principle is the solidarity of all men and the loyalty to life and to humanity which must always take precedence over the loyalty to any particular group. In fact, even this way of putting it is not correct. Any true love for another person has a particular quality: for I love in that person not only the person but humanity itself, or, as a Christian or Jewish believer would say: God. In the same way, if I love my country, this love is at the same time a love for man and mankind; and if it is not that, it is an attachment based on one's incapacity for independence and, in the last analysis, another manifestation of idolatry.

The crucial question is how these new-old principles can become effective. Those inside religion hope that they can transform their religion into the full practice of humanism, but many of them know that while this may prove to be true for some sectors of the population, there are others who for many obvious reasons cannot accept the theistic concepts and rituals so closely interwoven with them that it is almost impossible to separate the two.

Whatever new psychospiritual systems may arise, they will not be "fighting" religion, although they will be a challenge to those in the various religions who have made an ideology of religious teaching and an idol of God. Those who worship the "living God" will have no difficulty in sensing that they have more in common with the "unbelievers" than they have in what separates them; they will have a deep sense of solidarity with those who do not worship idols and who try to do what the believers call "God's will."

8

The conclusion seems unavoidable that the ideas of activation, responsibility, participation—that is, of the humanization of technological society—can find full expression only in a movement which is not bureaucratic, not connected with the political machines, and which is the result of active and imaginative efforts by those who share the same aims. Such a movement itself, in its organization and method, would be expressive of the aim to which it is devoted: to educate its members for the new kind of society in the process of striving for it.

The growing perception and responsibility of our World Age point to the new reality that the individual person and the collective person supplement and integrate each other; that the thrall of totalitarianism of both left and right has been shaken in the universal desire to recapture the authority of truth and human totality. Mankind can finally place its trust not in a proletarian authoritarianism, not in a secularized humanism, both of which have betrayed the spiritual property right of history, but in a sacramental brotherhood and in the unity of knowledge.

We stand at the brink of an age of a world in which human life presses forward to actualize new forms. The false separation of man and nature, of time and space, of freedom and security, is acknowledged, and we are faced with a new vision of man in his organic unity and of history offering a richness and diversity of quality and majesty of scope hitherto unprecedented. Encourage a renaissance of hope in society and of pride in man's decision as to what his destiny will be.

CHAPTER 35

The Never-Ending Pursuit of Learning

by Zakir Husain

The late Zakir Husain was the first Moslem President of predominately Hindu India. He wrote this article only a few months before his death in May 1969. The influence of this gentle scholar brought considerable unity to an oft-divided nation and this brief sample of his philosophy might well be considered as a message to the citizens of the world.

THE DEVELOPMENT OF the individual enriches and improves society, and a well-organized, free, and just society provides wider opportunities for the individual to grow. In certain situations, however, a greater emphasis deliberately has to be placed on the social purposes of education, and education has to be used as an instrument of social change. This situation is found especially in developing countries like India.

We want to raise our standard of living substantially, and to assure a minimum income to each family, or, at least, to each planned family. We want to create a new social order based on justice, equality, freedom, and the dignity of the individual. We want to adopt modern science and technology, and, side by side, develop a sense of social responsibility; to generate moral and spiritual values based on our own great traditions and on the valuable contributions of other cultures. This is not a utopian or even an overambitious program. It is the minimum needed for an honorable national existence. In implementing it, we can have no greater ally than education, which is the most powerful instrument of national development. What we need most urgently, therefore, is a revolution in education which can trigger off the necessary cultural, economic, and social revolution.

The large-scale reconstruction of national life which we envisage can be accomplished only with the help of an intelligentsia of adequate size and competence, and of deep commitment to the service of the masses and to the development of the nation. It is only the universities which can provide this leadership; and if they can do so, all difficulties which now loom large on the horizon and seem to hinder our progress will vanish like darkness at sunrise.

How can the universities fulfil this heavy responsibility? In my view, they will have to develop five important functions for this purpose. The traditional universities had three main functions—teaching, research, and the training of leadership in a few select fields. Modern universities will have to continue to expand these functions to cover all walks of life, and to add two others: service to the community, and adult education. This is especially important in developing countries.

Intensive drives have to be organized for liquidating mass illiteracy, and teachers and students in higher education can play a valuable role in them. They can make a still greater contribution through the training of rural leadership. Studies have shown that the size of this leadership is small. If the university teachers can meet this leadership in small seminars or groups, and discuss with them the major issues facing the country, and its programs of development, the entire character of Government policies, the quality of public participation in them, and the efficiency of their implementation will be revolutionized.

We have no time to lose. The next five or ten years will probably be the crucial period. The university students can be a great force for good and can regenerate the entire life of the nation. On the other hand, if education continues to be ineffective, if a climate of hard work and dedication cannot be generated, if the crisis of confidence between teachers and students continues to persist, if the link between the universities and the community remains weak, and if indiscipline continues, this very student body may accelerate social disintegration. The need for immediate and effective action on right lines is thus obvious and cannot be overstressed.

It is in this sense that I would like to recall what Pandit Jawaharlal Nehru said at the Convocation of the University of Allahabad some years ago: "A University stands for tolerance, for reason, for the adventure of ideas and for the search of truth. If it stands for the onward march of the human race towards ever higher goals then it is well with the people."

CHAPTER 36

Rounded Development of the Human Personality

by F. F. Korolev

Selections from a translation by International Arts and
Sciences Press. For Russian language article see *Convergence* Vol. 1, No. 4, December 1968. Korolev is a
leading adult educator in Russia.

1

WHAT PRECISELY IS the rounded development of the individual? It means molding a person who will perform both physical and mental work, will produce both material and spiritual values, will be harmoniously developed physically and spiritually, and will be active in public affairs. It means inculcating lofty ethical ideals and esthetic tastes, and varied material and spiritual needs.

Rounded development does not mean, of course, that a person must know everything in all spheres of work, or be a master, expert or virtuoso in all fields.

Nevertheless man's rounded development is inseparably connected with abolition of the old division of labor and, chiefly, with the complete eradication of distinctions between workers who do mental and physical work. It is not a matter of doing away with one or another type of work, but of seeing to it that every member of society takes part in creating both material and spiritual values. Neither physical nor mental work can disappear. What can disappear is the division of people into isolated social groups permanently and exclusively engaged in either physical or mental work.

It is obvious that the scientific and technical revolution taking place in all spheres of the national economy and the profound changes in the content and nature of work make new demands on the individual and on the character training and education he is given.

370 / THIS CYBERNETIC AGE

In a message to school children, the scientists I. I.
Artobolevskii, I. P. Bardin, A. A. Blagonravov, I. G. Bruevich,
V. I. Dsheuskin and B. S. Stepanenko write: "One must be
a highly educated man to operate machines, and even more
so to invent them. It will soon be as shameful not to know
how diesel and jet engines, electric motors and automated
machine—tools work as it is now not to know how to read and
write. Knowledge of the principles of technology will become
universal. That is why it is especially important to study
the construction of machines and the history of their invention, and to try to visualize their future. 'Love, study and know
machinery!' "

Automation of production leads to a sharp increase in the
proportion of engineering and technical personnel on the one
hand, and, on the other, to a situation where the worker's
tasks reach the level of work performed by the engineer or
technician. Physical and mental work are drawing closer
together. A new type of worker is appearing in ever increasing
numbers, a worker whose job combines physical and mental
work, who creates material values, operates a system of machines, and takes an active part in technical creative work.

Automation links functionally different machine-tools,
machines and devices into a single system and leads to the
utilization of the same types of machinery in industry, transport and agriculture. This provides a broad foundation for
polytechnical education, which is one of the major means
for the rounded development of the individual.

The material base for rounded development is being created
before our eyes, for automation radically undermines the old
division of labor and the one-sidedness that still exists in the
development of workers who do mental work and workers
who do physical work. As mechanization and automation are
extended in material production there will be constantly greater
merging of physical and mental work. Mental and physical
functions are already combined in the work of the modern

steel worker. Calculations, control of the production process and other functions falling into the category of mental work consume about 60 percent of his working time.

2

The rounded development of the individual is proceeding in the very process of labor which is changing before our eyes. When one considers that millions of workers and collective farmers combine their work in production with study in general education evening schools, specialized secondary or higher schools, that millions of working people are attending all sorts of courses in order to improve their work skills, it becomes clear that the rounded development achieved in the process of work is strongly reinforced and assisted by an organized, purposeful educational process which pursues the same aim. Two and one-half million workers learn new trades every year. About five million improve their work skills, over four million combine production work with study in schools, technical schools and higher educational institutions. "The advanced enterprises —the Magnitogorsk and Kuznetsk metallurgical combines, the Kupava cloth factory and many other industrial enterprises," it has been pointed out in *Pravda,* have set themselves the task, and are successfully achieving it, "of having all factory and office workers under 40 obtain at least an eight-year education in the present Seven-Year Plan period, and from 25 to 30 percent—a specialized secondary education or a higher education. There are today a good many industrial enterprises where every worker is engaged in study."

It should be noted that it is not only socialist production which demands the rounded development of the human personality and creates the objective conditions for it; modern science cannot be reconciled with narrow specialization, with the one-sided development of the individual.

Today we find not only a continuous differentiation of scientific knowledge and greater specialization, but also a process of integration. Differentiation of the sciences in our time, unlike the 19th century, leads not to their further dissociation but to their synthesis. The branching off of sciences and their isolation are accompanied by a process of unification based on the interpenetration, interconnection and interaction of the various areas of knowledge. In natural science the so-called transitional sciences—physical chemistry, chemical physics, biophysics and biochemistry—are the connecting links, the cement between the basic divisions of natural science. Cybernetics, a mid-20th century science which seeks the general laws of the functioning of guided and self-guided systems, including the functioning of the human brain, plays a special role in the synthesis of scientific knowledge.

3

The boundaries between many sciences are disappearing to some extent; the sharp gulf is being eliminated as methods and means of scientific cognition pass from some sciences to others, from chemistry to biology, from biology to chemistry, from physics to biology, etc. More and more problems arise whose solution requires a many-sided approach, the unification of many branches of science. In scientific research the efforts of workers doing mental and physical work are combined in the process of creativity even more distinctly than they are in production.

Thus we see that the nature and content of physical and mental work is changing radically both in material production and in intellectual creativity.

Today a higher educational level is needed if there is to be a rise in labor productivity, if there is to be active participation in public life, and if all of the individual's potentialities are to be manifested. According to the 1959 national census, 13,400,000 persons have a higher education or a specialized secondary education, and 58,600,000 persons have a higher, secondary or incomplete secondary education. More than one-third of the country's industrial workers have a seven-year, secondary or higher education. This is a tremendous achievement of socialism. But we cannot stop here, and we shall not. We shall go further—to compulsory education and, later, to universal higher education. The achievement of universal compulsory secondary education and universal higher education will be, in essence, a new communist cultural revolution. Nor does its essence lie merely in raising the level of education. The main thing is that the content of education is enriched as man's spiritual needs become broader and more profound.

4

Leisure, which will constantly increase as working time is reduced, will lose its former meaning of simply rest from work. Because of the changed nature of work, with automation and the shorter working day, man will not need much time in which to restore his physical and spiritual powers after work, and idleness as a negative feature of human behavior will disappear. The individual will spend less time than he does now on securing food, clothing and shelter. People will devote their leisure to voluntary scientific research, to cultural, social and artistic creativeness, in all spheres. There will be a constant increase in the number of scholars, writers, artists and actors for whom science and the arts will not be professional occupations, not specializations, but voluntary manifestations of inclinations, aspirations and talents. The lofty joy of voluntary creative endeavor will be within the reach of all.

It would, however, be a great mistake to suppose that the

education of roundly developed people is completed in the schools. By its very essence the problem of rounded development is not solved in the school or during the period of school instruction alone. It is a matter of the entire life and activity of the individual.

Strictly speaking, the education of fully developed people starts in the pre-school period. Different aspects and traits of personality develop in children's games, in work, in independent artistic activity. At this stage of character training, of course, rounded development assumes very elementary forms. In the secondary and higher schools the basis for rounded development is already laid, and this development continues throughout life in the performance of social labor, in the process of diversified activity.

CHAPTER 37

Checklist of Enemies

by Norman Cousins

A footnote on Norman Cousins appears at the beginning of Chapter 4. This section is adapted from a chapter in his book "In Place of Folly".

1

THE ENEMY IS not solely the unfettered sovereign national state, violating the natural rights of man and jeopardizing his natural environment.

Nor is the enemy solely an atomic muscled totalitarian power with a world ideology.

The enemy is many people. He is a man whose only concern about the world is that it stay in one piece during his own lifetime. He is invariably up to his hips in success and regards his good fortune not as a challenge to get close to the real problems of the age but as proof of the correctness of everything he does. Nothing to him is less important than the shape of things to come or the needs of the next generation. Talk of the legacy of the past or of human destiny leaves him cold. Historically, he is the disconnected man. Hence, when he thinks about the world at all, it is usually in terms of his hope that the atomic fireworks can be postponed for fifteen or twenty years. He is an enemy because he is detached from the kind of concern for the rights of unborn legions that will enable the world itself to become connected and whole.

The enemy is a man who not only believes in his own helplessness but actually worships it. His main article of faith is that there are mammoth forces at work which the individual cannot possibly comprehend, much less alter or direct. And so he expends vast energies in attempting to convince other people that there is nothing they can do. He is an enemy because of the proximity of helplessness to hopelessness.

The enemy is a man who has a total willingness to delegate his worries about the world to officialdom. He assumes that only the people in authority are in a position to know and act. He believes that if vital information essential to the making of public decisions is withheld, it can only be for a good reason. If a problem is wholly or partially scientific in nature, he will ask no questions even though the consequences of the problem are political or social. He is an enemy because government, by its very nature, is unable to deal effectively today with matters concerned with human survival. It is now necessary to tame the national sovereignties and create a design of the whole. If this is to be done, it can be done not by the national sovereignties themselves but by insistent acts of the public will.

The enemy is any man in government, high or low, who keeps waiting for a public mandate before he can develop big ideas of his own, but who does little or nothing to bring about such a mandate. Along with this goes an obsessive fear of criticism. To such a man, the worst thing in the world that can happen is to be accused of not being tough-minded in the nation's dealings with other governments. He can take in his stride, however, the accusation that he is doing something that may result in grave injury to the human race. He lives entirely on the plane of plot-and-counter-plot, where the dominant reality is represented by scoring points on a day-by-day basis. He figures security largely in terms of statistics—generally in terms of the kind of force that can be put to work in a showdown situation—rather than in terms of the confidence and good will a nation may enjoy among its neighbors in the world. He is an enemy because he sees no connection between his own authority and the need to act in behalf of the human community.

The enemy is any man in the pulpit who by his words and acts encourages his congregation to believe that the main purpose of the church or the synagogue is to provide social respectability for its members. He talks about the sacredness of life but he never relates that concept to the real and specific threats that exist today to such sacredness. He identifies himself as a man of God but feels no urge to speak out against a situation in which the nature of man is likely to be altered and cheapened, the genetic integrity of man punctured, and distant generations condemned to a lower species. He is a dispenser of balm rather than an awakener of conscience. He is preoccupied with the need to provide personal peace of mind rather than to create a blazing sense of restlessness to set things right. He is an enemy because the crisis today is as much a spiritual crisis as it is a political one.

At a time when everything we are and everything we have are in jeopardy, it may help to know the faces of the enemy.

BOOKS FOR FURTHER STUDY

Allport G. *Becoming,* Yale University Press.
Anderson, U. S. *Success Cybernetics,* Parker, West Nyack, N.Y., 1966.
Ashley, Montague, *On Being Human,* Schuman.
Barack, Arnold B. *1975 and Changes to Come,* Harper & Row, N.Y., 1962.
Berrill, N. J. *Man's Emerging Mind,* Fawcett.
Boguslaw, *The New Utopians,* Prentice-Hall, Englewood Cliffs, N.J., 1965.
Bois, J. S. *The Art of Awareness,* Harper & Row.
Boulding, Kenneth E. *The Image,* University of Michigan Press.
Boulding, Kenneth E. *The Meaning of the 20th Century,* Harper & Row, N.Y., 1964.
Brooks, John. *The One and the Many,* Harper & Row, N.Y., 1962.
Brown, Harrison. *The Challenge of Man's Future,* Viking, N.Y., 1954.
Brown, Wm. C. *Explorations in Awareness,* Harper & Row.
Brozen, Yale. *Automation: The Impact of Technological Change,* American Enterprise Institution for Public Policy Research, 1963.

Buchanan, R. A. *Technology and Social Progress,* Pergamon Press, London, 1965.

Burdick, Eugene. *Failsafe,* Dell, N.Y., 1962.

Burke, Kenneth. *Permanence and Change,* Bobbs Merril, New York, 1965.

Calder, Nigel (Ed.). *Unless Peace Comes,* Viking Press, N.Y., 1968.

Calder, Nigel (Ed.). *The World in 1984,* Vols. 1 & 2, Penguin Books, Middlesex, 1965.

Calder, Ritchie. *After the Seventh Day,* Simon & Schuster, N.Y., 1961.

Carothers, J. Edward. *Can Machines Replace Men?* Friendship, N.Y., 1966.

Churchman, C. West. *Challenge to Reason,* McGraw-Hill, N.Y., 1968.

Cousins, Norman, et al. *Issues, 1968,* University Press of Kansas, Kansas, 1968.

Cousins, Norman, *In Place of Folly,* Washington Square Press, N.Y., 1962.

Dechert, Charles R. (Ed.). *Social Impact of Cybernetics,* Clarion, N.Y., 1967.

Diebold, John. *Beyond Automation,* McGraw-Hill, N.Y., 1964.

De Ropp, R. S. *The Master Game,* Delacorte.

Dewey, J. *Human Nature and Conduct,* Random House.

Drucker, Peter. *The New Society,* Harper and Row, N.Y., 1962.

Drucker, Peter. *America's Next Twenty Years,* Harper and Brothers, N.Y., 1955.

Drucker, Peter. *The Future of the Industrial Man,* New American Library, N.Y., 1965.

Drucker, Peter. *Landmarks of Tomorrow,* Harper, N.Y., 1959.

Drucker, Peter. *Age of Discontinuity,* Harper & Row, N.Y., 1969.

Durant, W. *The Story of Philosophy,* Simon and Schuster.

Eisenstadt, S. N. *Modernization, Project and Change,* Prentice-Hall, Englewood Cliffs, N.J., 1966.

Evans, T. & Stewart, M. *Pathway to Tomorrow: The Impact of Automation on People,* Pergamon, 1967.

Field, J. *A Life of One's Own,* Penguin.

Fromm, Erich. *The Revolution of Hope,* Harper & Row, N.Y., 1968.

Fromm, Erich. *The Art of Loving,* Harper & Row, N.Y., 1956.

Fromm, Erich. *The Sane Society,* Fawcett, Greenwich, Conn., 1955.

Fromm, Erich (Ed.). *Symposium on Humanism,* Doubleday, N.Y., 1965.

Fromm, Erich. *Beyond the Chains of Illusion,* Simon and Schuster, N.Y., 1963.

Fromm, Erich. *Heart of Man,* Harper & Row, N.Y., 1964.

Fromm, Erich. *Man for Himself,* Fawcett, Greenwich, Conn., 1968.

Fry, Northrop. *The Modern Century,* Oxford University Press, Toronto, 1967.

Gabor, D. *Inventing the Future,* Secker and Warburg, London, 1963.

Gallaher, A. *Perspectives in Developmental Change,* University of Kentucky Press, Lexington, 1968.

Gallup, George. *The Miracle Ahead,* Harper & Row, N.Y., 1964.

Ginzherg, Eli. *Technology and Social Change,* Columbia University Press, N.Y., 1964.

Goldstein, K. *Human Nature,* Oxford University Press.

Gordon, M. *Sick Cities,* N.Y., Macmillan, 1963.

Green, Arnold W. *Sociology: An Analysis of Life in Modern Society,* 5th ed. McGraw-Hill, N.Y., 1968.

Hayakawn, S. I. *Language in Thought and Action,* Harcourt, Brace.

Hebb, D. O. *The Organization of Behavior,* Wiley.

Hoffer, Eric. *The Ordeal of Change,* Harper and Row, N.Y., 1952.

Hunt, Elgin F. & Karlin, Jules. *Society Today and Tomorrow,* Collier-Macmillan, N.Y., 1967.

Jeffress, L. A. (Ed.). *Cerebral Mechanisms in Behavior,* Wiley.

Johnson, W. *People in Quandaries,* Harper & Row.

Huxley, Aldous. *Brave New World,* Bantam Books, New York, 1st copyright, 1932.

Huxley, Aldous. *Island, Chatto and Windus,* London.

Kahn, Herman. *Thinking about the Unthinkable,* Horizon Press, 1962.

Kahn, Herman. *The Year 2000,* Macmillan, N.Y., 1967.

Kelly, G. A. *The Psychology of Personal Constructs,* Norton.

Keyes, K. *How to Develop Your Thinking Ability,* McGraw-Hill.

Kluckhohn, C. *Mirror for Man,* McGraw-Hill.

Korzybski, A. *Manhood of Humanity,* Dulton.

Lee, I. J. *Language Habits in Human Affairs,* Harper & Row.

Lechman, Milton. *This High Man,* Strauss and Company, N.Y., 1963.

Lewis, K. *Dynamic Theory of Personality,* McGraw-Hill.

Maltz, Maxwell. *Psycho-Cybernetics,* Simon and Schuster, N.Y., 1960.

Mathur, J. C. *New Lamps for Aladdin,* Orient Longmans, Calcutta, 1965.

May, Rollo. *Man's Search for Himself,* Norton, N.Y., 1953.

Mayo, Elton. *The Human Problems of an Industrial Civilization,* Viking Press, N.Y., 1960.

Michael, Donald N. *The Next Generation,* Random, N.Y., 1963.

Montagu, Ashley. *The Human Revolution,* World Publishing, Cleveland, Ohio, 1961.

Montagu, E. *The Man Who Never Was,* Bantam Books, N.Y., 1965.

Morrison, Elting E. *Men, Machines and Modern Times,* M.I.T. Press, Cambridge, Mass., 1966.

Ong, S. F. & Walter J. *Knowledge and the Future of Man,* Holt, Rinehart and Winston, N.Y., 1968.

Philipson, Morris (Ed.). *Automation: Implications for the Future,* Vintage, N.Y., 1964.

Platt, John R. *The Step to Man,* Wiley, N.Y., 1966.

Rahakrishan, S. *East and West.* Allen and Unwin.

Russell, Bertrand. *The Future of Science,* Philosophical Library Inc., N.Y., 1959.

Russell, Bertrand. *Has Man a Future?* Penguin, N.Y., 1962.

Russell, Bertrand. *New Hopes for a Changing World,* Humanities, N.Y., 1960.

Slater, P. E. *Microcosm,* Wiley, N.Y., 1966.

Spicer, E. H. (Ed.). *Human Problems in Technological Change,* Wiley, 1952.

Swados, Harvey. *Years of Conscience: The Muckrakers,* Meridian, Cleveland, 1962.

Theobald, Robert. *Human Rights in a Cybernated Age,* Pennsylvania State University, 1963.

Theobald, Robert (Ed.). *Social Policies for America in the 70's,* Doubleday, N.Y., 1968.

Theobald, Robert. *Problems of War and Peace in the Society of Nations,* Committee on International Relations, University of California, 1967.

Vickers, Geoffrey. *The Undirected Society: Essays on the Human Implications of Industrialization in Canada,* University of Toronto Press, Toronto, 1959.

Walker, Charles R. *Modern Technology and Civilization,* McGraw-Hill, N.Y., 1962.

Weinberg, Meyer, & Shabat, O. *Society and Man,* Prentice-Hall, 1965.

Wells, H. G. *The Time Machine,* Berkeley Publishing, 1964.

Wooldridge, Dean E. *Mechanical Man,* McGraw-Hill, N.Y., 1968.

CHAPTER 38

Afterwords

by Don Toppin

ON OCTOBER 4TH, 1957, Sputnik I orbited the earth and became the first earth satellite. On July 20th, 1969, Neil Armstrong set foot on the moon stating "One small step for a man; one giant leap for mankind". It is assumed that he meant "all mankind" because, significant as was "one small step", Neil Armstrong must have known that, like Newton, he actually had stood on the shoulders of giants.

It would be impossible to create a chronological table showing all forerunner achievements which made the landing conceivable and possible. We might briefly note some of these events:

3500 B.C.	Wheel and axle used for transport
3000 B.C.	Beginning of hieroglyphics
2500 B.C.	Construction of the Great Pyramid
1500 B.C.	First evidence of the pulley
400 B.C.	Invention of the catapult by the Greeks
270 B.C.	Archimedes devises the endless screw
60 B.C.	Hero of Alexandria makes important inventions including the aeolipile and the screw press
1 A.D.	The birth of Christ and the beginning of recorded time
600 A.D.	Persia develops the horizontal windmill

1100 A.D.	Papermaking industry develops in southern Europe
1190 A.D.	The magnetic compass reaches Europe from the East
1440 A.D.	Gutenberg invents the printing press in Germany
1492 A.D.	Columbus discovers America
1495 A.D.	Leonardo da Vinci foresees such inventions as the flying machine
1510 A.D.	Copernicus introduced the theory that the earth and other planets move around the sun
1609 A.D.	Galileo builds the first modern telescope
1642 A.D.	Pascal invents the first calculating machine
1642 A.D.	Torricell invents the barometer to demonstrate the existence of atmospheric pressure
1660 A.D.	Van Guericke invents a frictional electrical device—the first machine to generate electricity
1680 A.D.	Huygens introduces the principle of internal combustion
1700 A.D.	Sir Isaac Newton formulated the law of gravitation and initiated the science of modern physics
1746 A.D.	Pieter van Musschenbrock constructs the first electrical condenser
1752 A.D.	Benjamin Franklin demonstrates the concept of "positive" and "negative" electricity
1780 A.D.	James Watt perfects the steam engine
1800 A.D.	Volta invents the electric battery
1803 A.D.	Dalton advances his theory of the atomic composition of all matter
1822 A.D.	Babbage develops a complex computing machine, forerunner to the modern computer
1826 A.D.	Niepce makes first successful photography
1831 A.D.	Faraday constructs electric generator
1834 A.D.	Jacobi develops battery-powered electric motor

1844 A.D.	Morse builds first electric telegraph
1866 A.D.	Successful laying of first transatlantic cable
1875 A.D.	Crookes develops cathode-ray tube
1876 A.D.	Bell patents the telephone
1882 A.D.	Edison establishes the first large scale electric power system in New York City. He had also invented the phonograph and the incandescent electric lamp
1886 A.D.	Benz and Daimler construct first petrol-engine automobile
1895 A.D.	Installation of the Niagara Falls hydro-electric plant
1901 A.D.	Marconi sends first wireless signal across the Atlantic
1903 A.D.	Wright Brothers make first successful powered-airplane flight
1905 A.D.	Einstein announces his theory of relativity
1906 A.D.	Fessenden transmits first modulated radio-wave broadcast
1907 A.D.	DeForest invents three-electrode vacuum tube which was important toward the development of radio
1908 A.D.	Ford introduces assembly line mass production of "Model T" automobiles
1920 A.D.	The first radio station opens in Pittsburg
1922 A.D.	Jenkins invents telephoto
1925 A.D.	The first successful sound-motion pictures are produced
1927 A.D.	Lindberg flies across the Atlantic
1927 A.D.	First transatlantic telephone service is established
1929 A.D.	Zworykin designs a practical television system with his "iconoscope" (pick-up tube) and "kinescope" (receiving tube).
1935 A.D.	Watson-Watt develops radar
1939 A.D.	First turbojet plane is introduced in Germany

1942 A.D.   Manhattan project commenced for development of atomic bomb

1942 A.D.   Fermi constructs first nuclear reactor

1942 A.D.   Braun develops the long-range V-2 rocket

1944 A.D.   IBM and Harvard develop the Mark 1 computer

1945 A.D.   U.S. test explodes first atomic bomb at New Mexico

1947 A.D.   Weiner introduces the science of cybernetics

1951 A.D.   The transistor is invented by Shockley, Bardeen and Brattain

1954 A.D.   The first solar battery is developed in U.S.A.

1954 A.D.   Townes invents the maser

1956 A.D.   Britain constructs a system of atomic generating stations

1957 A.D.   Russia launches Sputnik I

1958 A.D.   The laser is invented by Townes and Schawlow

1958 A.D.   Van Allen discovers high-energy radiation belt in outer space

1958 A.D.   First U.S. satellite, Explorer I, orbits the earth

1959 A.D.   Russia's Lunar II becomes the first satellite to reach the moon

1961 A.D.   Yuri Gagarin makes the first manned orbital space flight

1962 A.D.   U.S. satellite Tel star provides first direct telephone and television communication between U.S. and Europe

1966 A.D.   Russia's Lunar IX transmits television photos of the lunar surface

1967 A.D.   Saturn 5 becomes the largest and most powerful rocket ever sent into space

1968 A.D.   Apollo 8 transmits live television, by man, from the moon

1969 A.D.   Armstrong, Aldrin and Collins become the heroes in "man's first landing on the moon" and most of the inhabitants of the earth watched by television, or listened by radio, as Armstrong proclaimed "one giant leap for mankind".

And indeed it was!

"The media were the message" and all mankind participated in witnessing, almost unknowingly, the greatest triumph of applied cybernetics. Insights of men, living and dead, had been marshalled toward the achievement of one single goal. Every component had been tested and retested. Every step was programmed by computer. Every invention in communications had been synthesized successfully into a "total concept" system. All mankind, men of diverse backgrounds and birthplaces, made the successful mission possible. The Russians inspired President Kennedy to appropriate the money for the National Aeronautics and Space Administration (NASA). The Germans contributed Werner Von Braun, now top man at the Marshall Space Flight Centre which gave birth to the Saturn V rocket boosters, in spite of the fact that he had been a main creator of the V-2 rockets which plagued London during World War Two.

The plaque left on the moon reads simply: "Here men from the planet earth first set foot upon the moon, July 1969 A.D. We come in peace for all mankind." Messages from leaders of seventy-three countries were also left. Prime Minister Pierre Elliott Trudeau of Canada said, "Man reached out and touched the tranquil moon. May that high accomplishment allow man to rediscover the earth and find peace."

That is what this book is all about! If science and technology can be used in coordination with men, money, materials, machines and management, through cybernetics, to place a man on the moon, and to provide global communication and participation, then, it should be relatively simple to reach the greater goal of world peace which must, as a matter of process, involve the elimination of violence and poverty.

Jack Gould, esteemed television columnist for the New York Times wrote on Sunday, July 27, 1969:

"The meaning of the Apollo 11 landing—scientifically, socially and philosophically—will be debated for months, but thanks to TV and radio, the layman will have his own first-hand thoughts on the course of the forthcoming dialogue. Through pooled TV coverage untold millions of viewers around the world were there when it happened.

Such individual involvement would seem certain to be a factor in molding man's opinions about meeting other challenges that so often seem insurmountable. When interplanetary travel can be forecast down to the split-second, the various crises on earth inevitably fall into a different perspective.

The success of Apollo 11 in reaching the moon was a lesson in the limitless powers of mankind to make the impossible seem feasible, given the commitment of resources and the determination and skill to achieve the dreams that for so many generations appeared beyond grasp.

The effect of TV's Apollo coverage was to present, in personalized terms, the fact that civilization underestimates its own potential and sadly and frequently becomes bogged down in bureaucratic squabbles and partisan expediency. The arrival of Apollo II on the moon was a reaffirmation of the lost virtues of teamwork in society."

Is it too much to suggest that teamwork, through the interdisciplinarian science of cybernetics, might eliminate bureaucratic squabbles and partisan expediency to the point where civilized men of all nations will agree on attaining the objective of resolving the major issues on earth?

2

It has been observed that to stop science would create more problems than solutions. Many scientists must feel humble as they look back over the surprises of the past few years. Yet knowledge is predicted to double again by 1975. We have good reason for great optimism because, as science grows, it penetrates deeper into mystery and, if emphasis is placed on human development in contrast to human destruction, human knowledge may be visualized as an expanding sphere whose volume grows larger as its diameter increases. When the scientific cybernetic approach is shifted to the social sciences, as is already being done in biology, chemistry, engineering, etc., the future looks very bright—but there are problems and much need for adjustments.

McLuhan [1] comments that: (1) "In the age of structures, knowledge necessarily replaces experience and planned effect replaces mere narrative sequence. Under satellite conditions, the great centralist structures of maxi-states and big-business organizations are being reshaped into small nucleated patterns. This accounts for what Peter Drucker notes as "the growing disparity between apparent power and actual control in government—in the international arena government has all but disintegrated. The 'sovereign state' no longer functions as the effective organ for public tasks." (2) Electric speed-up and the environment of telecommunications creates innumerable mini-states that are not specialist or exclusive. These new forms are inclusive as are those of family and tribal government.

"Any visually-organized attempt to cope with such inclusive structures as those created by the new electric environments

[1] Magazine edition, Dewline Newsletter, by Marshall McLuhan, Human Development Corporation, 1969, Vol. I, No. 8.

leads to direct conflict, whether at the parent-child level or at the business or international level. It is not generally understood that the structure of these new patterns is not one of explosion, nor of expansion, but of implosion. It is the pulling out of the spaces between components. Telecommunications pulls out the space and time distance between all operations, all information, all associations. This is the structure of the new organization at every level and in every region of the contemporary world. It is the antithesis of bureaucratic structure. It ends the organization chart just as it ends party politics based on policies. It ends subjects and credits in universities. It substitutes knowledge for experience, and creates learning by immersion. It replaces job-holding by role-playing. For the manager, it requires fusion of the roles of emperor and clown, of environment-maker and image-prober.

"Drucker [2] observes that in 1900 there were fewer than fifty sovereignties in the whole world—twenty in Europe and twenty in the Americas, with the rest of the world having fewer than a dozen. World War I increased the number to about sixty. Now we have more than one hundred and sixty, with new "mini-states" joining the ranks almost every month. The other side of this process of decentralization is the rise of the 'superpowers', the monopolizers of advanced technologies. These superpowers have themselves become service environments for the rest of the globe (and each other) and cease to be sovereign states in the old sense. These are the powers with the atomic weapons, the 'overkill' that produces 'the peace that passeth all technology'.

"In conclusion, it might be helpful to indicate some of the forms of the new mini-states compressed within the vast service environment of the new global theatre. They include the teenagers, the hippies and the elderly. Both 'mother Bell' and AT&T constitute mini-states that are part of the world service environment. IBM and RCA are similar 'alma maters' or

2 *The Age of Discontinuity* by Peter Drucker, Harper & Row, 1969.

'world mothers' of our new tribal condition. Universities are mini-states, as are trade and credit unions. All major media, railways, newspapers, and broadcasting systems are mini-states. The American negro is a mini-state first created by jazz. Jazz became and remains part of the world service and cultural environment. This reversal is as incongruous as the process by which in the 1920's the communities of the world were integrated by popular negro jazz. The avant-garde is a mini-state as much as is the global rock-music community or the teenage market. Of course, the armed services are mini-states as is the police force. Jet city, the 'urb' as 'orb', is a new maxi-state enveloping all the metropolitan areas which it has supplanted. The de-Romanization of the Roman Catholic Church is a prominent instance. The individual Catholic and the 'Mystical Body' now constitute mini-states. These closed structures are the exact opposite of the schismatic Catholic of the sixteenth century. The sixteenth century drop-out from the Catholic Church was prompted by private interpretation and fragmentary specialism. The twentieth century drop-out is motivated by a sense of wholeness and involvement. All existing metros are now undergoing the same dissolution as all other centralist structures, large or small. Mini-states, then, are not centralized governments in any form, but are resonating spheres of existence whose centres are everywhere and whose boundaries are nowhere."

3

Because of the high speed of extensions and expansions at the outer diameters, there are serious dichotomies. Theoretically, at the moment, mankind should be entering an era of unity but, temporarily, because of their new information and fears, there is a tendency for men to gather more closely into protective tribal groups, supposedly for self-protection. Global communication systems offer the potential of global participation as was evident with the "man on the moon". But television has already shown that pictures of affluent families with swimming pools simply tell minority groups that they too should be uniting to grab these benefits themselves. The oppressed must be satisfied on terms which are compatible with those of other humans and this, I am confident, can happen through increased productivity by cybernation and the sharing of rewards and responsibilities. There are already substantial trends.

But of greater urgency is the fact that a slow system cannot long survive within a fast system. Government systems, though not necessarily the people within the systems, are traditionally slow. First, the tenure of office for a public-elected official is uncertain and, usually, short. To some degree, the turn-over problem also applies to civil servants who are often dependent upon the elected representatives. There is also a tendency within any bureaucracy for executives to rapidly reach the point of maximum inefficiency, as recently noted by "The Peter Principal". Each man stakes out his territory and protects himself like a tom-cat. To avoid embarrassment, there is always the temptation to hire someone less efficient rather than the man who will get things done. So slow systems tend to become slower—rather than to adjust to change.

Hence, there are wheels within wheels; some moving slowly; some not moving at all; some moving in conflicting directions (i.e., municipal, federal, state, provincial, professional, unions, associations, etc.). Each tribe has its interests to protect. Conflictions can be great and hardly anyone is concerned with the new problems and potentials of the global community itself.

So we have the information overload, the increasing speed at the outer perimeters and the slow-down, almost sabotage, of the low-speed wheels within wheels. But, at the center of every wheel is the hub and the hub surrounds the "hole". Taking a literary liberty, let's spell it "whole". In other words, the centre of your universe is you. You are the "whole" and you can relate to the outer dimensions. Moreover, around you is a community; your relatives; friends, business and professional associates and often sympathetic members of the slow-moving "in-between" bureaucracies—some of whom are amazingly "with it" in off-hours. You have your area of influence. You do not have to be known as a non-conformist; you can adopt a "minimal change" attitude within your groups . . . providing you understand.

In this respect, we commend the efforts of various groups, including the Human Development Association which meets regularly in Montreal, and Viewpoints Institute in Los Angeles. The brochure, in part, says: "Briefly, this world view divides the history of the development of western man, from its earliest unknown origins in pre-historic times to the modern day, into five major stages (plus one intervening dark age):

—the primitive (from ? to 650 B.C.)
—the age of reason (650 B.C. to 350 A.D.)
—the age of classical science (1500 A.D. to 1900 A.D.)
—the age of relativity science (1900 A.D. to the present)
—the age of unity (from the present to ?)

"Each stage carries with it its own viewpoint and methods of thinking, and constitutes an advance over each preceding one. It should not be thought that each succeeding age has rejected all that has gone before. Rather, in each case, some of the errors of the past have been corrected and a broader more comprehensive viewpoint and methodology has been developed.

One of the major problems facing the world today is that the vast majority of the human race is still at the primitive stage of development; a few millions have reached the age of reason; a few hundred thousands, the age of classical science; a few thousands, the age of relativity; a handful, the age of unity.

We are faced with the vast educational task of bringing enormous numbers of people forward, as rapidly as possible, through to the more advanced stages of development."

4

The world is changing faster than you can read this sentence. Since this book was commenced a great deal has happened which may be just as important, if less sensational, as the man on the moon.

It is clear that automation, through cybernetics, is here to stay and is no longer a subject for debate. As someone commented, "In the future, there will be two kinds of people; those who relate to cybernation and those who don't." We hope this book has been commencement exercise in successfully relating.

The revolution of youth is now world-wide, and it is against authoritarian institutionalism of all kinds. Dr. Offer's [3] project in Chicago produced evidence that normal teen-agers get along very well with their parents, especially if they are instrumentalists and not institutionalists. Basically, they are a fine group. But, they won't be fooled. A young student friend spent the summer in Europe. Her parents had escaped from Communism and are now happy in Canada. Many of her young friends are young revolutionaries who are violently revolting within themselves about the USSR attempt to be safe from "capitalist domination". "Why?" she asked "Do you not come to America?" They replied that they would like to have the material advantages of America but that they preferred the "humanitarianism of Russia to the violence, chaos and war policies of USA." Everywhere, youth continues to dissent about

[3] This Chicago project scientifically investigated "Revolt of Youth".

war, violence and poverty and everywhere there is dissatisfaction about the inability of present institutions to solve the great problems of the day and to get on to the great issue of self-fulfillment.

The Duke of Edinborough recently said: "Everything good has been brought about by people being dissatisfied. But people lose this dissatisfaction when they become part of the establishment. Establishments could be changed from within if those people could remain dissatisfied."

On the matter of dissent, Sir Eric Ashby, Vice-Chancellor, University of Cambridge, told the 10th Commonwealth Universities Congress: "All fruitful innovation in intellectual matters depends on the mastery of the discipline of dissent. First, the pupil must become familiar with orthodoxy; he must absorb and understand what is already known about his subject. But this is only the first step in a full education, although it is as far as many students ever get.

"The pupil then has to learn how to question orthodoxy, but to do so in a special kind of way. Not like the nihilist, whose object is to destroy what is believed or practiced and to put nothing in its place; nor like the pendant who questions and corrects only trivialities.

"It has to be a constructive dissent which fulfills one overriding condition: it must shift the state of opinion about the subject in such a way that other experts in the subject are prepared to concur. This is done either by producing acceptable new data or by re-interpreting old data in a convincing way.

"It is a very austere form of dissent and it is difficult to learn. But it is this discipline of dissent which has rescued knowledge, in fields as wide apart as theology and physics, from remaining authoritarian and static."

A local High School principal [4] had some sound advice

---

[4] From the Huntsville Forester, Douglas C. Stone, Principal of Huntsville High School.

when he scolded parents for their conformity and told his graduating class: "These are the words for today and tomorrow—adaptability, flexibility and involvement. You young people have them, you believe in them, use, and will expand upon them. We older ones will have to learn their meaning quickly."

Which brings me back to my main point which is simply this: nobody really wants war, poverty and violence, yet all three are supported by the establishment, largely because of the gaps in communication, comprehension, coordination and planning—and sometimes short-sighted vested interests. Everyone wants peace and basic economic security in order to live a life of self-fulfillment with "liberty and pursuit of happiness".

As I pursued my study of "Communication and Cybernation", it became increasingly evident that here are the concepts which can, for the first time, eliminate war, violence and poverty. As I explored the thoughts of hundreds of distinguished thinkers, some of whom are represented briefly in this book, it became dramatically clear that this book had assumed a social purpose which could have a much greater influence than the simple primer on the "nature of the age" which was originally intended.

The oppressed are now in the majority. Over 50% of the world's population are under twenty-five; over 50% are non-white; and over 50% illiterate. There is the odd person who still believes that Communism (USSR or China) or Capitalism (USA) will conquer the world. But how can an obsolete concept conquer anything and how especially can these countries conquer the world when they have failed to solve their own problems at home. As someone recently said: "The great american dream has become the great american nightmare." I have spelled america in lower case to imply that I am including Canada and Pan-American countries. Even in Canada and USA, almost thirty percent of the population live in poverty and over forty percent have less than a Grade Nine education; a sad commentary on our industrial, political and educational systems and a weak showing for "the affluent society."

When asked the difference between capitalism and communism, U Thant, General Secretary of the United Nations, replied, "Under communism, man exploits man; under capitalism, it is visa-versa." But, as I keep saying, both terms are anachronisms; as Galbraith points out, all states tend to converge in nature under the impact of technological change. Moreover, China suspects Russia of returning to capitalism.

As Malcolm Muggeridge recently said: "Words like conservative, progressive, revolution, left, right, etc., become meaningless jargon in the world today. The liberation of man comes from people who understand and see visions—meaning they can see beyond the immediate preoccupations." It is in this respect that the Korolevs and Sakharovs may have a greater impact than Sputnik.

"The Soviet Union proceeds from principles of peaceful co-existence and co-operation with countries with different social systems," according to Vadim Ardatovsky [5] of the Novosti Press Agency. "It is implementing them in practice, in relations with many countries. We have good neighbourly relations with Finland, Iran, Afghanistan. There is a certain change for the good in relations with Turkey. Mutual understanding in important political questions exists with France with which, just like with Italy, the Soviet Union is widely cooperating in the field of economics."

As I write, Kosygin is on a holiday in Hungary meditating, according to the press, on how he can proceed with peace talks with Nixon. Nixon is on holiday, probably, wondering how he can proceed with peace talks with Kosygin. Neither leader is unaware of the futility of further escalation through ABM (Anti-Ballistic Missiles) or MIRV (Multiple Indepen-

[5] "Russia Today", January, 1969.

dently targetable Re-entry Vehicle)—a system which works like a flying-bus carrying missiles instead of people and programmed to drop these bombs over major cities in a matter of minutes. US claims that the USSR is testing MIRV but, according to Pentagon scientist John Foster, there is no evidence to support this conclusion.

Satellite surveillance has made phased disarmament realizable but Mr. Kosygin and Mr. Nixon are committed to enormous institutions which insist on saying "go" while the world says "stop". If these two men can come together and courageously say "stop", I enthusiastically predict that the frustrations of mankind, especially youth, will rapidly diminish and the youth of the world will rapidly unite on a non-political basis to use technology for the humanization of the earth.

Around about 1936, Winston Churchill made a widely-reported speech in which he suggested that England might well benefit by following the example of Hitler in Germany. On a radio broadcast a few days later, with youthful naivete, I made the simple prediction that Nazism would inevitably lead to war. A letter was sent out from national radio headquarters stating that, in the future, all commentaries must be submitted in writing one week in advance. Fortunately, both Canada and I recovered from this brief period of speech censorship. The point is, as the saying somehow goes, "out of the mouths of babes cometh wisdom". All leaders might be wise to listen at this time to the voices of informed, though disillusioned, youth around the world.

Strength is no longer synonomous with security and I have yet to find anyone under twenty-five who wants war. As a matter of fact the greatest source of protest seems to be against those institutions which are subsidized through military contracts. But these same industries might be just as happy to make their profits through contracts from the research, development and manufacture of cybernated equipment which can be used for the benefit of all mankind. Underdeveloped countries have immediate markets for industries within developed countries.

5

As to the future, assuming that the ballistic build-up is halted forever, there can be great optimism about "This Cybernetic Age—the age of unity".

Newspaper items almost daily report events which indicate movement toward the fulfillment of many of the things which have been discussed by our distinguished collaborators:

—A National Goals Research Staff has been established to analyze and synthesize the efforts of both public and private institutions which are involved in forecasting the future. It should be linked with the UN.

—The pilot plan on the guaranteed annual income in Maryland, has been, for the most part, so great a success that the President has announced an extension for the nation which will be closely tied in with programs for training and public works, but time is running out.

—The latest figures show that poverty is decreasing and that some of the Manpower Development plans, weak as they were, have produced some results.

—Some people within formal educational institutions have become deeply committed to the process of change.

—Industry has become aware of the inadequacy of much of the formal educational process and, more and more, are becoming interested in the "individual" as contrasted with the "certificate". Private educational organizations must be encouraged and supported.

—The concept of the "Global Shopping Centre" as identified by Peter Drucker is becoming recognized by a multitude of multi-national industries and, we should add

402 / THIS CYBERNETIC AGE

for the sake of the socialist countries, governments. As Drucker emphasizes, the world-wide communication of goods, services, standards and ways of life will become ever more evasive.

—The concepts of the "Global Village" as envisioned by Barbara Ward and the "Global Theatre" of Marshall McLuhan are becoming real and "Global College" has been born which will provide education,[6] in Global English, to anyone, anywhere, at any time, at any level —and at a cost which is amazingly low.

—Computer networks, the use of terminals, in libraries, homes and businesses and the provision of computer services as a public utility are becoming a reality.

—Learning research centres are being established in schools using multi-media equipment to individualize the learning process.

—Communication by satellite is now taken for granted (i.e., the crowning of the Prince of Wales and the pictures from Mars).

—The science of cybernetics as it applies to the individual has become recognized through such books as "Psycho-Cybernetics" and "Success Cybernetics".

—The current generation of recruits entering the so-called knowledge organizations is bringing new attitudes and concerns.

—Soaring meat prices may encourage more development of the artificial meat industry.

—Automation fears are diminishing. Human values need not be destroyed and the list could go on and on.

As a matter of fact, everything seems to channel into the areas of human development; development of self in relationship to others in the community, business and the world. Even

[6] For information, write to Don Toppin, Box 960, Bracebridge, Muskoka, Ontario, Canada.

the limitations of institutionalism, provincialism and politics become less frightening when it is realized that change can take place from within and, in fact, does. The supply of goods and services can become unlimited. Through cybernetics, the new developments in biology, chemistry, engineering, etc. can make further scientific development unlimited.

If the full forces of cybernation can be unleashed, in harmony with the new scientific knowledge and resources, towards achieving the objective of maximizing the production of goods and services at minimized per unit costs, the ten percent increase in gross national product, as already predicted by the Hudson Institute, would pay for all conceivable extensions which have been noted in this book. If only eight percent of this income went into the central pool, stockholders and entrepreneurs would also increase their profits. As productivity rises and unit costs are reduced, real wages should increase and consumer costs decrease leaving more spendable income. But neither wages nor consumer costs should be allowed to rise at a rate which exceeds productivity. At the moment, Japan becomes the model with both productivity and wages increasing side-by-side while per unit costs decrease largely because of automation.

So far we have not even mentioned the benefits which could be derived if, for example, the defence budget of every nation could be reduced at least fifty percent with this money going directly to the United Nations as a contribution to an international police force until such time as it is reasonable to appropriate it to worthier purposes. This would also avoid excessive unemployment of military personnel.

Moreover, 1. Many of the new developments either create new money or reduce present costs. 2. A guaranteed income would have the effect of bolstering the entire economy through increased purchasing power for consumer goods. 3. Education costs can be dramatically decreased by modern instructional technology as already proven and direct payments to worthy students would go a long way toward making educational organizations democratic and self-supporting as some already are.

The potential of applied cybernetics is enormous as the moon landing has proven. Global communications systems will make it possible for all men to know their brothers. There will be time, money and resources to help when help is needed. Ray Bradbury, interviewed in London, England, by Mike Wallace on the CBS Evening News, July 21, 1969, said, "When we move out into the mystery and loneliness of space, when we begin to discover that we really are three billion lonely people on a small world, I think it's going to draw us much closer together."

Marshall McLuhan, as guest of honor at the Lord Mayor's banquet in London on the occasion of the 21st Anniversary of the Formal Birth of Cybernetics, said, among other things: "Cybernetics is from the Greek word cybernetes—navigator, ruler, steersman. Today's cybernetics means programming a comprehensive awareness of human needs and satisfactions. The specialist is finished, in Echo Land, in the world of resonance and total interface of cultures and technologies. Echo Land is a world of resonance, designated by electric engineers and modern chemistry alike on the material bond of being. Resonance is the term used by scientists for the nature of the chemical bond. Because every event now has its effects on every part of the world at the same time it is impossible to have a fixed point of view or a single goal. Since Sputnik, the planet has become a global theatre. I used to say village but it's changed to a theatre with a proscenium of satellites. Space capsule earth now becomes content of satellite environment, of electrical information, i.e., the future belongs to the computer programmer of total environments. Echo Land has become ecological, social and political reality. Now people want roles, not goals, i.e., involvement, self-effacement. Private identity becomes a meaningless burden in a world when you are totally involved with everyone else. At computer speed one penny can do all the economic transactions of the globe. It's up to the computer people to put back into the world equilibrium and consciousness."

Norman Cousins in an editorial in the September 20, 1969 issue of Saturday Review tells about a fascinating television debate which he watched in his hotel room in Lagos, Nigeria, on the proposition that the human race is decadent. The Nigerian student who took the affirmative pointed at the tragedy in store for any leader who genuinely tried to upgrade the conditions of life, then referred to the assassinations of four men, John F. Kennedy, Robert F. Kennedy, Martin Luther King and Tom Mboya. He stated that violence was the dominant characteristic of our time and cited large numbers of television programs glorifying brutality or cruelty—mostly from the USA. He then said that most of the energies of mankind had turned to the manufacture of weapons which could smash civilization beyond recognition or repair. He also spoke about the great disparity of wealth in the world with 80% of the goods produced or owned by only 6% of the world's peoples. He talked of dead fish, of pollution, of poisons from automobiles, of the high divorce rate, of depravity in entertainment. We are not merely decadent but downright degraded. He was applauded; his points could not be refuted.

Then his opponent stepped forward—a lovely and attractively dressed young lady. She began by saying that at any given time in history it would be possible to point to any number of serious faults in the human record. But the general movement of history was forward. Man was not perfect but he was at least perfectible. Whatever his propensity for error, she declared, he had an unerring instinct for justice that was at least equal to his instinct for survival. Man's ability to define the right and his insistence on achieving it, even at fearsome cost, were his main tools in fashioning an ever-better life. She spoke of the inexorable process by which peoples liberated themselves from outside rule, beginning with the American Revolution in 1776 and extending to the national freedom movements in Africa today. The young lady did not despair of man's ability to use his science for his own good. She felt that human intelligence was on the verge of its greatest victories; disease, ignorance, poverty, and venality would eventually all fall before it. Meanwhile, all humanity could exult over man's voyage to the moon, representing as it did the combined triumph of man's knowledge, technology and spirit. She emphasized the expedition to the moon as offering proof of man's ability to meet any problem worth meeting. She was declared the winner.

Dr. Harvey Cox of the Harvard Divinity School writes in "The Futurist"; "In modern terms the prophetic mood has confidence in the worth of moral and political action. It sees the world as one that man is unavoidably summoned to shape in accord with his hopes and memories. It rejects the notion that this or that elect group can escape cosmic ruination or is destined to rule the rest of us. It sees the future with its manifold possibilities undoing the determinative grip of the past, of the beginning.

"Prophesy insists that the future will be shaped not by invisible malevolent forces or by irresistible inherent tendencies but by what men decide to do. This unconditioned openness to the future also allows prophesy to escape from the paralysis of past decisions and policies. The prophetic call always requires repentance, the candid recognition that one has made mistakes but will now do something different. Policies need not be papered over with spurious claims that they are simply extensions of decisions made in the past. The prophetic perspective requires incessant innovation and the continuous reappraisal of past policies because tomorrow will not be just an unfolding of yesterday's tendencies but will include aspects of unprecedented novelties.

"Can we not put aside both falling firmament and sprouting spores as our image of history and act on the conviction that there is no future except the one we make? The answer to this question will be given not in our creedal recitations but in how we make our individual and political decisions in the years ahead."

Come! Let us reason together! The problems are great but the rewards are greater! We have nothing to lose since the instruments of death have already made death a reality if we fail to adjust. We have everything to gain since the instruments of life can, for the first time, be available to all. This cybernetic age can truly become the golden age of unity, freedom, and self-realization with peace and abundance for all.

THE CANDLE OF FELLOWSHIP
FOR THIS CYBERNETIC AGE

I will light the candle of fellowship tonight. I know that the experiences of unity in human relations are more compelling than the concepts, the fears, the prejudices, which divide. Despite the tendency to feel my race superior, my nation the greatest nation, my faith the true faith, I must beat down the boundaries of my exclusiveness until my sense of separateness is completely enveloped in a sense of fellowship. There must be free and easy access by all, to all the rich resources accumulated by groups and individuals in years of living and experiencing. I will light the candle of fellowship tonight, a candle that must burn forever.

Adapted from an extract from
"The Inward Journey" by Dr.
Howard Thurman, reprinted,
courtesy of Harper & Bros.,
New York and Abitibi Provincial
Paper Ltd.

BOOKS FOR FURTHER STUDY
LAST MINUTE RECOMMENDATIONS

Asimov, Isaac. *Is Anyone There?* Doubleday. 320 pages.
$5.95

Ayers, Robert U. *Technological Forecasting.* McGraw-Hill. An excellent review of the state of the art—and one that can be understood by non-technologists.

Bennis, Benne and Chin. *The Planning of Change.* Holt, Rinehart, Winston, 383 Madison Avenue, New York, New York, 10017. New edition excellent for professionals.

Birenbaum, William M. *Overlive: Power, Poverty and the University.* Dial/Delacorte. 224 pages. $6.25

Bowen and Kavesh (Eds.). *Automation and Economic Progress.* Spectrum. Paperback. 167 pages. $1.95

Bravo, Francisco. *Christ in the Thought of Teilhard de Chardin.* University of Notre Dame Press. $6.25

Calder, Nigel (Editor). *Unless Peace Comes: A Scientific Forecast of New Weapons.* Viking Compass. 243 pages. Paperback. $1.95

Calder, Nigel (Editor). *The World of 1984.* Penguin. 420 pages. Paperback. $1.90

Churchman, C. West. *The Systems Approach.* Dial/Delacorte. 256 pages. $9.50

Collins, N. L. and Michie, D. (Eds.). *Machine Intelligence 1.* Oliver and Boyd.

Cox, Donald W. *Explorers of the Deep.* Hammond. 96 pages. $4.50

Crossman, Frederick J. *Science and Contemporary Society.* University of Notre Dame Press. $9.95

Dale, E. and Michie, D. (Eds.). *Machine Intelligence 2.* Oliver and Boyd.

Diebold, John. *Man and the Computer: Technology as an Agent of Social Change.* Frederick A. Praeger, Inc. April 1969.

Direnzo, Gordon J. *Personality, Power and Politics.* University of Notre Dame Press. $9.95

Donovan, John C. *The Politics of Poverty.* Penguin Books. cloth $7.25   paper $1.85

Drucker, Peter F. (Editor). *Preparing Tomorrow's Business Leaders Today.* $10.00

Drucker, Peter F. *The Age of Discontinuity: Guidelines to Our Changing Society.* Harper & Row. 394 pages. $7.95

Eurich, Alvin C. *Campus 1980: The Shape of the Future in American Higher Education.* Delacorte. 327 pages. $6.95

Ewald, William R. *Environment for Man: The Next Fifty Years.* Indiana University Press.

Feinberg, Gerald. *The Prometheus Project: Mankind's Search for Long-Range Goals.* Doubleday. 215 pages. $4.95

Finnocchiaro, Mary. *Teaching English as a Second Language.* Harper & Row. $8.75

George, F. H. *Cybernetics and Biology.* University reviews in Biology No. 6. Oliver and Boyd.

Glasser, William. *Schools Without Failure.* Harper & Row. 224 pages. $6.25

Gross, Bertram M. *A Great Society?* Basic. 326 pages. $8.50

Hubbard, Earl. *The Search is On.* Pace Publications, 385 South Flower Street, Los Angeles, California 90017. Paperback. A view of man's future from the new perspective of space. $1.95

Innis, Harold. *The Bias of Communication.* University of Toronto Press, University of Toronto, Toronto, Ontario. Empire and Communications.

Jungk and Galtung (Eds.). *Mankind 2000*. Universitetsforlaget, Oslo. 368 pages. Papers presented at the "First International Future Research Conference in Oslo.
$14.50

Leonard, George B. *Education and Ecstasy*. Dial/Delacorte. 256 pages. $7.50

Lobkowicz, Nicholas. *Theory and Practice*. University of Notre Dame Press. $11.25

MacNeil, Robert. *The People Machine*. Harper & Row. 384 pages. $8.75

McNamara, Robert S. *The Essence of Security*. Harper & Row. 192 pages. $6.25

Peace Division, American Friends Service Committee. *In Place of War*. Grossman. paper $1.85   cloth $4.95

Platt, John R. *The Step to Man*. John Wiley. 216 pages.
$5.95

Raphael, D. D. *Political Theory and the Rights of Man*. Indiana University Press. $7.25

Reed, Edward. *Beyond Coexistence*. The Requirements of Peace. Grossman. 320 pages. $9.50

Reichardt, Jasia. *Cybernetic Serendipity: The Computer and the Arts*. Frederick A. Praeger, Inc. June 1969.

Rosenfield, Albert. *The Second Genesis: The Coming Control of Life*. Prentice-Hall. Deals with test tube babies, etc.

Staff of "The Wall Street Journal". *The Innovators: How Today's Inventors Shape Your Life Tomorrow*. Dow Jones. 110 pages. Paperback. $1.85

Staff of "The Wall Street Journal". *Here Comes Tomorrow: Living and Working in the Year 2000*. Dow Jones Books. Paperback. 196 pages. $1.85

Steadman, John M. *The Myth of Asia*. Simon & Schuster. 353 pages. $6.95

Theobald, Robert. (Editor). *Dialogue on Technology*. Bobbs-Merrill. Paperback. 109 pages. $1.25

Theobald, Robert. *An Alternative Future for America.* Swallow. 186 pages. Paperback. $1.95
Theobald, Robert. *Committed Spending: A Route to Economic Security.* Doubleday & Company, Inc. 1968.
Theobald, Robert. *Social Policies in the '70's.* Doubleday & Company, Inc.
Thurman, Howard. *The Inward Journey.* Harper & Row.
Warshofsky, Fred. *The 21st Century: The New Age of Exploration.* Viking. $6.95

APPENDIX I

BASIC ENGLISH VOCABULARY
FOR GLOBAL COMMUNICATION

Ten words account for a fourth of all that we say, read or write. They are: and, be, have, I, it, me, of, the, will, you.

The following words make up nearly 50 per cent (or half) of all the words used by adults in writing and speaking the English language: a, about, all, are, as, at, but, can, come, day, dear, do, for, from, get, go, good, had, he, hear, her, if, in, is, letter, much, my, no, not, on, one, our, put, say, she, so, that, there, they, this, time, though, to, very, was, we, when, with, would, write, your, yours.

These are the 200 most-used nouns (pictured things): Angle, ant, apple, arch, arm, army, baby, bag, ball, band, basin, basket, bath, bed, bee, bell, berry, bird, blade, board, boat, bone, book, boot, bottle, box, boy, brain, brake, branch, brick, bridge, brush, bucket, bulb, button, cake, camera, card, carriage, cart, cat, chain, cheese, chest, chin, church, circle, clock, cloud, coat, collar, comb, cord, cow, cup, curtain, cushion, dog, door, drain, drawer, dress, drop, ear, egg, engine, eye, face, farm, feather, finger, fish, flag, floor, fly, foot, fork, fowl, frame, garden, girl, glove, goat, gun, hair, hammer, hand, hat, head, heart, hook, horn, horse, hospital, house, island, jewel, kettle, key, knee, knife, knot, leaf, leg, library, line, lip, lock, map, match, monkey, moon, mouth, muscle, nail, neck, needle, nerve, net, nose, nut, office, orange, oven, parcel, pen, pencil, picture, pig, pin, pipe, plane, plate, plough, pocket, pot, potato, prison, pump, rail, rat, receipt, ring, rod, roof, root, sail, school, scissors, screw, seed, sheep, shelf, ship, shirt, shoe, skin, skirt, snake, sock, spade, sponge, spoon, spring, square, stamp, star, station, stem, stick, stocking, stomach, store, street, sun, table, tail, thread, throat, thumb, ticket, toe, tongue, tooth, town, train, tray, tree, trousers, umbrella, wall, watch, wheel, whip, whistle, window, wing, wire, worm.

These most-used words describe "Operations": a, about, after, again, against, all, almost, among, and, any, as at, be, because, before, between, but, by, come, do, down, east, enough, even, ever, every, far, for, forward, from, get, give, go, have, he, here, how, I, if, in, keep, let, little, make, may, much, near, no, north, not, now, of, off, on, only, or, other, out, over, please, put, quite, say, see, seem, send, so, some, south, still, such, take, than, that, the, then, there, this, though, through, till, to, together, tomorrow, under, up, very, well, west, when, where, while, who, why, yes, yesterday, you.

These words describe "Qualities" (General): able, acid, angry, automatic, beautiful, black, boiling, bright, broken, brown, cheap, chemical, chief, clean, clear, common, complex, conscious, cut, deep, dependent, early, elastic, electric, equal, fat, fertile, first, fixed, flat, free, frequent, full, general, good, great, grey, hanging, happy, hard, healthy, high, hollow, important, kind, like, living, long, male, married, material, medical, military, natural, necessary, new, normal, open, parallel, past, physical, political, poor, possible, present, private, probable, quick, quiet, ready, red, regular, responsible, right, round, same, second, separate, serious, sharp, smooth, sticky, stiff, straight, strong, sudden, sweet, tall, thick, tight, tired, true, violent, waiting, warm, wet, wide, wise, yellow, young.

(Opposites): awake, bad, bent, bitter, blue, certain, cold, complete, cruel, dark, dead, dear, delicate, different, dirty, dry, false, feeble, female, foolish, future, green, ill, last, late, left, loose, loud, low, mixed, narrow, old, opposite, public, rough, sad, safe, secret, short, shut, simple, slow, small, soft, solid, special, strange, thin, white, wrong.

This list of "nouns" describes "General things": account, act, addition, adjustment, advertisement, agreement, air, amount, amusement, animal, answer, apparatus, approval, argument, art, attack, attempt, attention, attraction, authority, back, balance, base, behaviour, belief, birth, bit, bite, blood, blow, body, brass, bread, breath, brother, building, burn, burst, business, butter, canvas, care, cause, chalk, chance, change, cloth, coal, colour, comfort, committee, company, comparison, competition, condition, connection, control, cook, copper, copy, cork, cotton, cough, country, cover, crack, credit, crime, crush, cry, current, curve, damage, danger, daughter, day, death, debt, decision, degree, design, desire, destruction, detail, development, digestion, direction, discovery, discussion, disease, disgust, distance, distribution, division, doubt, drink, driving, dust, earth, edge, education, effect, end, error, event, example, exchange, existence, expansion, experience, expert, fact, fall, family, father, fear, feeling, fiction, field, fight, fire, flame, flight, flowers, fold, food, force, form, friend, front, fruit, glass, gold, government, grain, grass, grip, group, growth, guide, harbour, harmony, hate, hearing, heat, help, history, hole, hope, hour, humour, ice, idea, impulse, increase, industry, ink, insect, instrument, insurance, interest, invention, iron, jelly, join, journey, judge, jump, kick, kiss, knowledge, land, language, laugh, law, lead, learning, leather, letter, level, lift, light, limit, linen, liquid, list, look, loss, love, machine, man, manager, mark, market, mass, meal, measure, meat, meeting, memory, metal, middle, milk, mind, mine, minute, mist, money, month, morning, mother, motion, mountain, move, music name, nation, need, news, night, noise, note, number, observation, offer, oil, operation, opinion, order, organization, ornament, owner, page, pain, paint, paper, part, paste, payment, peace, person, place, plant, play, pleasure, point, poison, polish, porter, position, powder, power, price. print, process, produce, profit, property, prose, protest, pull, punishment, purpose, push, quality, question, rain, range, rate, ray, reaction, reading, reason, record, regret, relation, religion, representative, request, respect, rest, reward, rythm, rice, river, road, roll, room, rub, rule, run, salt, sand, scale, science, sea, seat, secretary, selection, self, sense, servant, sex, shade, shake, shame, shock, side, sign, silk, silver, sister, size, sky, sleep, slip, slope, smash, smell, smile, smoke, sneeze, snow, soap, society, son, song, sort, sound, soup, space, stage, start, statement, steam, steel, step, stitch, stone, stop, story, stretch, structure, substance, sugar, suggestion, summer, support, surprise, swim, system, talk, taste, tax teaching, tendency, test, theory, thing, thought, thunder, time, tin, top, touch, trade, transport, trick, trouble, turn, twist, unit, use, value, verse, vessel, view, voice, walk, war, wash, waste, water, wave, wax, way, weather, week, weight, wind, wine, winter, woman, wood, wool, word, work, wound, writing, year.

These general rules apply:

Plurals in 's'
Derivatives in 'er', 'ing',
'ed' from 300 nouns
Adverbs in 'ly' from qualifiers
Degree with 'more' and 'most'
Question by inversion and 'do'
Operators and pronouns conjugate
in full
Measurement, numerals, currency,
calendar, and international terms in
English form.

From this basic list, a rich, effective English vocabulary can be developed. For further information, send for the brochure on "Instant English": Global College, Box 960, Bracebridge, Muskoka, Ontario, Canada.

APPENDIX II

A GLOSSARY OF TIMELY TERMS

abacus: a device for making arithmetic calculations
absolute: unrestrained
absorption: complete attention; the act of taking in
accelerate: speed up
accessability: easiness to use
accordance: agreement
accrue: to happen as a natural growth or addition
acoustic: pertaining to organs of hearing; to sound
acquiesce: to submit or comply quietly
acuity: sharpness
ad-hocracy: with respect to this subject or thing
advent: arrival
advocate: support; in favour of
aesthetic: characterized by the love of beauty
affluence: wealth
agrarian: relating to land or land tenure
agronomists: the art or science of managing land or crops
alienated: turned away from
allegation: a statement offered as a plea, excuse or justification
allegedly: supposedly; so-called
ameliorate: improve
amenities: pleasing; courtesies
amid: among
analogy: agreement; similarity
analog (analogue): (computer) one that solves a mathematical prob-
    lem by using physical similarities, as electric voltage or shaft
    rotations
analogous: equivalent
analytical: proceeding by analysis
anarchic: not regulated by law
anathema: detested or loathed
ancillary: accessory; something added to make completeness

animate: alive, possessing life

annihilation: the act of destroying and ruining

anthropology: the science that deals with the origins, physical and cultural development, racial characteristics, and social customs and beliefs of mankind

antithetic: directly opposed or contrasted

apathy: absence of emotion, passion or excitement; lack of interest

apocalyptic: affording a revolution or prophecy

apolyptic: instrumental

apropos: opportune, pertinent

arbitrary: subject to individual will or judgment without restriction

archaic: antiquated; old-fashioned

archetypes: the original patterns of models after which things are made

armageddon: the place where the final battle will be won between good and evil

artefact: any object made by man

artisan: a craftsman

ascended: climbed

ascertain: to find out definitely

aspirations: goals, ambitions

assertion: a positive statement or declaration

astrodome: a transparent dome on top of the fuselage of an aircraft, through which observations are made for navigation into space

atrophy: decline, decrease, as from disuse

attainable: capable of being reached or being accomplished

attrition: a wearing down or rubbing against

audio: reception of sound

augur: to predict

automation: the technique, method or system or operating or controlling a mechanical or productive process by highly automatic means

autonomous: self-governing

avid: enthusiastic

bilingual: able to speak one's own language and another one equally well

biological: pertaining to life or living matter

biosphere: the part of the earth's crust, waters and atmosphere where living organisms can exist

bourgeoisie: members of the middle class (in Marxist theory) opposed to the wage-earning class.

Buddhism: a religion founded in India by Buddha

Buddhist Eightfold Path: four noble truths

bureaucracy: the body of officials and administrators especially of government

burgeoning: budding or sprouting

capacious: very large; roomy

capitalism: an economic system in which businesses are mainly privately owned and operated instead of state-owned

capitalist: a person who has capital (money) invested in business enterprises

capitalize: take advantage of

catalysts: people who cause activity and enthusiasm

cermet: a blend of a metal and a ceramic substance

certitude: freedom from doubt

chiaroscuro: the distribution of light and shade in a picture

chiasmus: a reversal in parallel phrases or words

clandestine: executed with secrecy or concealment

cliche: commonplace statement

coaxial cable: a cable that consists of an insulated conducting tube through which a central, insulated conductor runs

coerce: to compel by force

collaboration: working together; cooperation

communism: a theory or system of social organization based on the holding of all property in common; ownership by state or community

complacency: self-satisfaction; a feeling of quiet pleasure or security

computation: calculation

comprehend: grasp; understand

conceivably: imaginably

conception: idea

concomitant: existing or occurring with something else, often in a lesser way

concurrent: occurring or existing side by side

conflagration: a destructive fire

conformity: correspondence in form, nature or character

Confucianism: doctrine containing traditional Chinese principles of ethics, morals and politics, founded by Confucius

congenial: suited or adapted in spirit, feeling, temper

conglomerate: anything composed of differing elements

connotation: the suggested meaning of a word or expression in addition to its explicit meaning

consensus: majority of opinion

continuum: a continuous extent, series or whole

contradistinction: distinction by opposition

contrivance: mechanical device

contours: outlines

convergence: a coming together

coordination: harmonious combination or interaction, as of functions or parts

cornucopia: an abundant or overflowing supply

corollary: an easily drawn conclusion

cosmic: a part of the material universe outside of the earth

cosmological: argument for the existence of God
countenance: facial expression (color, composed appearance)
cranium: the part of the skull which encloses the brain
credibility: extent to which one can believe
curriculum: course of study

debilitating: making weak or feeble
decadence: deterioration, decay
defer: put off to a future time
delineate: to trace the outline of
demagogue: person who gains power and popularity by arousing the emotions, passions and prejudices of people
demise: end of existence
demographic: pertaining to the science of vital and social statistics
deprecate: disapprove; protest against
dervish: a member of any of the various Muslim orders some of whom carry on ecstatic observances such as violent dancing and whirling
despoliation: the act of stripping off things of value
despotism: absolute power
dichotomy: division into two parts of kinds
dictatorship: (of the Proletariat) (in Marxism): absolute rule by the working class, preceding the establishment of a classless society
didactic: intended for instruction
diffusion: a spreading out
digital: (computer technology) using numerical digits expressed in a scale to represent variables in a problem
disaffection: absence of good will
discretionary: subject to one's own judgment
discriminatory: constituting a difference
disintegration: the act of breaking up
disparity: lack of similarity or equality
dissemination: broadcasting; dispersement
dissent: to differ in sentiment or opinion
dissipated: indulging in excessive devotion to pleasure
diurnal: daily; pertaining to each day
diversification: the act of practice of manufacturing a variety of products, investing in a variety of securities, selling a variety of merchandise, etc., so that an economic slump will not be disastrous
dogmatism: arrogant stating of opinions as truths
dynamics: the pattern of change of growth in any field
dynamo: an energetic person; an electric generator

ecology: branch of sociology concerned with the spacing of people and institutions and the resulting interdependency

efficacy: effectiveness
electorate: the body of persons entitled to a vote in elections
elemental: simple
emission: sending forth
empathy: deep understanding of the feelings and thoughts of another
empirical: derived from experiments
encyclical: a wide circulation
engender: produce
ennoble: to dignify
entrepreneurial: organizer; business manager
enterprise: a project undertaken or to be undertaken especially an
    important one or that requires boldness or energy
entitlements: rights or claims to something
envisage: to look at and think about
epitomize: to contain or represent in small compass; typify
equilibrium: balance
erroneous: containing error
espouse: make one's own, as a cause
ethics: body of moral principles or values
eugenic: bringing about improvement in the type of offspring produced
evolve: develop gradually
exhortation: a discourse or address conveying urgent advice or
    recommendations
expedite: make easier and faster
exploit: use selfishly for one's own ends
exponential: of or pertaining to the constant
extrapolate: to estimate the value of a variable outside its tabulated
    range
extramural: outside the walls or boundaries

fatalistic: accepting all things and events as inevitable
felicity: the state of being happy
ferment: agitation, unrest, excitement
fervor: a great warmth and earnestness of feeling
fluid: changing readily
folly: lack of understanding or sense—foolishness
fostered: encouraged
foetus: the young of an animal in the womb or egg

ganglion: a gray mass of tissue
geodesic: pertaining to the geometry of curved surfaces (geodesic
    line-shortest line connecting two points)

hallucinogenic: producing something that does not exist outside the
    mind

haptic: ability to grasp or perceive
hegemony: leadership
heretical: pertaining to an opinion or doctrine at variance with the orthodox or accepted doctrine
heterarchies: a system of persons or things ranked by differences
hiatus: a break or interruption in the continuity of work
hierarchy: a system of persons or things ranked one above the other
Hinduism: the common religion of India
holocaust: a great or complete devastation or destruction
homogenize: to form by blending unlike elements
homeostasis: the tendency of a system to maintain internal stability
homo sapien: man
hyper: to imply excess or exaggeration
hyperbole: obvious exaggeration
hypocrisy: a pretense of having a virtuous character; moral, religious beliefs or principles which do not exist
hypothetically: supposedly

icon: a picture image or other representation
ideology: a system of ideas
ideological: pertaining to impractical planning
idolatry: the religious worship of idols
ignominious: humiliating
imperceptible: very slight, gradual or subtle
impervious: not permitting penetration or passage
implode: to burst inward
imponderable: that which cannot be precisely determined, measured or evaluated
impotent: lacking power or ability
imprecation: curse
incisible: able to cut marks, figures, cleanly, not ragged
incommensurable: having no common measure or standard of comparison
incommensurate: disproportionate or inadequate
inexorably: not to be persuaded or moved
ingenuity: cleverness, skillfulness
innate: inherent in the essential character of something
innovation: something new or different introduced
institutionalism: the belief that society must establish and maintain public organizations
Instrumentalism: the belief that thought should be used to control environment and ideas used to further experience and progress
intangibles: not definite; things that cannot be touched
integral: necessary to the completeness of the whole
integrity: soundness of moral principle, character, honesty

interface: the facts and theories shared by two or more disciplines or fields of study
interministerial: within the ministry of religion
intricate: entangled; involved
intrinsic: belonging to a thing by its very merit—inward
invariably: constantly
irony: words that express meaning different from or opposite of literal meaning
irrespective: ignoring; without regard for
Islam: religion of Muslims based on words and religious systems founded by the prophet Mohammed

Jainism: a dualistic, dedicated religion founded by a Hindu reformer
Judaism: religion of the Jews based on the Old Testament
juggernaut: any large overpowering destructive force or object
jurisprudence: the science or philosophy of law

kinesthetic: pertaining to muscle sense

laser: light amplification by stimulated emission of radiation
laggard: one who lags, lingers or loiters
litany: a prolonged or monotonous account
literacy: the ability to read and write
luddite: a member of any or various bands of workmen in England (1811-16, named after Ned Ludd) organized to destroy manufacturing machinery under the belief that its use diminished employment

maelstrom: restless, disordered, or disturbed affairs
Maginot Line: a zone of French fortification erected along the French-German border in the years preceding World War II.
magnitude: moral greatness
malleable: adaptable
mandate: authorization to act
mandatory: containing a command
manifest: evident, obvious
manifesto: a public declaration of intentions, opinions, objectives
Maoism: doctrines by Mao Tse-tung, Chinese Communist Leader
Marxism: a system of thought developed by Karl Marx
maser: microwave amplification by stimulated emission of radiation
mastodon: of immense size, power and influence
mater et magistra: Latin—mother and teacher
maximize: increase to the greatest possible degree
mediator: go-between
menial: low, degrading

meritocracy: rule by virtue of worth
metaphorical: comparing
millennium: a period of 1,000 years
miscegenation: interbreeding between members of different races
mnemonic: assisting the memory
modality: the natural way of action or existence; one of the primary senses
modules: a readily interchangeable unit
monadology: study of any simple single-celled organism
monumental: of enduring significance
mosaic: being made up of many fragments
multilateral: having many sides
mundane: of or pertaining to the common world
myriad: a very great number

nascent consensus: general agreement beginning to develop
neurosis: emotional disorder
nomenclature: a set or system of names or terms
nucleation: having a core or a central part
nullified: deprived of value of effectiveness

obfuscation: confusion, bewilderment
obsessive: extreme domination of thoughts
obsolete: out of date
odious: hateful
olefactory: pertaining to the nose and the sense of smell
ominous: threatening
onslaught: a furious attack
optimum: the best or most favorable point, degree or amount
orthodox: approved or conventional
ostensible: given out or outwardly appearing as such
ostentatious: characterized by display intended to impress
outmoded: gone out of style

palliative: something that tries to conceal the gravity of something by making excuses and apologies
papyrus: a tall aquatic plant used as a paper by the Egyptians
paradigm: an example
paradox: a statement or proposition seemingly self-contradictory or absurd, but in reality expressing a possible truth
pari passu: Latin for with equal pace or progress; side by side; equally
partisan: supporter of a person or cause
pathogenic: disease-producing
pathological: pertaining to the science or the study of the origin, nature and course of diseases

pauper: a very poor person without means of support

penumbra: the imperfect shadow outside the complete shadow of an opaque body

Periclean Era: When Athens was intellectually and materially superior

peril: exposure to danger, injury, loss, risk or destruction

peripheral: concerned with the superficial aspects

permeate: pass through

permutation: alteration; transformation

pervasive: extending its presence; influence throughout

phenomenon: a fact or occurrence or circumstance observed

philosophy: the rational investigation of the truths and principles of being, knowledge or conduct

phoenix: a person or thing that has become renewed or restored after suffering calamity or apparent annihilation

phonetic: pertaining to speech, sound

photoelectric: pertaining to the electronic effects produced by light

photosynthesis: the combining of complex organic materials using sunlight as the source of energy

pluralistic: referring to the theory that there is more than one basic substance or principle

polarizing: presence of two opposite principles

ponderous: of great weight

potential: something possible; capable of being or becoming

pragmatic: pertaining to the practical point of view

precariously: with danger or risk

preclude: to prevent the presence of

preconscious: absent from but capable of being brought into consciousness

precursor: that which or the one who comes before

prelude: the beginning of an event of higher importance

prerequisite: something required beforehand

prevail: exists everywhere

primitive: one of the first of its kind in existence

pristine: having its original purity

prodigy: a marvellous example

profound: intense, extreme

prognostication: forecasting of a prediction

projection: prediction of the future

proletariate: the working class

proliferate: to grow or produce by multiplication of parts

propagate: to spread and increase

proponent: a person who puts forward a proposition or proposal

prospectus: a report which describes something forthcoming

proximity: nearness

prudence: good judgment

psyche: the human soul, spirit or mind

psychological: pertaining to the science of the mind
psychospiritual: of the mind and the soul
pummel: to beat or thrash as with fists
purveyor: a person who provides or supplies

rapproachement: establishment of relations
rationale: statement of reasons
raison d'etre: reason for being or existence
reactionary: a person who favors action in a reverse direction manner
receptiveness: the quality of being able or quick to receive knowledge
     or ideas
redeploy: to transfer from one theatre of operations to another
redundance: an overflowing or an excess amount—unnecessary
relevant: to the purpose
remotest: farthest out of the way; secluded
reprehensible: deserving of reproof, rebuke, or censure
resonance: the prolongation of sound by reflection
resurgence: revival or rising again
revile: to speak of obusively or with contempt
revolutionary: complete change
rhetoric: the ability to use language effectively

sabbatical: bringing a period of rest
salient: prominent; conspicuous
sanctioned: supported in action
satanic: devil-like
satellite: anything that depends or accompanies or serves something
     else
saturated: impregnated or soaked thoroughly
scanner: a device for exposing an image on film
schizophrenic: having a mental disorder; marked by a withdrawn in-
     tellectual and emotional deterioration
sector: circle
secularized: separate from religious or spiritual connection or influence
semantic: arising from the different meanings of words
sentient: having the power of perception by the senses
serfdom: slavery
shibboleth: a peculiarity of behavior or dress which makes a particu-
     lar set of persons stand out
Shintoism: the native religion of Japan, primarily a system of nature
     and ancestor worship
simultaneous: happening at the same time
socialism: an economic system in which the community owns and con-
     trols means of production, capital and land
sociological: pertaining to the science of social relations

solenoid: electric conductor wound as a helix with small pitch, or as two or more coaxial helices, so that the current through the conductor establishes a magnetic field within the conductor

solidarity: union—because of common responsibilities and interests; community of interests, feelings, purposes

spatial: pertaining to space

speculative: contemplating; abstract reasoning

stabilization: holding at a certain level

stolid: unemotional, immovable

strategical: forming an important and essential part

stupefaction: overwhelming; the state of being stupefied or numbed

subliminal: existing or operating below the threshold of consciousness

sublimity: the state or quality of being elevated or lofty in thought, language, etc.

subscribe: to promise, as by signing an agreement

subversive: that which is meant to overthrow, destroy or corrupt

summation: review of total conclusions

sumptuous: splendid or superb

superfluous: unnecessary or needless

supersede: to set aside as useless or to replace in power and authority

suppress: to do away with

sustain: to support; to undergo; endure

synchronous: occurring at the same time

syncopate: contracted by omitting one or more sounds from the middle

synonymous: implying the same idea

syntax: the study of the rules for the formation of grammatical sentences in a language

synthesized: formed by combining parts

tactile: pertaining to the sense of touch

tactile-kinetic: affecting the sense of touch caused by motion

t'ang dynasty: (In China) marked by territorial expansion, the invention of printing and the high development of poetry

tantamount: equivalent

Taoism: a philosophical system evolved by Lao-tzu and Chuang-tzu

technology: science and industry

technostructure: the structure of technology

technocrat: one who advocates control, reform and reorganization based on the findings of technologists

tempo: rate of movement

tenacity: the quality or property of being stubborn or obstinate

tentatively: for an indefinite period

theistic: one who believes in one God or one ruler of the universe

thermonuclear: thermo—heat or hot; nuclear—refers to atomic weapons

thermionic: referring to an ion emitted by incandescent material
thrall: slave
totalitarianism: the practices and principles of a centralized government in which those in control grant neither recognition nor tolerance to parties of differing opinion
transcend: to rise above or go beyond the limits
transducer: a device that receives energy from one system and re-transmits it, often in a different form
transient: temporary
transition: period of change
transitory: not permanent
transformation: change
transisterized: equipped with a circuit employing transistors
trivia: matters or things very unimportant
truism: a self-evident or obvious truth

ubiquitous: present everywhere
unalienable: (as rights) that which cannot be taken away from oneself
unambiguous: clear
unalleviate: to not make easier or lessen
unassailable: not open to attack
universal: world wide
unprecedented: never before experienced
unscrupulous: not held back by conscience or principles
usurpation: wrongful infringement
Utopia: a place of ideal perfection

valency: the relative combining capacity of an atom or group
venal: in return for a bribe
verification: evidence that establishes or confirms the accuracy or truth of
verisimilitude: the appearance or semblance of truth
verity: truth
viable: capable of living, vivid real
vignette: a small pleasing picture or view
versatility: all-round handy
virtually: just about
vista: a far-reaching intellectual view
vital: of critical importance
volition: willing, choosing
vying: competing, contending

zenith: highest point
Zoroastrianism: an Iranian religion

APPENDIX III

STATISTICS ON "THE GOOD EARTH"

Country	Population	Political System	Free Press	Annual Income Per Head	Per-centage Illiterate	War or Peace	Life Span
Afghanistan	13,800,000	Strong King: No parties	No	$ 56	90%	Peace	Not Known
Albania	1,625,000	Communist	No	290	28.5%	Peace	63
Algeria	10,453,600	President backed by army	No	207	81%	Peace	35
Argentina	22,520,000	Military rule: parties suspended	No	757	13.6%	Peace	63
Austria	7,073,000	Democratic: Nazi parties banned	Yes	1,111	Less than 1%	Peace	66
Australia	11,750,000	Democratic	Yes	1,868	Less than 1%	Fighting in Vietnam	67
Bahrein	182,000	Strong sheikh: no parties	No	322	74.7%	Peace	Not Known
Barbados	250,000	Democratic	Yes	404	1.1%	Peace	62
Belgium	9,556,380	Democratic	Yes	1,612	3.3%	Peace	67
Bolivia	4,334,121	President backed by army	Yes	177	67.9%	Fighting guerillas	49
Botswana	543,000	Democratic	Yes	Not Known	78%	Peace	Not Known
Brazil	87,209,000	Military rule: main parties suspended	No	271	39.3%	Peace	39
Britain	51,000,000	Democratic	Yes	1,628	Less than 1%	Peace	67

Country	Population	Political System	Free Press	Annual Income Per Head	Percentage Illiterate	War or Peace	Life Span
Bulgaria	8,285,000	Communist	No	$1,030	Less than 1%	Peace	67
Burma	25,800,000	Military rule: one party	No	69	42.3%	Civil War	40
Burundi	3,000,000	Military rule: one party	No	75	Not known	Peace	35
Cambodia	6,260,000	Strong premier: one party	No	118	69.2%	Peace	44
Cameroons	5,200,000	Democratic	Yes	124	Not known	Peace	34
Canada	20,630,000	Democratic	Yes	2,075	Less than 1%	Peace	68
Central African Republic	1,466,000	Military rule: one party	No	127	Not known	Peace	33
Ceylon	11,504,000	Democratic	Yes	138	22%	Peace	61
Chad	3,400,000	Strong president: one party	No	69	50%	Peace	Not Known
Chile	8,750,000	Democratic	Yes	497	16.4%	Peace	49
China	760,000,000	Communist	No	Not Known	46.1%	Peace	Not Known
Colombia	19,300,000	Democratic: Communist party banned	Yes	297	37.7%	Fighting guerillas	44
Congo (Brazzaville)	870,000	Military rule:	No	161	84.6%	Peace	37

Country	Population	Political System	Free Press	Annual Income Per Head	Percentage Illiterate	War or Peace	Life Span
Costa Rica	800,000	Democratic	Yes	$ 379	15.7%	Peace	61
Cuba	7,900,000	Communist Party dominant	No	Not Known	Less than 1%	Peace	Not Known
Cyprus	614,000	Strong president	Yes	672	24.1%	Peace	63
Czechoslovakia	14,200,000	Communist: Soviet enforcement	No	1,347	Less than 1%	Peace	67
Dahomey	2,370,000	President backed by army	No	71	Not known	Peace	37
Denmark	4,800,000	Democratic	Yes	1,895	Less than 1%	Peace	70
Dominica	3,500,000	Strong president	No	230	40.1%	Peace	56
Ecuador	5,500,000	Democratic but weak	Yes	197	32.7%	Peace	Not Known
El Salvador	3,000,000	Democratic	Yes	252	51%	Peace	56
Ethiopia	22,500,000	Strong emperor: no parties	No	46	Not known	Border disputes	Not Known
Finland	4,500,000	Democratic	Yes	1,546	Less than 1%	Peace	64
France	46,500,000	Democratic	Yes	1,616	3.6%	Peace	67
Gabon	470,000	Strong president: one party	No	46	87.6%	Peace	25
Gambia	315,486	Democratic	Yes	73	Not known	Peace	43
Germany (East)	17,000,000	Communist	No	1,635	Less than 1%	Peace	68

Country	Population	Political System	Free Press	Annual Income Per Head	Percentage Illiterate	War or Peace	Life Span
Germany (West)	59,700,000	Democratic	Yes	$1,591	Less than 1%	Peace	67
Ghana	7,945,000	Military rule: all parties banned	Yes	298	20%	Peace	38
Greece	8,500,000	Military rule: all parties banned	No	651	19.6%	Peace	67
Guatamala	4,575,000	Strong president	No	278	70.6%	Peace	48
Guinea	3,500,000	Strong president: one party	No	98	Not known	Peace	26
Guyana	675,000	Democratic but weak	Yes	286	24.1%	Peace	59
Haiti	4,500,000	Dictator-president: parties banned	No	82	89.5%	Peace	32
Honduras	2,300,000	President backed by army	No	208	64.8%	Peace	44
Hungary	10,100,000	Communist	No	1,215	3.2%	Peace	67
Iceland	196,000	Democratic	Yes	2,165	Less than 1%	Peace	70
India	500,000,000	Democratic	Yes	82	72.2%	Naga War	41
Indonesia	112,300,000	Military rule: Communist party banned	No	91	57.1%	Peace	Not Known
Iran	25,700,000	Strong king: Communist party banned	No	222	87.2%	Peace	42

Country	Population	Political System	Free Press	Annual Income Per Head	Per-centage Illiterate	War or Peace	Life Span
Iraq	8,200,000	President backed by army: one party	No	$ 227	85.5%	War with Israel	Not Known
Ireland	2,800,000	Democratic	Yes	845	Less than 1%	Peace	68
Israel	2,600,000	Democratic	Yes	1,211	15.8%	War with Arab neighbours	70
Italy	53,600,000	Democratic	Yes	989	8.4%	Peace	67
Ivory Coast	3,840,000	Strong president: one-party state	No	225	Not known	Peace	35
Jamaica	1,859,000	Democratic	Yes	447	18.1%	Peace	62
Japan	100,100,000	Democratic	Yes	829	2.2%	Peace	68
Jordan	2,100,000	Strong king: no parties	No	201	67.6%	War with Israel	52
Kenya	8,600,000	Strong president	Yes	101	Not known	Peace	40
Kinshasa	13,600,000	President backed by army: one party state	No	109	84.6%	Peace	37
Korea (North)	12,500,000	Communist	No	Not Known	Not known	Border clashes with S. Korea	47

Country	Population	Political System	Free Press	Annual Income Per Head	Percentage Illiterate	War or Peace	Life Span
Korea (South)	29,200,000	Strong president: Communist party banned	Yes	$ 123	29.4%	Border clashes with North	51
Kuwait	468,000	Strong sheikh: no parties	No	3,415 (oil income)	53.2%	Peace	68 (Govt. estimate)
Laos	2,300,000	Premier, backed by army: feuding political factions	No	101	Not known	Fighting Communist guerillas	Not Known
Lebanon	1,750,000	Weak democracy	Yes	356	20%	Peace	65
Liberia	1,000,000	Strong president	No	153	91.1%	Peace	60 (Govt. estimate)
Libya	1,500,000	Strong king: no parties	No	713	87.1%	Peace	Not Known
Luxembourg	334,790	Democratic	Yes	1,671	Less than 1%	Peace	61
Madagascar	6,300,000	Weak democracy	Yes	99	66.5%	Peace	37
Malawi	4,000,000	Strong president: one-party state	No	49	93.5%	Peace	Not Known
Malaysia	9,855,000	Weak democracy: Communist party banned	Yes	261	77.7%	Peace	55
Mali	4,700,000	Military rule: one-party state	No	69	Not known	Peace	27

Country	Population	Political System	Free Press	Annual Income Per Head	Percentage Illiterate	War or Peace	Life Span
Malta	319,000	Democratic	Yes	$ 493	42.4%	Peace	67
Mauritania	1,100,000	Strong president: one-party state	No	111	Not known	Peace	40
Mauritius	700,000	Weak democracy	Yes	216	38.4%	Peace	58
Mexico	45,671,000	Weak democracy	Yes	468	34.6%	Peace	55
Mongolia	1,100,000	Communist	No	Not Known	4.6%	Peace	Not Known
Morocco	13,300,000	Strong king	No	182	86.2%	Peace	47
Nepal	9,500,000	Strong king: parties abolished	No	90	94.9%	Peace	44
Netherlands	12,500,000	Democratic	Yes	1,428	Less than 1%	Peace	71
New Zealand	2,600,000	Democratic	Yes	1,848	Less than 1%	Fighting in Vietnam	68
Nicaragua	1,700,000	Concealed dictatorship: parties officially free	No	326	50.4%	Peace	Not Known
Niger	3,300,000	Strong president: one-party state	No	82	99.1%	Peace	37
Nigeria	55,653,000	Military rule: parties suspended	No	79	40% (approx.)	Civil war with Biafra	Not Known
Norway	3,700,000	Democratic	Yes	1,629	Less than 1%	Peace	71

Country	Population	Political System	Free Press	Annual Income Per Head	Percentage Illiterate	War or Peace	Life Span
Pakistan	93,720,000	Strong president	No	$ 120	81.2%	Peace	53
Panama	1,300,000	Military rule	No	468	30.1%	Peace	57
Paraguay	1,800,000	Strong president	No	199	25.7%	Peace	Not Known
Peru	11,700,000	Military rule	No	233	39.4%	Peace	51
Philippines	27,000,000	Democratic but weak	Yes	242	28.1%	Fighting in Vietnam	48
Poland	31,800,000	Communist	No	1,115	4.7%	Peace	64
Portugal	9,234,000	Premier dictator	No	395	38.1%	Fighting in African colonies	60
Rhodesia	4,500,000	White minority rule	Yes	207	Not known	Fighting African guerillas	White 66 African 50
Rumania	19,100,000	Communist	No	785	11.4%	Peace	65
Rwanda	3,300,000	Strong president	No	75	Not known	Peace	Not Known
Saudi Arabia	6,000,000	Strong king	No	157	79%	Peace	Not Known
Senegal	3,500,000	Strong president	No	190	94.4%	Peace	37
Singapore	2,000,000	Democratic	Yes	555	33.9%	Peace	Not Known
Sierra Leone	2,183,000	Military rule	No	134	60%	Peace	Not Known

Country	Population	Political System	Free Press	Annual Income Per Head	Percentage Illiterate	War or Peace	Life Span
Somalia	2,500,000	Democratic	Yes	$ 65	93%	Peace	Not Known
South Africa	18,200,000	White minority rule	No	512	68.5%	Peace	White 64 African 44
Spain	32,000,000	Dictatorship	No	623	17.6%	Peace	67
Sudan	13,000,000	Democratic but weak	No	94	88%	Civil war	Not Known
Swaziland	389,000	Strong king	Yes	Not Known	77.2%	Peace	48
Sweden	7,760,000	Democratic	Yes	2,509	Less than 1%	Peace	71
Switzerland	5,500,000	Democratic	Yes	2,155	Less than 1%	Peace	68
Syria	4,600,000	Military rule: one party	No	172	70.5%	Israel	Not Known
Taiwan	12,993,000	Dictatorship by Chiang Kai-shek	No	209	20%	Peace	64
Tanzania	12,231,000	Strong president: one party	No	69	Not known	Peace	35
Thailand	32,000,000	Military rule: Communists banned	No	128	32.3%	Fighting in Vietnam	53
Togo	1,650,000	Military rule	No	94	Not known	Peace	31

Country	Population	Political System	Free Press	Annual Income Per Head	Percentage Illiterate	War or Peace	Life Span
Trinidad and Tobago	974,000	Democratic	Yes	$ 565	26.2%	Peace	62
Tunisia	4,457,000	Strong president	No	190	84.3%	Peace	53
Turkey	31,391,000	Democratic but weak	No	290	61.9%	Peace	52
U.A.R.	30,000,000	Strong president: one party	No	170	80.5%	War with Israel	51
Uganda	7,700,000	Strong president	No	87	74.9%	Peace	50
U.S.A.	196,842,000	Democratic	Yes	3,305	2.2%	Fighting in Vietnam	66
U.S.S.R.	234,700,000	Communist	No	1,513	1.5%	Peace	66
Upper Volta	5,000,000	Military rule: one party	No	46	82%	Peace	35
Uruguay	2,750,000	Strong president	No	567	9.7%	Peace	Not Known
Venezuela	9,350,000	Democratic	Yes	785	34.2%	Fighting Communist guerillas	66
Vietnam (North)	17,800,000	Communist	No	Not Known	35.5%	Fighting in Vietnam	Not Known
Vietnam (South)	15,100,000	Strong president backed by army	No	121	Not known	Fighting Communists	35 (approx).

Country	Population	Political System	Free Press	Annual Income Per Head	Percentage Illiterate	War or Peace	Life Span
Yemen (North)	4,500,000	Military rule: one party	No	$ 100	60% (approx.)	Civil war against Royalists	50 (approx.)
Yemen (South)	1,500,000	Strong president: one party	No	129	55% (approx.)	Peace	50 (approx.)
Yugoslavia	18,549,000	Communist	No	695	23.5%	Peace	62
Zambia	3,700,000	Strong president	Yes	208	58.6%	Peace	40

Reprinted courtesy Toronto Telegram.

Appendix IV

QUESTIONS TO CONSIDER

PART ONE

1. Discuss two of the main potentials of cybernation and global communication systems.
2. What are the "main choices" faced by mankind?
3. How does thermo-nuclear warfare change the rationale behind all wars?
4. Why are we socially ill-equipped to eliminate confusion, frustration, conflict, poverty and war? Discuss.
5. Illustrate the process of cybernetics.
6. Why, according to Galbraith, are all states, both capitalist and communist, converging in character?
7. Why, according to Sakharov should socialism merge with capitalism?
8. Why are the terms *capitalism* and *communism* becoming outdated?
9. Discuss briefly the consensus about cybernation.
10. What does McLuhan consider to be the role of machines in our present and future society?
11. What does youth mean by the "hypocrisy of the parents" double standard of important social values?
12. What is the dilemma of the church?
13. What relationship exists between technology and the activities of young revolutionists?
14. Why is marketing and distribution a problem in a free economy?
15. Can we have peace without economic collapse? Discuss.

PART TWO

1. Discuss the effects of some of man's greatest innovations on his culture.
2. Discuss the importance of and relation between education and cybernation.

3. What constitutes a "learning environment"? When and how should they be modified for improvement?
4. Discuss Charles Kollingsworth's "Nest of Change."
5. Are all of the larger civilizations encountering the same problems with cybernation? Why?
6. Discuss two forms of action that might be implemented to eliminate school drop-outs and unskilled laborers.
7. List four or five myths about automation. Why are they myths?
8. a. What is cybernation?
   b. Discuss the nature of present day technology.
   c. List some fundamental differences between present day technology and early automation.
9. a. What changes are taking place in our society because of cybernation?
   b. Do these changes affect you? Discuss.
10. Have culture and civilizations evolved through the effects or production of machines? Discuss.
11. State and discuss some of the new problems facing managers and ways of solving or dealing with them.
12. Is it possible, by educating everyone on cybernation, to close the existing communications gaps? Explain.

PART THREE

1. What main communications factors distinguish men from animals?
2. Comment on the advantages, disadvantages and current and past relevance of both centralism and decentralism.
3. Comment on Colin Cherry's theories of signals and signs.
4. Discuss Trevor Roper's observation that "society tends to invest in itself."
5. Discuss the role radio has played in shaping our local and global society.
6. What factors, according to Marshall McLuhan are contributing to various levels and degrees of civil war?
7. How do developments in music and the arts relate to other forms of social progress, technology included.
8. What are the effects of information overload and how can they be used in other applications?
9. What could be used as a basis and testing ground for consensus-forming systems? Explain and discuss.
10. Discuss Project Delphi.
11. a. How must we plan our future in terms of cybernation and communication?

    b. Discuss the effects of communications speeds on forms of social organization.
12. Discuss Gordon Thompson's statement "today's complexities become tomorrow's routine" giving examples.
13. a. How will adult education be a development of human resources?
    b. Discuss possible structures of an "interactive communications environment."
14. What basic changes have taken place in the concepts of education in Japan and in the U.S. Account for these changes.
15. Discuss the advantages and dangers of following each of the two present trends in communications development.

PART FOUR

1. Identify and discuss one of the critical political changes of our time and in our culture.
2. Discuss the role of the rich countries in improving underdeveloped areas, the effects on the incumbent culture of such accelerated development and the net desirability of such development.
3. In what ways and to what extent do you feel that we have already advanced towards world awareness?
4. What possible methods can there be for establishing international rule of law?
5. What are the advantages and significance of cultural and social differences with regard to global unity?
6. Lester Pearson's concept of what should be of present world concern is "modification of national sovereignty in the interest of greater international unity." Discuss with reference to problems involved, steps to be taken and feasibility.
7. a. What were man's first two attempts at world government? Why have they not succeeded?
    b. Why is the world ready to discuss possible world government?
    c. Outline several areas of interdependence between nations.
    d. What might be the benefits of world government?
    e. What factors are obstructing world government?
8. Discuss some organizations already in existence to promote world government.
9. a. Discuss the present general disillusionment with foreign aid.
    b. What is a possible basis for scaling the contributions of wealth by the rich nations? What, if anything, would this solve?
10. In Part Four, several experts have expressed their opinions on world problems. Compare these with regard to scope and the intensity of problem, proposed solutions and plans, and obstacles to these plans.

PART FIVE

1. Compare and contrast Pearson's and Sakharov's statements and opinions on the subject of the incompatability of world ideologies.
2. How would Dr. Sakharov scale the contributions of the rich countries? Compare this to McNamara's scale in Part Four and evaluate both.
3. What is the relation between the education and scientific "states" and the techno structure? How is this relationship paradoxical?
4. Discuss Theobald's proposal of a new principle in jurisprudence.
5. Outline briefly Dwight MacDonald's position on the necessity to provide for the individual.
6. In attacking the problem of job security in the U.S., Theobald allocates responsibility to the government, Stone to business. Discuss.
7. Explain and discuss Ezra Pound's dictum, "the artists are the antennae of the race" with reference to Parts I-IV. How does art mimic the forms of communication?
8. Discuss the relation between sensory and perceptual bias and technological and cultural change.
9. Does acceleration of change make meaningful perception possible or impossible? Why?
10. a. What is the role of education in society? Discuss.
    b. What is the relation between education and entertainment? Discuss.
11. Discuss Parker's closing statement, "the human spirit is actually moving toward the great mythic contours which will ultimately delineate a new and integral man, profound in his corporate arts."
12. Explain the cliché to archetype pattern as it applies to communication. Does it operate in the arts? In business? In government? Explain.

PART SIX

1. What conflicts are apparent in the processes of technological and social change? Do these remain the same for any culture or period of change? Discuss.
2. Discuss Hare's statement, "the introduction of change is eased if the symbols of change present no apparent alteration or modification of the culture's widely held symbols."
3. Discuss Huxley's statement "the great issue . . . is what are you

going to do with these things?"

4.
  a. What approaches must we avoid in solving the current problems of man and machine?

  b. What specific steps might Morrison take to solve these problems?

5.
  a. What elements must we take into account when considering the humanizing of industrial society?

  b. What is one basic principle in humanizing our society? What does it imply?

6.
  a. What needs, other than material considerations, must be satisfied if man is to be happy?

  b. How have the authors faced this question?

  c. What new attitudes towards life must man develop?

  d. What is the relation of these needs and attitudes to religion?

7.
  a. Compare Fromm's ideas on the importance of guaranteed income with Theobald's concept of Basic Economic Security.

  b. Fromm postulates activation, responsibility and participation for today's man. How and why did he arrive at these conclusions, and what do they (a) mean and (b) suggest? Does he feel we have made a beginning? Why? Do you? Why?

8.
  a. What is our idea of the relation of the individual to society?

  b. What cultures, past and present, have evolved a concept of individualism, and at what point in their development was it evolved?

  c. What cultures, past and present, have evolved different concepts for relating the single person to the various levels of his society? How many such basic concepts exist and how are they the same or different?

  d. Certain modern philosophers have re-examined our concept of an individualist—structured society and found it inappropriate or lacking for our present and—they think—future needs. Discuss.

9. What new functions and/or orientations must the schools and universities develop to ease and further our present course of social change?

10.
  a. Outline briefly Norman Cousins' "checklist of enemies."

  b. What guidelines did he use in establishing the list?

  c. What additions or deletions would you make on the list and how, if at all, would you change the guidelines? Why?

  d. Relate his list, and your own if it differs, to specifics in your community and country and the world.